Unintentional-injury deaths were up 2% in 2002 compared to the revised 2001 total. Unintentional-injury deaths were estimated to total 99,500 in 2002 and 98,000 in 2001.

The resident population of the United States was 280,306,000 in 2002, an increase of 1% from 2001.

The death rate in 2002 was 35.5 per 100,000 population — 1% greater than the rate in 2001 and 4% greater than the lowest rate on record, which was 34.0 in 1992.

A more complete summary of the situation in 2002 and recent trends is given on page 2.

The graph on page v shows the overall trends in the number of unintentional-injury deaths, the population, and the death rate per 100,000 population.

It is important to note that, beginning with the 1999 reference year, the data used in many tables in *Injury Facts*® is now based on the tenth revision of the *International Classification of Diseases.* The implications of this change are noted, where appropriate, throughout the book and especially in the Technical Appendix.

Changes in the 2003 Edition

In a continuing effort to improve *Injury Facts*®, some of the chapters have been combined. The Work and Occupational Health chapters have been consolidated into the Occupational chapter. The Public, Home, and Environmental Health chapters have been combined into the Home and Community chapter.

Changes have also been made in the design of the pages to make them easier to read and easier to photocopy from the book or to print from the CD-ROM.

Look for *new* data on …

• Occupational injury and illness profile data for four industries representing almost one fourth of Council members

• Work-related terrorism deaths from September 11, 2001

• Traumatic brain injuries

• Graduated driver licensing

• Cellular telephones and traffic crashes

• Children and choking

• Children's products

• BB/pellet gun injuries

• And more

and *updated* or *expanded* data on …

• General mortality

• Industry division profiles

• Occupational injury and illness incidence rates by industry

• Workers' compensation claims and costs

• Comparing safety of transportation modes

• State traffic laws

• Highway work zones

• Sports injuries

• Consumer product-related injuries

• Home fires by community size

• Environmental health issues

• State-level data

• And more

We welcome your comments and suggestions to improve *Injury Facts*®. Information on how to contact us is given on page ii.

UNINTENTIONAL-INJURY DEATHS, DEATH RATES, AND POPULATION, UNITED STATES, 1903–2002

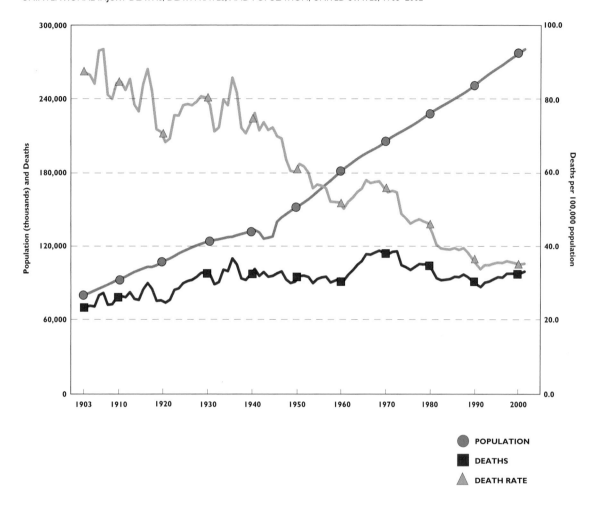

POPULATION

DEATHS

DEATH RATE

INJURY FACTS®

NATIONAL SAFETY COUNCIL

Unintentional-injury deaths were up 2% in 2002 compared to the revised 2001 total. Unintentional-injury deaths were estimated to total 99,500 in 2002 and 98,000 in 2001. The 2002 estimate is also up 2% from the 2000 final count of 97,900. The 2002 figure is 15% greater than the 1992 total of 86,777 (the lowest annual total since 1924) and 15% below the 1969 peak of 116,385 deaths.

The death rate in 2002 was 35.5 per 100,000 population — 4% greater than the lowest rate on record, which was 34.0 in 1992. The 2002 death rate was 1% greater than the 2001 revised rate of 35.3.

Comparing 2002 to 2001, public and work deaths decreased while home and motor-vehicle deaths increased. The population death rates in the public and work classes declined, in the motor-vehicle class it was unchanged, and in the home class the rate increased.

The motor-vehicle death total was up 1% in 2002. The motor-vehicle death rate per 100,000,000 vehicle-miles was 1.56 in 2002, down 0.6% from the revised 2001 rate (1.57) and down 1.3% from the revised 2000 rate of 1.58.

According to the latest final data (2000), unintentional injuries continued to be the fifth leading cause of death, exceeded only by heart disease, cancer, stroke, and chronic lower respiratory diseases. Preliminary death certificate data for 2001 indicate that unintentional injuries will remain in fifth place.

Nonfatal injuries also affect millions of Americans. In 2001, about 2.6 million people were hospitalized for injuries and about 39.4 million were treated in hospital emergency departments. In 2000, about 9.5 million visits to outpatient departments and about 89.9 million visits to physicians' offices were due to injuries. In 1998, about 34.0 million people — about one in eight — sought medical attention because of an injury.

The economic impact of these fatal and nonfatal unintentional injuries amounted to $586.3 billion in 2002. This is equivalent to about $2,100 per capita, or about $5,600 per household. These are costs that every individual and household pays whether directly out of pocket, through higher prices for goods and services, or through higher taxes.

Beginning with 1999 data, which became available in September 2001, deaths are now classified according to the 10th revision of the *International Classification of Diseases.* Overall, about 3% more deaths are classified as due to "unintentional injuries" under the new classification system than under the 9th revision. The difference varies across causes of death. See the Technical Appendix for more information on comparability. Caution should be used in comparing data classified under the two systems.

ALL UNINTENTIONAL INJURIES, 2002

Class	2002 Deaths	Change from 2001	Deaths per 100,000 Persons	Disabling Injuries[a]
All Classes[b]	**99,500**	**+2%**	**35.5**	**20,400,000**
Motor-vehicle	44,000	+1%	15.7	2,300,000
Public nonwork	*41,700*			*2,200,000*
Work	*2,100*			*100,000*
Home	*200*			*([c])*
Work	4,900	–3%	1.7	3,700,000
Nonmotor-vehicle	*2,800*			*3,600,000*
Motor-vehicle	*2,100*			*100,000*
Home	33,300	+5%	11.9	8,000,000
Nonmotor-vehicle	*33,100*			*8,000,000*
Motor-vehicle	*200*			*([c])*
Public	19,600	–2%	7.0	6,500,000

Source: National Safety Council estimates (rounded) based on data from the National Center for Health Statistics, Bureau of Labor Statistics, state departments of health, state traffic authorities, and state industrial commissions. The National Safety Council adopted the Bureau of Labor Statistics' Census of Fatal Occupational Injuries count for work-related unintentional injuries retroactive to 1992 data. See the Glossary for definitions and the Technical Appendix for revised estimating procedures.
[a] Disabling beyond the day of injury. Disabling injuries are not reported on a national basis, so the totals shown are approximations based on ratios of disabling injuries to deaths developed by the National Safety Council. The totals are the best estimates for the current year. They should not, however, be compared with totals shown in previous editions of this book to indicate year-to-year changes or trends. See the Glossary for definitions and the Technical Appendix for estimating procedures.
[b] Deaths and injuries above for the four separate classes add to more than the All Classes figures due to rounding and because some deaths and injuries are included in more than one class. For example, 2,100 work deaths involved motor vehicles in transport and are in both the Work and Motor-vehicle totals, and 200 motor-vehicle deaths occurred on home premises and are in both Home and Motor-vehicle. The total of such duplication amounted to about 2,300 deaths and 100,000 injuries in 2002.
[c] Less than 10,000.

UNINTENTIONAL-INJURY DEATHS BY CLASS, UNITED STATES, 2002

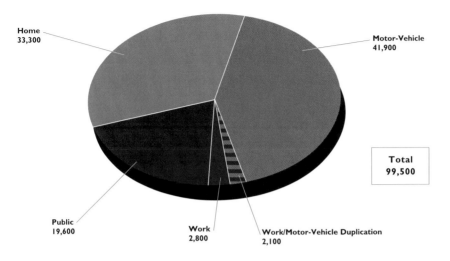

Home
33,300

Motor-Vehicle
41,900

Total
99,500

Public
19,600

Work
2,800

Work/Motor-Vehicle Duplication
2,100

UNINTENTIONAL DISABLING INJURIES BY CLASS, UNITED STATES, 2002

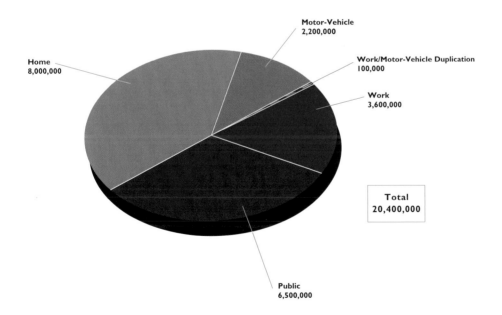

Motor-Vehicle
2,200,000

Work/Motor-Vehicle Duplication
100,000

Work
3,600,000

Home
8,000,000

Total
20,400,000

Public
6,500,000

COSTS OF UNINTENTIONAL INJURIES BY CLASS, 2002

The total cost of unintentional injuries in 2002, $586.3 billion, includes estimates of economic costs of fatal and nonfatal unintentional injuries together with employer costs, vehicle damage costs, and fire losses. Wage and productivity losses, medical expenses, administrative expenses, and employer costs are included in all four classes of injuries. Cost components unique to each class are identified below.

Motor-vehicle costs include property damage from motor-vehicle accidents. Work costs include the value of property damage in on-the-job motor-vehicle accidents and fires. Home and public costs include estimated fire losses, but do not include other property damage costs.

Besides the estimated $586.3 billion in economic losses from unintentional injuries in 2002, lost quality of life from those injuries is valued at an additional $1,272.0 billion, making the comprehensive cost $1,858.3 billion in 2002.

Cost estimating procedures were revised extensively for the 1993 edition of *Accident Facts*®. New components were added, new benchmarks adopted, and a new discount rate assumed (see the Technical Appendix). In general, cost estimates are not comparable from year to year. As additional or more precise data become available, they are used from that point forward. Previously estimated figures are not revised.

CERTAIN COSTS OF UNINTENTIONAL INJURIES BY CLASS, 2002 ($ BILLIONS)

Cost	Total[a]	Motor-Vehicle	Work	Home	Public Nonmotor-Vehicle
Total	**$586.3**	**$242.7**	**$146.6**	**$126.7**	**$88.3**
Wage and productivity losses	286.4	79.6	74.0	80.3	56.3
Medical expenses	106.6	28.0	27.7	30.2	22.3
Administrative expenses[b]	88.7	62.0	26.3	5.5	4.3
Motor-vehicle damage	71.1	71.1	2.8	(c)	(c)
Employer cost	22.6	2.0	12.5	4.7	3.8
Fire loss	10.9	(c)	3.3	6.0	1.6

Source: National Safety Council estimates. See the Technical Appendix.
[a]Duplication between work and motor-vehicle, which amounted to $18.0 billion, was eliminated from the total.
[b]Home and public insurance administration costs may include costs of administering medical treatment claims for some motor-vehicle injuries filed through health insurance plans.
[c]Not included; see comments above.

COST OF UNINTENTIONAL INJURIES BY CLASS, 2002

TOTAL COST $586.3 BILLION

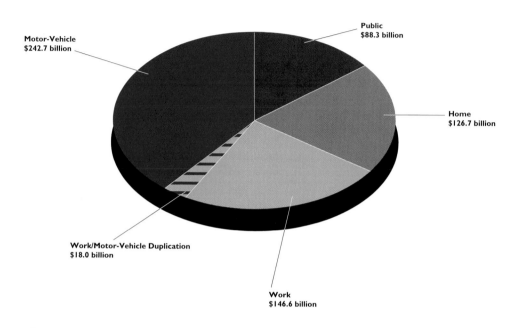

Motor-Vehicle
$242.7 billion

Public
$88.3 billion

Home
$126.7 billion

Work/Motor-Vehicle Duplication
$18.0 billion

Work
$146.6 billion

COSTS OF UNINTENTIONAL INJURIES BY COMPONENT

Wage and Productivity Losses

A person's contribution to the wealth of the nation usually is measured in terms of wages and household production. The total of wages and fringe benefits together with an estimate of the replacement-cost value of household services provides an estimate of this lost productivity. Also included is travel delay for motor-vehicle accidents.

Medical Expenses

Doctor fees, hospital charges, the cost of medicines, future medical costs, and ambulance, helicopter, and other emergency medical services are included.

Administrative Expenses

Include the administrative cost of public and private insurance, and police and legal costs. Private insurance administrative costs are the difference between premiums paid to insurance companies and claims paid out by them. It is their cost of doing business and is a part of the cost total. Claims paid by insurance companies are not identified separately, as every claim is compensation for losses such as wages, medical expenses, property damage, etc.

Motor-Vehicle Damage

Includes the value of property damage to vehicles from motor-vehicle accidents. The cost of normal wear and tear to vehicles is not included.

Employer Costs

This is an estimate of the uninsured costs incurred by employers, representing the dollar value of time lost by uninjured workers. It includes time spent investigating and reporting injuries, giving first aid, hiring and training of replacement workers, and the extra cost of overtime for uninjured workers.

Fire Loss

Includes losses from both structure fires and nonstructure fires such as vehicles, outside storage, crops, and timber.

Work—Motor-Vehicle Duplication

The cost of motor-vehicle crashes that involve persons in the course of their work is included in both classes, but the duplication is eliminated from the total. The duplication in 2002 amounted to $18.0 billion and was made up of $3.8 billion in wage and productivity losses, $1.6 billion in medical expenses, $9.4 billion in administrative expenses, $2.8 billion in vehicle damage, and $0.4 billion in uninsured employer costs.

COST OF UNINTENTIONAL INJURIES BY COMPONENT, 2002

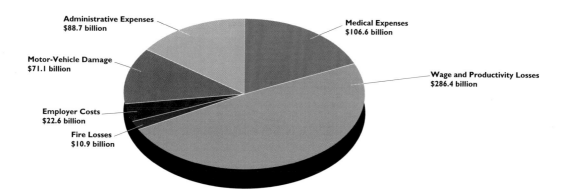

TOTAL COST $586.3 BILLION

Administrative Expenses
$88.7 billion

Medical Expenses
$106.6 billion

Motor-Vehicle Damage
$71.1 billion

Wage and Productivity Losses
$286.4 billion

Employer Costs
$22.6 billion

Fire Losses
$10.9 billion

COST EQUIVALENTS

The costs of unintentional injuries are immense — billions of dollars. Since figures this large can be difficult to comprehend, it is sometimes useful to reduce the numbers to a more understandable scale by relating them to quantities encountered in daily life.

The table below shows how the costs of unintentional injuries compare to common quantities such as taxes, corporate profits, or stock dividends.

COST EQUIVALENTS, 2002

The Cost of...	Is Equivalent to...
...All Injuries ($586.3 billion)	...70 cents of every dollar paid in federal personal income taxes, **or** ...57 cents of every dollar spent on food in the U.S.
...Motor-Vehicle Crashes ($242.7 billion)	...purchasing 720 gallons of gasoline for each registered vehicle in the U.S., **or** ...more than $1,300 per licensed driver.
...Work Injuries ($146.6 billion)	...34 cents of every dollar of corporate dividends to stockholders, **or** ...22 cents of every dollar of pre-tax corporate profits, **or** ...exceeds the combined profits reported by the top 19 Fortune 500 companies.
...Home Injuries ($126.7 billion)	...a $95,600 rebate on each new single-family home built, **or** ...47 cents of every dollar of property taxes paid.
...Public Injuries ($88.3 billion)	...a $9.7 million grant to each public library in the U.S., **or** ...a $107,300 bonus for each police officer and firefighter.

Source: National Safety Council estimates.

DEATHS DUE TO UNINTENTIONAL INJURIES, 2002

TYPE OF EVENT AND AGE OF VICTIM

All Unintentional Injuries

The term "unintentional" covers most deaths from injury and poisoning. Excluded are homicides (including legal intervention), suicides, deaths for which none of these categories can be determined, and war deaths.

	Total	Change from 2001	Death Rate[a]
Deaths	99,500	+2%	35.5

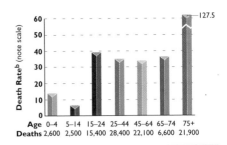

Motor-Vehicle Accidents

Includes deaths involving mechanically or electrically powered highway-transport vehicles in motion (except those on rails), both on and off the highway or street.

	Total	Change from 2001	Death Rate[a]
Deaths	44,000	+1%	15.7

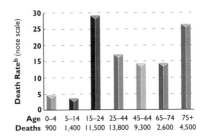

Poisoning

Includes deaths from drugs, medicines, other solid and liquid substances, and gases and vapors. Excludes poisonings from spoiled foods, salmonella, etc., which are classified as disease deaths.

	Total	Change from 2001	Death Rate[a]
Deaths	15,700	+12%	5.6

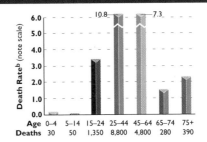

Falls

Includes deaths from falls from one level to another or on the same level. Excludes falls in or from transport vehicles, or while boarding or alighting from them.

	Total	Change from 2001	Death Rate[a]
Deaths	14,500	+1%	5.2

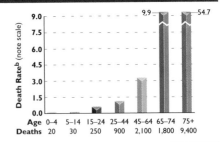

Suffocation by Ingested Object

Includes deaths from unintentional ingestion or inhalation of food or other objects, resulting in the obstruction of respiratory passages.

	Total	Change from 2001	Death Rate[a]
Deaths	4,200	+5%	1.5

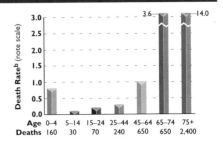

See footnotes on page 9.

DEATHS DUE TO UNINTENTIONAL INJURIES, 2002 (CONT.)

Drowning

Includes nontransport-related drownings such as those resulting from swimming, playing in the water, or falling in. Excludes drownings in floods and other cataclysms, which are classified to the cataclysm, and boating-related drownings.

	Total	Change from 2001	Death Rate[a]
Deaths	3,000	−9%	1.1

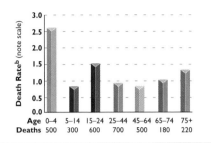

Fires, Flames, and Smoke

Includes deaths from exposure to fires, flames, and smoke, and from injuries in fires — such as falls and being struck by falling objects. Excludes burns from hot objects or liquids.

	Total	Change from 2001	Death Rate[a]
Deaths	2,900	−15%	1.0

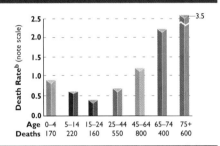

Mechanical Suffocation

Includes deaths from hanging and strangulation, and suffocation in enclosed or confined spaces, cave-ins, or by bed clothes, plastic bags, or similar materials.

	Total	Change from 2001	Death Rate[a]
Deaths	2,900	−15%	0.5

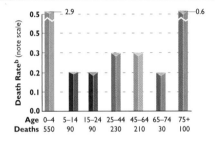

Natural Heat or Cold

Includes deaths resulting from exposure to excessive natural heat and cold (e.g., extreme weather conditions).

	Total	Change from 2001	Death Rate[a]
Deaths	1,000	−9%	0.4

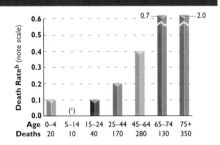

All Other Types

Most important types included are: firearms, struck by or against object, machinery, electric current, and air, water, and rail transport.

	Total	Change from 2001	Death Rate[a]
Deaths	12,900	−1%	4.6

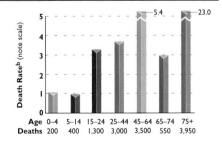

Note: Category descriptions have changed due to adoption of ICD-10. See Technical Appendix for comparablity.
[a]*Deaths per 100,000 population.*
[b]*Deaths per 100,000 population in each age group.*
[c]*Deaths rate less than 0.05.*

LEADING CAUSES OF DEATH

Unintentional injuries are the fifth leading cause of death overall and first among persons in age groups from 1 to 34. By single years of age, unintentional injuries are the leading cause from 1 to 39.

Causes are ranked for both sexes combined. Some leading causes for males and females separately may not

be shown. Beginning with 1999 data, deaths are classified according to the 10th revision of the International Classification of Diseases. See the Technical Appendix for comparability.

DEATHS AND DEATH RATES BY AGE AND SEX, 2000

Cause	Number of Deaths			Death Rates[a]		
	Total	Male	Female	Total	Male	Female
All Ages[b]						
All Causes	**2,403,351**	**1,177,578**	**1,225,773**	**873.0**	**875.2**	**870.9**
Heart disease	710,760	344,807	365,953	258.2	256.3	260.0
Cancer (malignant neoplasms)	553,091	286,082	267,009	200.9	212.6	189.7
Stroke (cerebrovascular disease)	167,661	64,769	102,892	60.9	48.1	73.1
Chronic lower respiratory diseases	122,009	60,004	62,005	44.3	44.6	44.1
Unintentional injuries	**97,900**	**63,817**	**34,083**	**35.6**	**47.4**	**24.2**
Motor-vehicle	43,354	29,451	13,903	15.7	21.9	9.9
Falls	13,322	7,122	6,200	4.8	5.3	4.4
Poisoning	12,757	9,138	3,619	4.6	6.8	2.6
Inhalation, ingestion of food, object	4,313	2,152	2,161	1.6	1.6	1.5
Drowning	3,482	2,735	747	1.3	2.0	0.5
All other unintentional injuries	20,672	13,219	7,453	7.5	9.8	5.3
Diabetes mellitus	69,301	31,602	37,699	25.2	23.5	26.8
Influenza and pneumonia	65,313	28,658	36,655	23.7	21.3	26.0
Alzheimer's disease	49,558	14,438	35,120	18.0	10.7	25.0
Nephritis and nephrosis	37,251	17,811	19,440	13.5	13.2	13.8
Septicemia	31,224	13,537	17,687	11.3	10.1	12.6
Under 1 Year						
All Causes	**28,035**	**15,718**	**12,317**	**728.7**	**799.9**	**654.3**
Congenital anomalies	5,743	3,028	2,715	149.3	154.1	144.2
Short gestation, low birth weight, n.e.c.	4,397	2,391	2,006	114.3	121.7	106.6
Sudden infant death syndrome	2,523	1,509	1,014	65.6	76.8	53.9
Maternal complications of pregnancy	1,404	791	613	36.5	40.3	32.6
Complications of placenta, cord, membranes	1,062	569	493	27.6	29.0	26.2
Respiratory distress	999	643	356	26.0	32.7	18.9
Unintentional injuries	**881**	**501**	**380**	**22.9**	**25.5**	**20.2**
Mechanical suffocation	449	258	191	11.7	13.1	10.1
Motor-vehicle	168	90	78	4.4	4.6	4.1
Inhalation, ingestion of food, object	77	44	33	2.0	2.2	1.8
Drowning	75	43	32	1.9	2.2	1.7
Fires and flames	37	20	17	1.0	1.0	0.9
All other unintentional injuries	75	46	29	1.9	2.3	1.5
Bacterial sepsis	768	447	321	20.0	22.7	17.1
Diseases of the circulatory system	663	357	306	17.2	18.2	16.3
Intrauterine hypoxia and birth asphyxia	630	352	278	16.4	17.9	14.8
1 to 4 Years						
All Causes	**4,979**	**2,824**	**2,155**	**33.2**	**36.8**	**29.3**
Unintentional injuries	**1,826**	**1,098**	**728**	**12.2**	**14.3**	**9.9**
Motor-vehicle	651	368	283	4.3	4.8	3.9
Drowning	493	316	177	3.3	4.1	2.4
Fires and flames	290	174	116	1.9	2.3	1.6
Inhalation, ingestion of food, object	92	56	36	0.6	0.7	0.5
Mechanical suffocation	59	36	23	0.4	0.5	0.3
All other unintentional injuries	241	148	93	1.6	1.9	1.3
Congenital anomalies	495	259	236	3.3	3.4	3.2
Cancer (malignant neoplasms)	420	233	187	2.8	3.0	2.5
Homicide	356	198	158	2.4	2.6	2.2
Heart disease	181	107	74	1.2	1.4	1.0
Influenza and pneumonia	103	54	49	0.7	0.7	0.7
Septicemia	99	53	46	0.7	0.7	0.6
Certain conditions originating in the perinatal period	79	52	27	0.5	0.7	0.4
Benign neoplasms	53	33	20	0.4	0.4	0.3
Chronic lower respiratory diseases	51	28	23	0.3	0.4	0.3

See source and footnotes on page 12.

DEATHS AND DEATH RATES BY AGE AND SEX, 2000, Cont.

Cause	Number of Deaths			Death Rates[a]		
	Total	Male	Female	Total	Male	Female
5 to 14 Years						
All Causes	**7,413**	**4,401**	**3,012**	**18.7**	**21.7**	**15.5**
Unintentional injuries	**2,979**	**1,861**	**1,118**	**7.5**	**9.2**	**5.8**
Motor-vehicle	1,772	1,043	729	4.5	5.1	3.8
Drowning	375	267	108	0.9	1.3	0.6
Fires and flames	266	145	121	0.7	0.7	0.6
Mechanical suffocation	93	73	20	0.2	0.4	0.1
Firearms	67	62	5	0.2	0.3	0.0
All other unintentional injuries	406	271	135	1.0	1.3	0.7
Cancer (malignant neoplasms)	1,014	569	445	2.6	2.8	2.3
Congenital anomalies	399	207	192	1.0	1.0	1.0
Homicide	371	227	144	0.9	1.1	0.7
Suicide	307	244	63	0.8	1.2	0.3
Heart disease	271	163	108	0.7	0.8	0.6
Chronic lower respiratory diseases	139	80	59	0.4	0.4	0.3
Benign neoplasms	99	49	50	0.2	0.2	0.3
Influenza and pneumonia	87	48	39	0.2	0.2	0.2
Stroke (cerebrovascular disease)	76	33	43	0.2	0.2	0.2
15 to 24 Years						
All Causes	**31,307**	**23,071**	**8,236**	**81.5**	**117.3**	**43.9**
Unintentional injuries	**14,113**	**10,460**	**3,653**	**36.7**	**53.2**	**19.5**
Motor-vehicle	10,560	7,516	3,044	27.5	38.2	16.2
Poisoning	1,160	920	240	3.0	4.7	1.3
Drowning	646	583	63	1.7	3.0	0.3
Falls	237	203	34	0.6	1.0	0.2
Firearms	202	183	19	0.5	0.9	0.1
All other unintentional injuries	1,308	1,055	253	3.4	5.4	1.3
Homicide	4,939	4,203	736	12.9	21.4	3.9
Suicide	3,994	3,424	570	10.4	17.4	3.0
Cancer	1,713	1,022	691	4.5	5.2	3.7
Heart disease	1,031	638	393	2.7	3.2	2.1
Congenital anomalies	441	268	173	1.1	1.4	0.9
Stroke (cerebrovascular disease)	199	106	93	0.5	0.5	0.5
Chronic lower respiratory diseases	190	120	70	0.5	0.6	0.4
Influenza and pneumonia	189	102	87	0.5	0.5	0.5
Human immunodeficiency virus infection	179	99	80	0.5	0.5	0.4
25 to 34 Years						
All Causes	**40,451**	**27,890**	**12,561**	**108.0**	**150.3**	**66.5**
Unintentional injuries	**11,769**	**9,059**	**2,710**	**31.4**	**48.8**	**14.4**
Motor-vehicle	6,884	5,135	1,749	18.4	27.7	9.3
Poisoning	2,380	1,820	560	6.4	9.8	3.0
Drowning	419	364	55	1.1	2.0	0.3
Falls	303	272	31	0.8	1.5	0.2
Fires and flames	241	157	84	0.6	0.8	0.4
All other unintentional injuries	1,542	1,311	231	4.1	7.1	1.2
Suicide	4,792	3,938	854	12.8	21.2	4.5
Homicide	4,164	3,361	803	11.1	18.1	4.3
Cancer	3,916	1,854	2,062	10.5	10.0	10.9
Heart disease	2,958	1,922	1,036	7.9	10.4	5.5
Human immunodeficiency virus infection	2,437	1,602	835	6.5	8.6	4.4
Diabetes mellitus	623	376	247	1.7	2.0	1.3
Stroke (cerebrovascular disease)	602	308	294	1.6	1.7	1.6
Congenital anomalies	477	279	198	1.3	1.5	1.0
Chronic liver disease and cirrhosis	415	280	135	1.1	1.5	0.7
35 to 44 Years						
All Causes	**89,798**	**57,297**	**32,501**	**200.0**	**257.1**	**143.8**
Cancer	16,520	7,344	9,176	36.8	32.9	40.6
Unintentional injuries	**15,413**	**11,444**	**3,969**	**34.3**	**51.3**	**17.6**
Motor-vehicle	6,927	4,940	1,987	15.4	22.2	8.8
Poisoning	4,663	3,384	1,279	10.4	15.2	5.7
Falls	608	496	112	1.4	2.2	0.5
Drowning	480	406	74	1.1	1.8	0.3
Fires and flames	402	268	134	0.9	1.2	0.6
All other unintentional injuries	2,333	1,950	383	5.2	8.7	1.7
Heart disease	13,181	9,286	3,895	29.4	41.7	17.2
Suicide	6,562	5,114	1,448	14.6	22.9	6.4
Human immunodeficiency virus infection	5,919	4,441	1,478	13.2	19.9	6.5
Chronic liver disease and cirrhosis	3,371	2,314	1,057	7.5	10.4	4.7
Homicide	3,219	2,319	900	7.2	10.4	4.0
Stroke (cerebrovascular disease)	2,599	1,297	1,302	5.8	5.8	5.8
Diabetes mellitus	1,926	1,151	775	4.3	5.2	3.4
Influenza and pneumonia	1,068	630	438	2.4	2.8	1.9

See source and footnotes on page 12.

LEADING CAUSES OF DEATH (CONT.)

DEATHS AND DEATH RATES BY AGE AND SEX, 2000, Cont.

Cause	Number of Deaths			Death Rates[a]		
	Total	Male	Female	Total	Male	Female
45 to 54 Years						
All Causes	**160,341**	**100,398**	**59,943**	**431.4**	**552.4**	**315.6**
Cancer	48,034	24,215	23,819	129.2	133.2	125.4
Heart disease	35,480	25,927	9,553	95.5	142.7	50.3
Unintentional injuries	**12,278**	**9,063**	**3,215**	**33.0**	**49.9**	**16.9**
Motor-vehicle	5,361	3,780	1,581	14.4	20.8	8.3
Poisoning	3,061	2,223	838	8.2	12.2	4.4
Falls	871	690	181	2.3	3.8	1.0
Fires and flames	439	303	136	1.2	1.7	0.7
Drowning	354	299	55	1.0	1.6	0.3
All other unintentional injuries	2,192	1,768	424	5.9	9.7	2.2
Chronic liver disease and cirrhosis	6,654	4,975	1,679	17.9	27.4	8.8
Stroke (cerebrovascular disease)	6,011	3,235	2,776	16.2	17.8	14.6
Suicide	5,437	4,149	1,288	14.6	22.8	6.8
Diabetes mellitus	4,954	2,821	2,133	13.3	15.5	11.2
Human immunodeficiency virus infection	4,142	3,296	846	11.1	18.1	4.5
Chronic lower respiratory diseases	3,251	1,661	1,590	8.7	9.1	8.4
Viral hepatitis	1,894	1,425	469	5.1	7.8	2.5
55 to 64 Years						
All Causes	**240,846**	**143,321**	**97,525**	**1,003.5**	**1,252.5**	**776.6**
Cancer	89,005	48,427	40,578	370.8	423.2	323.1
Heart disease	63,399	43,285	20,114	264.2	378.3	160.2
Chronic lower respiratory diseases	10,739	5,564	5,175	44.7	48.6	41.2
Stroke (cerebrovascular disease)	9,956	5,496	4,460	41.5	48.0	35.5
Diabetes mellitus	9,186	4,943	4,243	38.3	43.2	33.8
Unintentional injuries	**7,505**	**5,133**	**2,372**	**31.3**	**44.9**	**18.9**
Motor-vehicle	3,506	2,306	1,200	14.6	20.2	9.6
Falls	949	680	269	4.0	5.9	2.1
Poisoning	688	401	287	2.9	3.5	2.3
Fires and flames	369	241	128	1.5	2.1	1.0
Inhalation, ingestion of food, object	329	190	139	1.4	1.7	1.1
All other unintentional injuries	1,664	1,315	349	6.9	11.5	2.8
Chronic liver disease and cirrhosis	5,774	4,005	1,769	24.1	35.0	14.1
Nephritis and nephrosis	3,100	1,651	1,449	12.9	14.4	11.5
Suicide	2,945	2,265	680	12.3	19.8	5.4
Septicemia	2,899	1,513	1,386	12.1	13.2	11.0
65 to 74 Years						
All Causes	**441,209**	**247,408**	**193,801**	**2,425.7**	**3,013.5**	**1,942.1**
Cancer	150,131	83,191	66,940	825.4	1,013.3	670.8
Heart disease	122,405	74,589	47,816	673.0	908.5	479.2
Chronic lower respiratory diseases	31,157	16,210	14,947	171.3	197.4	149.8
Stroke (cerebrovascular disease)	23,649	12,042	11,607	130.0	146.7	116.3
Diabetes mellitus	16,674	8,226	8,448	91.7	100.2	84.7
Unintentional injuries	**7,698**	**4,639**	**3,059**	**42.3**	**56.5**	**30.7**
Motor-vehicle	3,038	1,802	1,236	16.7	21.9	12.4
Falls	1,660	991	669	9.1	12.1	6.7
Inhalation, ingestion of food, object	569	301	268	3.1	3.7	2.7
Fires and flames	401	232	169	2.2	2.8	1.7
Poisoning	278	147	131	1.5	1.8	1.3
All other unintentional injuries	1,752	1,166	586	9.6	14.2	5.9
Influenza and pneumonia	7,189	4,013	3,176	39.5	48.9	31.8
Nephritis and nephrosis	6,990	3,564	3,426	38.4	43.4	34.3
Septicemia	5,704	2,867	2,837	31.4	34.9	28.4
Chronic liver disease and cirrhosis	5,482	3,317	2,165	30.1	40.4	21.7
75 Years and Older[b]						
All Causes	**1,358,972**	**555,250**	**803,722**	**8,163.5**	**8,865.6**	**7,740.0**
Heart disease	471,361	188,630	282,731	2,831.5	3,011.8	2,722.8
Cancer	242,246	119,177	123,069	1,455.2	1,902.9	1,185.2
Stroke (cerebrovascular disease)	124,398	42,159	82,239	747.3	673.1	792.0
Chronic lower respiratory diseases	75,220	35,716	39,504	451.9	570.3	380.4
Influenza and pneumonia	51,371	20,698	30,673	308.6	330.5	295.4
Alzheimer's disease	45,564	12,635	32,929	273.7	201.7	317.1
Diabetes mellitus	35,740	13,972	21,768	214.7	223.1	209.6
Nephritis and nephrosis	24,237	10,886	13,351	145.6	173.8	128.6
Unintentional injuries	**23,438**	**10,559**	**12,879**	**140.8**	**168.6**	**124.0**
Falls	8,613	3,731	4,882	51.7	59.6	47.0
Motor-vehicle	4,487	2,471	2,016	27.0	39.5	19.4
Inhalation, ingestion of food, object	2,616	1,146	1,470	15.7	18.3	14.2
Fires and flames	740	364	376	4.4	5.8	3.6
Poisoning	436	184	252	2.6	2.9	2.4
All other unintentional injuries	6,546	2,663	3,883	39.3	42.5	37.4
Septicemia	19,083	7,219	11,864	114.6	115.3	114.3

Source: Adapted from Anderson, R.N. (2002). Deaths: Leading causes for 2000. National Vital Statistics Reports, 50(16), 13-19, 70; with additional National Safety Council tabulations of NCHS mortality data.
[a] Deaths per 100,000 population in each age group.
[b] Includes 356 deaths where the age is unknown.

LEADING CAUSES OF NONFATAL INJURIES

LEADING CAUSES OF NONFATAL UNINTENTIONAL INJURIES TREATED IN HOSPITAL EMERGENCY DEPARTMENTS BY AGE GROUP, UNITED STATES, 2001

Rank	All Ages	<1	1–4	5–9	10–14	15–24	25–34	35–44	45–54	55–64	65+
1	Falls 7,836,956	Falls 125,026	Falls 914,249	Falls 747,011	Falls 715,634	Struck by/against 989,434	Falls 768,445	Falls 850,414	Falls 712,426	Falls 499,676	Falls 1,642,135
2	Struck by/against 4,610,361	Struck by/against 34,708	Struck by/against 413,811	Struck by/against 484,794	Struck by/against 618,272	Motor-vehicle occupant 935,107	Overexertion 757,144	Overexertion 695,055	Overexertion 409,337	Struck by/against 183,838	Struck by/against 194,473
3	Overexertion 3,487,316	Other bite/sting[a] 11,225	Other bite/sting[a] 128,096	Cut/pierce 150,568	Overexertion 301,136	Falls 860,223	Struck by/against 712,407	Struck by/against 604,588	Struck by/against 373,750	Motor-vehicle occupant 176,285	Motor-vehicle occupant 185,956
4	Motor-vehicle occupant 3,041,622	Fire/burn 10,667	Foreign body 119,487	Pedalcyclist 110,505	Cut/pierce 183,215	Overexertion 829,338	Motor-vehicle occupant 628,788	Motor-vehicle occupant 522,125	Motor-vehicle occupant 337,577	Overexertion 171,736	Overexertion 162,782
5	Cut/Pierce 2,472,325	Foreign body 9,960	Cut/pierce 103,246	Other bite/sting[a] 88,872	Pedalcyclist 143,597	Cut/pierce 547,438	Cut/pierce 503,002	Cut/pierce 427,373	Cut/pierce 286,939	Cut/pierce 143,944	Cut/pierce 118,914
6	Other bite/sting[a] 849,703	Poisoning 8,345	Poisoning 82,534	Overexertion 84,270	Unknown/unspecified 125,492	Unknown/unspecified 206,808	Unknown/unspecified 128,825	Other bite/sting[a] 113,748	Other bite/sting[a] 92,078	Other bite/sting[a] 52,546	Other bite/sting[a] 59,955
7	Unknown/unspecified 829,324	Cut/pierce 7,513	Overexertion 70,546	Motor-vehicle occupant 81,681	Motor-vehicle occupant 114,376	Other bite/sting[a] 127,386	Foreign body 117,120	Foreign body 112,468	Poisoning 75,067	Foreign body 31,620	Unknown/unspecified 53,666
8	Foreign body 708,374	Motor-vehicle occupant 6,974	Fire/burn 68,794	Foreign body 66,969	Other bite/sting[a] 60,997	Other transport[b] 127,163	Other bite/sting[a] 114,775	Unknown/unspecified 107,891	Foreign body 72,239	Poisoning 31,434	Other transport[b] 45,645
9	Other transport[b] 583,142	Unknown/unspecified 5,956	Motor-vehicle occupant 50,662	Dog bite 56,258	Other transport[b] 59,285	Foreign body 111,918	Other transport[b] 97,283	Poisoning 106,094	Other specified[c] 67,395	Unknown/unspecified 31,060	Foreign body 34,227
10	Poisoning 519,164	Overexertion 5,761	Unknown/unspecified 49,768	Unknown/unspecified 53,710	Dog bite 49,019	Fire/burn 98,867	Fire/burn 91,334	Other specified 100,149	Unknown/unspecified 65,732	Other transport[b] 27,211	Poisoning 27,926
All Causes											
Number	27,566,102	2,390,596		2,054,155	2,513,402	5,354,332	4,331,097	4,043,273	2,757,602	1,472,324	2,649,321[d]
Per 1,000 population	99.2	126.5		105.1	124.0	137.0	116.9	90.5	71.4	60.0	75.6[d]

Source: NEISS All Injury Program, Office of Statistics and Programming, National Center for Injury Prevention and Control, CDC, and Consumer Product Safety Commission.
[a] *Other than dog bite.*
[b] *Includes occupant of any transport vehicle other than a motor vehicle or motor cycle (e.g., airplane, rail car, boat, ATV, animal rider).*
[c] *Includes electric current, explosions, fireworks, radiation, animal scratch, etc. Excludes all causes listed in the table and bb/pellet gunshot, drowning and near drowning, firearm gunshot, suffocation, machinery, natural and environmental conditions, pedestrians, and motorcyclists.*
[d] *Includes 6,918 cases with age unknown.*

Falls are the leading cause of nonfatal injuries that are treated in hospital emergency departments (ED) according to data from the All Injury Program, a cooperative program involving the National Center for Injury Prevention and Control, CDC, and the Consumer Product Safety Commission. Nearly eight million people were treated in the ED for fall-related injuries in 2001. Falls were the leading cause of nonfatal injuries for all age groups except 15–24 years old, for which struck by or against an object or person was the leading cause. Struck by or against, overexertion, and motor-vehicle crashes involving vehicle occupants were also leading causes for most age groups.

LEADING CAUSES OF UNINTENTIONAL-INJURY DEATH BY AGE, 2000

LEADING CAUSES OF UNINTENTIONAL-INJURY DEATH BY AGE, UNITED STATES, 2000

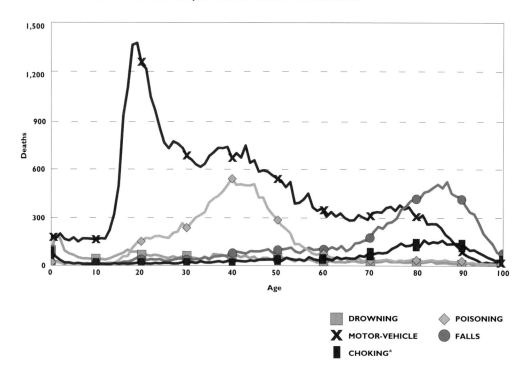

Motor-vehicle crashes, falls, poisonings, choking (suffocation by inhalation or ingestion of food or other object), drownings, fires and flames, and mechanical suffocation were the seven leading causes of unintentional-injury death in the United States in 2000. The graph above depicts the number of deaths attributed to the top five causes by single years of age through age 99.

Motor-vehicle crashes were the leading cause of unintentional-injury death overall and the leading cause of unintentional-injury death from age 2 to 77 in 2000. The distribution of 2000 motor-vehicle fatalities shows a sharp increase for persons aged 13 to 19, rising from 211 for 13-year-olds to 1,376 for 19-year-olds. The greatest number of motor-vehicle fatalities occurred to persons aged 18 and 19 in 2000.

The second leading cause of unintentional-injury death overall in 2000 was falls. Falls were the leading cause of unintentional-injury death of persons aged 78 and older and second leading cause from ages 57 through 77; deaths resulting from falls peaked at 514 for individuals age 87. Poisoning was the third leading cause of

unintentional-injury death in the United States in 2000. Poisoning fatalities reached a high of 532 for 40-year-old individuals and were the second leading cause of unintentional-injury death for persons aged 18 to 56.

Choking was the fourth leading cause of unintentional-injury death in 2000. Choking deaths peaked at age 86 with 149 deaths. It was the second leading cause of unintentional-injury deaths for age 89 and older. Drownings were the fifth leading cause of unintentional-injury death in 2000. Drowning fatalities reached a high of 184 for 1-year-olds (the leading cause for that age) and were the second leading cause of unintentional-injury death for ages 2, 3, 5, and 8 to 17.

The sixth leading cause of unintentional-injury death was fires and flames, which peaked at 80 for 2-year-olds. Mechanical suffocation was the seventh leading cause overall and the leading cause for infants under 1 year old with 449 deaths.

Source: National Safety Council tabulations of National Center for Health Statistics data. See the Technical Appendix for ICD-10 codes for the leading causes and comparability with prior years.
a Inhalation or ingestion of food or other objects.

UNINTENTIONAL-INJURY DEATH RATES BY AGE, 2000

UNINTENTIONAL-INJURY DEATH RATES BY AGE, UNITED STATES, 2000

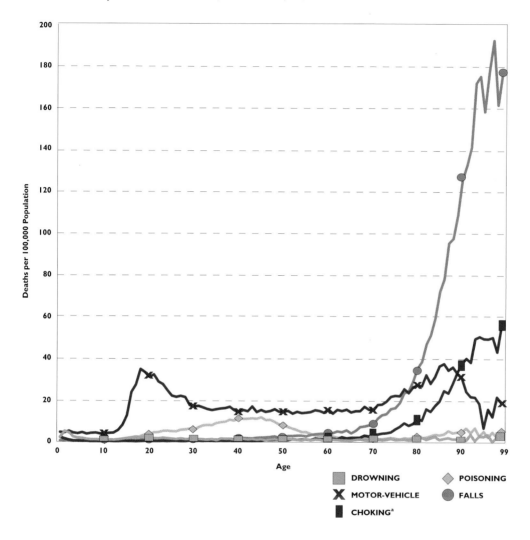

On a rate basis, motor-vehicle deaths by single year of age in 2000 rose to a high of 34.7 per 100,000 population for persons 18 years of age. This rate declined to an average of about 15.0 for those aged 30 to 70, then increased to another high at 37.4 for those 86 years of age.

While motor-vehicle crashes are a significant problem for all ages, deaths resulting from falls for certain older ages have even higher death rates. Beginning at about age 70, the death rate from falls increases dramatically. At age 78 the falls death rate surpasses that for motor-vehicle, with the death rate continuing to rise through 97 years of age where it reaches 192.6.

The poisoning death rate remains low until about age 20, where it begins rising to its peak rate of 11.7 at 45 years of age then falls again.

Death rates due to choking on inhaled or ingested food or other objects are quite low for most ages. Rates are slightly elevated for infants and toddlers and rise rapidly beginning at about age 70. The death rates for drownings show peaks at very young ages and again at some very old ages.

The graph above depicts death rates per 100,000 population for the five leading causes of unintentional-injury deaths in 2000 for single years of age through age 99.

Source: National Safety Council tabulations of National Center for Health Statistics data. See the Technical Appendix for ICD-10 codes for the leading causes and comparability with prior years.
a Inhalation or ingestion of food or other objects.

UNINTENTIONAL-INJURY DEATHS
BY SEX AND AGE

UNINTENTIONAL-INJURY DEATHS BY SEX AND AGE, UNITED STATES, 2000

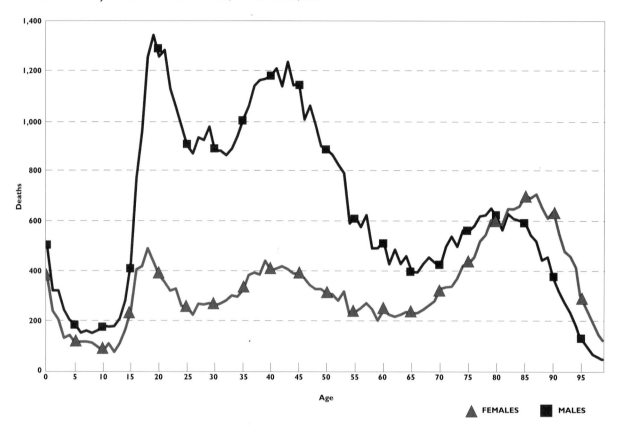

Males incur more deaths due to unintentional injuries than females at all ages from under one year old to age 80. The difference between the unintentional-injury death totals ranges from 36 at age 6 to 926 at age 21. The excess number of deaths for males compared to females is most evident from the late teenage years to the mid forties where the gap begins to narrow. Beginning at age 81, deaths of females exceed those of males by as little as 20 deaths at age 82 to as much as 266 at age 90.

Unintentional-injury deaths are at their lowest level for both sexes from about age 4 to about age 13. For males the highest number of deaths (1,343) occurs at age 19 and the totals remain high until the mid-forties. For females, however, the highest totals occur among the elderly from about age 75 and older. The greatest number of female deaths (708) occurs at age 87.

The graph above shows the number of unintentional-injury deaths for each sex by single years of age from under one year old to age 99. It is based on death certificate data from the National Center for Health Statistics.

UNINTENTIONAL-INJURY DEATH RATES BY SEX AND AGE

UNINTENTIONAL-INJURY DEATH RATES BY SEX AND AGE, UNITED STATES, 2000

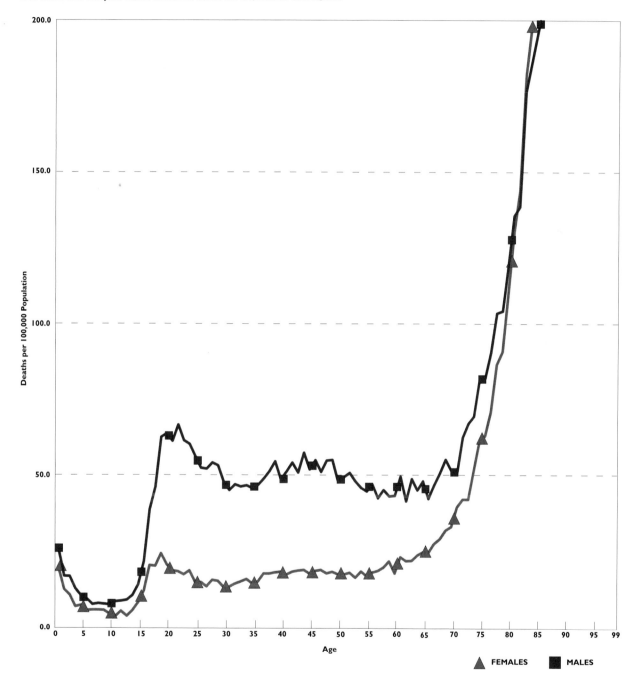

Males have greater unintentional-injury death rates at every age from under one year old to age 80. Above age 80, females have higher death rates at every age.

The graph above shows the unintentional-injury death rates for males and females by single years of age from under one year old to about age 80. It is based on National Center for Health Statistics mortality data and U.S. Census Bureau population data.

Death rates for both sexes are lowest from birth until the mid teenage years where rates rise rapidly. Rates then remain fairly constant until the late sixties where they again rise steadily with increasing age. Rates for males in their late nineties are generally between 500 and 600 per 100,000 population. Rates for females in their late nineties are greater than 1,500. For comparison, the overall unintentional-injury death rate for all ages and both sexes was 35.6.

ALL DEATHS DUE TO INJURY

MORTALITY BY SELECTED EXTERNAL CAUSES, UNITED STATES, 1999–2000

Type of Accident or Manner of Injury	2000[a]	1999
All External Causes of Mortality, V01–Y98[b]	**151,268**	**151,10**
Deaths Due to Unintentional (Accidental) Injuries, V01–X59, Y85–Y86	**97,900**	**97,860**
Transport Accidents, V01–V99, Y85	**46,749**	**46,423**
Pedestrian, V01–V09	5,870	6,047
Pedalcyclist, V10–V19	740	800
Motorcycle rider, V20–V29	2,765	2,316
Occupant of three-wheeled motor vehicle, V30–V39	23	33
Car occupant, V40–V49	14,813	14,549
Occupant of pick-up truck or van, V50–V59	3,268	3,133
Occupant of heavy transport vehicle, V60–V69	369	422
Bus occupant, V70–V79	20	62
Animal rider or occupant of animal-drawn vehicle, V80	97	110
Occupant of railway train or railway vehicle, V81	30	54
Occupant of streetcar, V82	1	1
Other and unspecified land transport accidents, V83–V89	16,850	16,992
Occupant of special industrial vehicle, V83	*15*	*18*
Occupant of special agricultural vehicle, V84	*273*	*348*
Occupant of special construction vehicle, V85	*37*	*38*
Occupant of all-terrain or other off-road motor vehicle, V86	*717*	*603*
Other and unspecified person, V87–V89	*15,808*	*15,985*
Water transport accidents, V90–V94	630	679
Drowning, V90, V92	*466*	*501*
Other and unspecified injuries, V91, V93–V94	*164*	*178*
Air and space transport accidents, V95–V97	777	715
Other and unspecified transport accidents and sequelae, V98–V99, Y85	496	510
Other specified transport accidents, V98	*2*	*8*
Unspecified transport accident, V99	*4*	*6*
Nontransport Unintentional (Accidental) Injuries, W00–X59, Y86	**51,151**	**51,437**
Falls, W00–W19	13,322	13,162
Fall on same level from slipping, tripping, and stumbling, W01	*565*	*611*
Other fall on same level, W00, W02–W03, W18	*1,885*	*820*
Fall involving bed, chair, other furniture, W06–W08	*650*	*624*
Fall on and from stairs and steps, W10	*1,307*	*1,421*
Fall on and from ladder or scaffolding, W11–W12	*412*	*375*
Fall from out of or through building or structure, W13	*506*	*550*
Other fall from one level to another, W09, W14–W17	*687*	*772*
Other and unspecified fall, W04–W05, W19	*7,310*	*7,989*
Exposure to inanimate mechanical forces, W20–W49	2,768	2,739
Struck by or striking against object, W20–W22	*877*	*842*
Caught between objects, W23	*84*	*93*
Contact with machinery, W24, W30–W31	*676*	*622*
Contact with sharp objects, W25–W29	*80*	*68*
Firearms discharge, W32–W34	*776*	*824*
Explosion and rupture of pressurized devices, W35–W38	*30*	*33*
Fireworks discharge, W39	*5*	*7*
Explosion of other materials, W40	*167*	*166*
Foreign body entering through skin or natural orifice, W44–W45	*36*	*38*
Other and unspecified inanimate mechanical forces, W41–W43, W49	*37*	*46*
Exposure to animate mechanical forces, W50–W64	204	214
Struck by or against another person, W50–W52	*61*	*52*
Bitten or struck by dog, W54	*26*	*25*
Bitten or struck by other mammals, W53, W55	*65*	*69*
Bitten or stung by nonvenomous insect and other arthropods, W57	*9*	*10*
Bitten or crushed by other reptiles, W59	*31*	*45*
Other and unspecified animate mechanical forces, W56, W58, W60, W64	*12*	*13*
Accidental drowning and submersion, W65–W74	3,482	3,529
Drowning and submersion while in or falling into bath-tub, W65–W66	*341*	*320*
Drowning and submersion while in or falling into swimming-pool, W67–W68	*567*	*530*
Drowning and submersion while in or falling into natural water, W69–W70	*1,135*	*1,212*
Other and unspecified drowning and submersion, W73–W74	*1,439*	*1,467*
Other accidental threats to breathing, W75–W84	5,648	5,503
Accidental suffocation and strangulation in bed, W75	*327*	*330*
Other accidental hanging and strangulation, W76	*333*	*307*
Threat to breathing due to cave-in, falling earth and other substances, W77	*64*	*47*
Inhalation of gastric contents, W78	*382*	*417*
Inhalation and ingestion of food causing obstruction of respiratory tract, W79	*744*	*640*
Inhalation and ingestion of other objects causing obstruction of respiratory tract, W80	*3,187*	*2,828*
Confined to or trapped in a low-oxygen environment, W81	*15*	*16*
Other and unspecified threats to breathing, W83–W84	*596*	*918*

See source and footnotes on page 19.

MORTALITY BY SELECTED EXTERNAL CAUSES, UNITED STATES, 1999–2000

Type of Accident or Manner of Injury	2000[a]	1999
Exposure to electric current, radiation, temperature, and pressure, W85–W99	419	479
Electric transmission lines, W85	99	127
Other and unspecified electric current, W86–W87	296	310
Radiation, W88–W91	0	0
Excessive heat or cold of man-made origin, W92–W93	12	18
High and low air pressure and changes in air pressure, W94	12	22
Other and unspecified man-made environmental factors, W99	0	2
Exposure to smoke, fire and flames, X00–X09	3,377	3,348
Uncontrolled fire in building or structure, X00	2,776	2,676
Uncontrolled fire not in building or structure, X01	68	78
Controlled fire in building or structure, X02	50	56
Controlled fire not in building or structure, X03	29	32
Ignition of highly flammable material, X04	65	73
Ignition or melting of nightwear, X05	9	6
Ignition or melting of other clothing and apparel, X06	116	112
Other and unspecified smoke, fire and flames, X08–X09	264	315
Contact with heat and hot substances, X10–X19	110	123
Contact with hot tap-water, X11	55	51
Other and unspecified heat and hot substances, X10, X12–X19	55	72
Contact with venomous animals and plants, X20–X29	80	61
Contact with venomous snakes and lizards, X20	12	7
Contact with venomous spiders, X21	5	6
Contact with hornets, wasps and bees, X23	54	43
Contact with other and unspecified venomous animal or plant, X22, X24–X29	9	5
Exposure to forces of nature, X30–X39	1,223	1,488
Exposure to excessive natural heat, X30	301	594
Exposure to excessive natural cold, X31	742	598
Lightning, X33	50	64
Earthquake and other earth movements, X34–X36	35	46
Cataclysmic storm, X37	49	129
Flood, X38	5	15
Exposure to other and unspecified forces of nature, X32, X39	41	42
Accidental poisoning by and exposure to noxious substances, X40–X49	12,757	12,186
Nonopioid analgesics, antipyretics, and antirheumatics, X40	176	168
Antiepileptic, sedative-hypnotic, antiparkinsonism, and psychotropic drugs n.e.c., X41	704	671
Narcotics and psychodysleptics [hallucinogens] n.e.c., X42	6,139	6,009
Other and unspecified drugs, medicaments, and biologicals, X43–X44	4,693	4,307
Alcohol, X45	302	320
Gases and vapours, X46–X47	631	597
Other and unspecified chemicals and noxious substances, X48–X49	112	114
Overexertion, travel and privation, X50–X57	185	191
Accidental exposure to other and unspecified factors and sequelae, X58–X59, Y86	7,576	8,414
Intentional self-harm, X60–X84, Y87.0	**29,350**	**29,199**
Intentional self-poisoning, X60–X69	4,859	4,893
Intentional self-harm by hanging, strangulation, and suffocation, X70	5,688	5,427
Intentional self-harm by firearm, X72–X74	16,586	16,599
Other and unspecified means and sequelae, X71, X75–X84, Y87.0	2,217	2,280
Assault, X85–Y09, Y87.1	**16,765**	**16,889**
Assault by firearm, X93–X95	10,801	10,828
Assault by sharp object, X99	1,805	1,879
Other and unspecified means and sequelae, X85–X92, X96–X98, Y00–Y09, Y87.1	4,159	4,182
Event of undetermined intent, Y10–Y34, Y87.2, Y89.9	**3,819**	**3,917**
Poisoning, Y10–Y19	2,557	2,595
Hanging, strangulation, and suffocation, Y20	104	110
Drowning and submersion, Y21	231	243
Firearm discharge, Y22–Y24	230	324
Exposure to smoke, fire, and flames, Y26	76	70
Falling, jumping, or pushed from a high place, Y30	55	59
Other and unspecified means and sequelae, Y25, Y27–Y29, Y31–Y34, Y87.2, Y89.9	566	516
Legal intervention, Y35, Y89.0	**359**	**398**
Legal intervention involving firearm discharge, Y35.0	270	299
Legal execution, Y35.5	80	88
Other and unspecified means and sequelae, Y35.1–Y35.4, Y35.6–Y35.7, Y89.0	9	11
Operations of war and sequelae, Y36, Y89.1	**16**	**23**
Complications of medical and surgical care and sequelae, Y40–Y84, Y88.0–Y88.3	**3,059**	**2,823**

Source: National Center for Health Statistics. Deaths are classified on the basis of the Tenth Revision of "The International Classification of Diseases" (ICD-10), which became effective in 1999.
Note: n.e.c. = not elsewhere classified.
[a]Latest official figures.
[b]Numbers following titles refer to External Cause of Injury and Poisoning classifications in ICD-10.

DEATHS BY AGE, SEX, AND TYPE

UNINTENTIONAL-INJURY DEATHS BY AGE, SEX, AND TYPE, UNITED STATES, 2000[a]

Age & Sex	All Types[b]	Motor-vehicle	Falls	Poisoning	Choking[c]	Drowning[d]	Fires/Flames	Mechanical Suffocation	Natural Heat/Cold	% Male, All Types
All Ages	**97,900**	**43,354**	**13,322**	**12,757**	**4,313**	**3,482**	**3,377**	**1,335**	**1,043**	**65%**
Under 5	2,707	819	44	46	169	568	327	508	27	59%
5–14	2,979	1,772	37	45	24	375	266	93	10	63%
15–24	14,113	10,560	237	1,160	45	646	192	102	38	74%
25–44	27,182	13,811	911	7,043	270	899	643	276	180	75%
45–64	19,783	8,867	1,820	3,749	620	571	808	188	254	72%
65–74	7,698	3,038	1,660	278	569	179	401	57	157	60%
75 & over	23,438	4,487	8,613	436	2,616	244	740	111	377	45%
Male	63,817	29,451	7,122	9,138	2,152	2,735	2,025	931	694	
Female	34,083	13,903	6,200	3,619	2,161	747	1,352	404	349	
Percent Male	65%	68%	54%	72%	50%	79%	60%	70%	67%	

Source: National Safety Council tabulations of National Center for Health Statistics mortality data.
[a]*Latest official figures.*
[b]*Includes types not shown separately.*
[c]*Inhalation or ingestion of food or other object.*
[d]*Excludes water transport drownings.*

Of the 97,900 unintentional-injury deaths in 2000, males accounted for 65% of all deaths. For women, the percentage was highest in the 75 and over age group. By type of accident, men accounted for 79% of all drowning deaths, but only 50% of deaths due to choking (inhalation or ingestion of food or other object obstructing breathing).

UNINTENTIONAL-INJURY DEATH RATES BY TYPE AND SEX, UNITED STATES, 2000

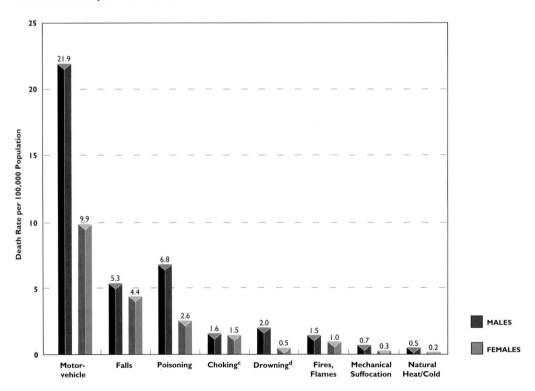

UNINTENTIONAL-INJURY DEATHS BY MONTH AND TYPE, UNITED STATES, 2000[a]

Month	All Types	Motor-vehicle	Falls	Poisoning	Choking[b]	Drowning[c]	Fires/Flames	Mechanical Suffocation	Natural Heat/Cold	Firearms	All Other Types
All Months	**97,900**	**43,354**	**13,322**	**12,757**	**4,313**	**3,482**	**3,377**	**1,335**	**1,043**	**776**	**14,141**
January	8,387	3,362	1,155	1,136	460	129	485	124	173	89	1,274
February	7,175	2,909	1,051	1,099	334	132	354	107	97	40	1,052
March	7,548	3,301	1,038	1,119	353	173	287	113	41	43	1,080
April	7,836	3,494	1,012	1,120	360	243	263	112	34	51	1,147
May	8,386	3,697	1,110	1,183	345	423	194	124	38	54	1,218
June	8,323	3,760	1,088	1,076	323	570	185	95	58	63	1,105
July	9,055	4,157	1,120	1,048	356	667	173	109	103	56	1,266
August	8,662	3,984	1,137	980	327	474	175	113	76	73	1,323
September	8,086	3,837	1,030	957	352	286	186	108	56	52	1,222
October	8,131	3,836	1,165	910	351	174	254	116	40	73	1,212
November	7,752	3,462	1,130	1,024	363	114	306	103	82	93	1,075
December	8,559	3,555	1,286	1,105	389	97	515	111	245	89	1,167
Average	**8,158**	**3,613**	**1,110**	**1,063**	**359**	**290**	**281**	**111**	**87**	**65**	**1,178**

Source: National Safety Council tabulations of National Center for Health Statistics mortality data.
[a]Latest official figures.
[b]Inhalation or ingestion of food or other object.
[c]Excludes water transport drownings.

UNINTENTIONAL-INJURY DEATHS BY MONTH, UNITED STATES, 2000

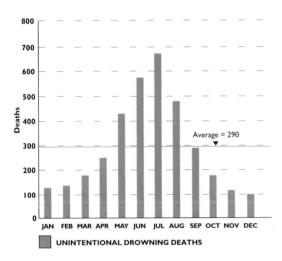

UNINTENTIONAL DROWNING DEATHS

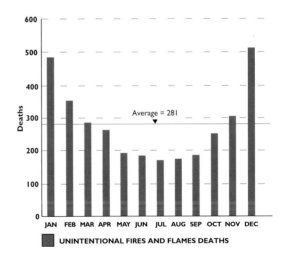

UNINTENTIONAL FIRES AND FLAMES DEATHS

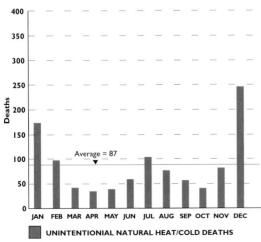

UNINTENTIONIAL NATURAL HEAT/COLD DEATHS

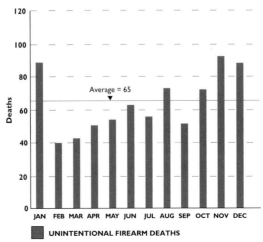

UNINTENTIONAL FIREARM DEATHS

See page 98 for motor-vehicle deaths by month.

YEARS OF POTENTIAL LIFE LOST

While unintentional injuries are the fifth leading cause of death in the United States, unintentional-injury victims tend to be younger than those for the four leading causes of death (heart disease, cancer, stroke, and chronic lower respiratory disease). Ranked by years of potential life lost (YPLL) before age 65, unintentional injuries were the leading cause of death, accounting for slightly more than two million years lost in 2000.

Heart disease was the leading cause of death in 2000 and ranked third in terms of YPLL at 1.4 million years. Cancer ranked second in both number of deaths and YPLL. Stroke was the third leading cause of death and ranked ninth in YPLL.

Within unintentional-injury deaths, motor-vehicle traffic crashes accounted for 44% of the deaths and 55% of the years of potential life lost in 2000. Poisoning accounted 16% of the YPLL and 13% of the deaths. Falls, which were the second leading cause of unintentional-injury deaths, ranked sixth on YPLL.

Years of potential life lost before age 65 are calculated by subtracting the age at death from 65 and adding the result across all persons who died from a particular cause.

Source: Centers for Disease Control and Prevention, National Center for Injury Prevention and Control.

YEARS OF POTENTIAL LIFE LOST BEFORE AGE 65, UNITED STATES, 1999–2000

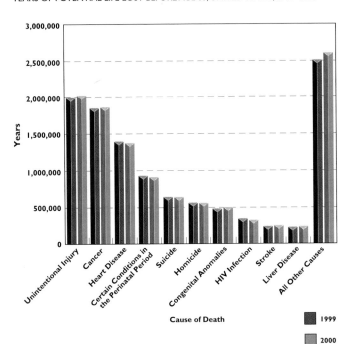

YEARS OF POTENTIAL LIFE LOST TO UNINTENTIONAL INJURIES BEFORE AGE 65, UNITED STATES, 1999–2000

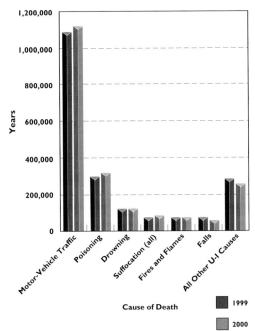

The National Health Interview Survey, conducted by the National Center for Health Statistics, is a continuous, personal-interview sampling of households to obtain information about the health status of household members, including injuries experienced during the 3 months prior to the interview. Responsible family members residing in the household supplied the information found in the survey. Of the nation's 102,528,000 households in 1998, 39,209 households containing 98,785 persons were interviewed. See below for definitions and comparability with other injury figures published in *Injury Facts®*.

NUMBER AND RATE OF LEADING EXTERNAL CAUSES OF INJURY AND POISONING EPISODES BY SEX AND AGE, UNITED STATES, 1998[a]

Sex and Age	Fall	External Cause of Injury and Poisoning[b]					
		Struck By or Against Person or Object	Transportation	Overexertion	Cutting/Piercing Instruments	Other Injury Causes	Poisoning
Total episodes (000)	10,523	4,886	4,459	4,679	2,837	4,983	1,654
Rate per 1,000 population							
Both sexes	39.12	18.16	16.58	17.39	10.55	18.52	6.15
Under 12 years	41.83	20.14	10.80	3.46	8.01	15.48	11.04
12–17 years	44.07	46.64	28.48	18.86	6.28	23.52	(c)
18–44 years	31.27	19.21	20.64	22.31	14.33	22.93	5.04
45–64 years	32.84	8.03	13.91	24.59	10.24	15.30	4.55
65–74 years	46.96	9.16	9.71	7.43	(c)	11.27	(c)
75 years and over	96.60	(c)	(c)	(c)	(c)	(c)	(c)
Male	**36.26**	**24.33**	**18.11**	**21.04**	**16.03**	**23.71**	**6.20**
Under 12 years	47.47	26.94	13.14	(c)	12.12	17.29	12.54
12–17 years	56.86	54.16	33.48	20.69	(c)	21.43	(c)
18–44 years	33.56	27.72	20.57	30.31	21.60	34.39	5.17
45–64 years	20.84	9.80	15.78	26.09	15.40	17.48	(c)
65 years and over	39.35	(c)	(c)	(c)	(c)	(c)	(c)
Female	**41.85**	**12.27**	**15.11**	**13.91**	**5.31**	**13.57**	**6.10**
Under 12 years	35.95	13.06	8.36	(c)	(c)	13.60	9.48
12–17 years	30.45	38.63	23.15	16.91	(c)	25.74	(c)
18–44 years	29.03	10.86	20.71	14.47	7.20	11.70	4.92
45–64 years	44.10	6.38	12.15	23.19	5.39	13.26	6.60
65 years and over	90.43	8.52	(c)	10.15	(c)	12.08	(c)

NUMBER AND PERCENT OF INJURY EPISODES BY PLACE OF OCCURRENCE AND SEX, UNITED STATES, 1998[b]

Place of Occurrence of Injury Episode[d]	Both Sexes		Male		Female	
	Number of Episodes (000)	%	Number of Episodes (000)	%	Number of Episodes (000)	%
Total episodes[e]	**31,837**	**100.0%**	**17,988**	**100.0%**	**13,849**	**100.0%**
Home (inside)	7,476	23.5%	3,262	18.1%	4,214	30.4%
Home (outside)	5,701	17.9%	3,501	19.5%	2,200	15.9%
School/child care center/preschool	2,141	6.7%	1,189	6.6%	952	6.9%
Hospital/residential institution	451	1.4%	186	1.0%	265	1.9%
Street/highway/parking lot	4,915	15.4%	2,373	13.2%	2,542	18.4%
Sport facility/recreation area/lake/river/pool	4,420	13.9%	3,040	16.9%	1,380	10.0%
Industrial/construction/farm/mine/quarry	2,231	7.0%	1,827	10.2%	404	2.9%
Trade/service area	1,969	6.2%	1,084	6.0%	885	6.4%
Other public building	928	2.9%	496	2.8%	432	3.1%
Other unspecified	1,605	5.0%	1,030	5.7%	575	4.1%

Source: Blackwell, D.L., & Tonthat, L. (2002, October). *Summary health statistics for the U.S. population: National Health Interview Survey, 1998.* Vital and Health Statistics, Series 10 (No. 207). Hyattsville, MD: National Center for Health Statistics.
[a]Latest official figures.
[b]Transportation includes motor vehicle, bicycle, motorcycle, pedestrian, train, boat, or airplane. "Other" includes fire/burn/scald related, animal or insect bites, machinery, and other causes. Poisoning does not include allergic/adverse reaction to medicine or other substances.
[c]Figure does not meet standard of reliability or precision.
[d]These estimates are based on data that describe where the respondent was at the time of the injury. The category "Sport facility/recreation area/lake/river/pool" also includes playgrounds, athletic fields, parks, streams, lakes, or oceans. "Trade/service area" includes restaurants, stores, banks, gas stations, etc. Poisoning episodes are not included in this table because poisoning victims were not asked this question in 1998.
[e]Numbers and percents may not sum to respective totals due to rounding.

Injury definitions

National Health Interview Survey definitions. The National Health Interview Survey (NHIS) figures include injuries due to intentional violence as well as unintentional injuries. An injury episode refers to a traumatic event in which the person was injured one or more times from an external cause. Poisoning episodes include ingestion of or contact with harmful substances and also overdoses or wrong use of any drug or medication, but exclude illnesses such as food poisoning or poison ivy. An injury or poisoning is included in the NHIS totals if it is *medically attended.* A *medically attended* injury or poisoning is one for which a physician has been consulted (in person or by telephone) for advice or treatment. Calls to poison control centers are considered contact with a health care professional and are included in this definition of medical attendance.

National Safety Council definition of injury. A disabling injury is defined as one that results in death, some degree of permanent impairment, or renders the injured person unable to effectively perform their regular duties or activities for a full day beyond the day of the injury. This definition applies to all unintentional injuries. All injury totals labeled "disabling injuries" in *Injury Facts®* are based on this definition. Some *rates* in the Work section are based on OSHA definitions of recordable cases (see Glossary).

Numerical differences between NHIS and National Safety Council injury totals are due mainly to the duration of disability. The Council's injury estimating procedure was revised for the 1993 edition of *Accident Facts®.* See the Technical Appendix for more information.

INJURY-RELATED HOSPITAL EMERGENCY DEPARTMENT VISITS, 2001

About 39.4 million visits to hospital emergency departments in 2001 were due to injuries.

About 37% of all hospital emergency department visits in the United States were injury related, according to information from the 2001 National Hospital Ambulatory Medical Care Survey conducted for the National Center for Health Statistics. There were approximately 107.5 million visits made to emergency departments, of which about 39.4 million were injury related. This resulted in an annual rate of about 38.4 emergency department visits per 100 persons, of which about 14.1 visits per 100 persons were injury related.

Males had a higher rate of injury-related visits than females. For males, about 15.8 visits per 100 males were recorded; for females the rate was 12.4 per 100 females. Those aged 15 to 24 had the highest rate of injury-related visits for males, and those aged 75 and over had the highest rate for females.

Falls and motor-vehicle accidents were the leading causes of injury-related emergency department visits,

accounting for about 20% and 12% of the total, respectively. In total, about 7.8 million visits to emergency departments were made in 2001 due to accidental falls, and about 4.8 million were made due to motor-vehicle accidents. The next leading types were struck against or struck accidentally by objects or persons with 4.4 million visits (over 11% of the total), and accidents caused by cutting or piercing instruments, which accounted for about 3.0 million visits (8% of the total).

By intentionality of the injury, nearly 73% of the injury-related emergency department visits were due to unintentional injuries, while about 4% were due to assault, 2% were due to self-inflicted injuries, and 21% were due to unknown or blank causes. About 9% of the injury-related emergency department visits were work-related, 61% were due to nonwork-related causes, and work-relatedness was unknown or blank for 30% of the injuries.

NUMBER AND PERCENT DISTRIBUTION OF EMERGENCY DEPARTMENT VISITS BY CAUSE OF INJURY, UNITED STATES, 2001

Cause of Injury and E-code[a]	Number of Visits (000)	%
All Injury-Related Visits	**39,389**	**100.0%**
Unintentional Injuries, E800–869, E880–E929	**28,342**	**72.0%**
Accidental Falls, E880.0–E66.9, E888	7,762	19.7%
Total Motor Vehicle Accidents, E810–E825	4,750	12.1%
Motor vehicle traffic, E810–E819	4,370	11.1%
Motor vehicle, nontraffic, E820–E825(.0–.5, .7–.9)	380	1.0%
Striking Against or Struck Accidentally by Objects or Persons, E916–E917	4,382	11.1%
Accidents Caused by Cutting or Piercing Instruments, E920	2,974	7.6%
Overexertion and Strenuous Movements, E927	1,699	4.3%
Accidents Due to Natural and Environmental Factors, E900–E909, E928.0–E928.2	1,496	3.8%
Accidental Poisoning by Drugs, Medicinal Substances, Biologicals, Other Solid and Liquid Substances, Gases and Vapors, E850–E869	720	1.8%
Accidents Caused by Fire and Flames, Hot Substances or Object, Caustic or Corrosive Material, and Steam, E890–E899, E924	502	1.3%
Pedalcycle, Nontraffic and Other, E800–E807(.3), E820–E825(.6), E826.1, E826.9	412	1.0%
Machinery, E919	321	0.8%

Cause of Injury and E-code[a]	Number of Visits (000)	%
Other Transportation, E800–807(.0–.2, .8–.9), E826(.0, .2–.8), E827–E829, E831, E833–E845	128	0.3%
Other Mechanism[b], E830, E832, E846–E848, E910–E915, E918, E921–E923, E925–E926, E928.8, E929.0–E929.5	2,384	6.1%
Mechanism Unspecified, E887, E928.9, E929.8, E929.9	937	2.4%
Intentional Injuries, E950–E959, E960–E969, E970–E978, E990–E999	**1,837**	**4.7%**
Assault, E960–E969	1,387	3.5%
Unarmed Fight or Brawl and Striking by Blunt or Thrown Object, E960.0, E968.2	925	2.3%
Assault by Cutting and Piercing Instrument, E966	96	0.2%
Assault by Other and Unspecified Mechanism[c], E960.1, E962–964, E965.5–E965.9, E967–E968.1, E968.3–E969	365	0.9%
Self-inflicted Injury, E950–E959	400	1.0%
Poisoning by Solid or Liquid Substances, Gases or Vapors, E950–E952	283	0.7%
Other and Unspecified Mechanism[d], E954–E955, E957–E959	117	0.3%
Other Causes of Violence, E970–E978, E990–E999	([e])	—
Adverse Effects of Medical Treatment, E870–E879, E930–E949	**1,445**	**3.7%**
Other and Unknown[f]	**7,765**	**19.7%**

Source: McCaig, L.F. & Burt, C.W. (2003). National Hospital Ambulatory Medical Care Survey: 2001 Emergency Department Summary (Advance Data, Number 335, June 4, 2003). Hyattsville, MD: National Center for Health Statistics.

Note: Sum of parts may not add to total due to rounding.

[a] *Based on the International Classification of Diseases, 9th Revision, Clinical Modification (ICD-9-CM).*
[b] *Includes drowning, suffocation, firearm missile, and other mechanism.*
[c] *Includes assault by firearms and explosives, and other mechanism.*
[d] *Includes injury by cutting and piercing instrument, suffocation, and other and unspecified mechanism.*
[e] *Figure did not meet standard of reliability or precision.*
[f] *Includes all other major E-code categories where the estimate was too low to be reliable and uncodable, illegible, and blank E-codes.*

NUMBER AND PERCENT DISTRIBUTION OF INJURY-RELATED EMERGENCY DEPARTMENT VISITS BY CHARACTERISTIC OF THE INJURY AND AGE, UNITED STATES, 2001

Characteristic of the Injury	All Ages		Under 18		18–64 Years		65 Years & Over	
	Number of Visits (000)	%	Number of Visits (000)	%	Number of Visits (000)	%	Number of Visits (000)	%
Total	39,389	100.0	10,187	100.0	24,933	100.0	4,268	100.0
Intentionality								
Self-inflicted	978	2.5	156	1.5	796	3.2	(a)	(a)
Assault	1,392	3.5	312	3.1	1,051	4.2	(a)	(a)
Unintentional	28,730	72.9	8,043	78.9	17,259	69.2	3,428	80.3
Unknown or blank	8,289	21.0	1,677	16.5	5,827	23.4	784	18.4
Work-related								
Yes	3,503	8.9	(a)	(a)	3,344	13.4	(a)	(a)
No	24,034	61.0	7,733	75.9	13,446	53.9	2,855	66.9
Unknown or blank	11,851	30.1	2,373	23.3	8,143	32.7	1,335	31.3

See source on page 24.
Note: Sum of parts may not add to total due to rounding.
aEstimate did not meet standard of reliability or precision.

RATE OF INJURY-RELATED VISITS TO EMERGENCY DEPARTMENTS BY PATIENT AGE AND SEX, 2001

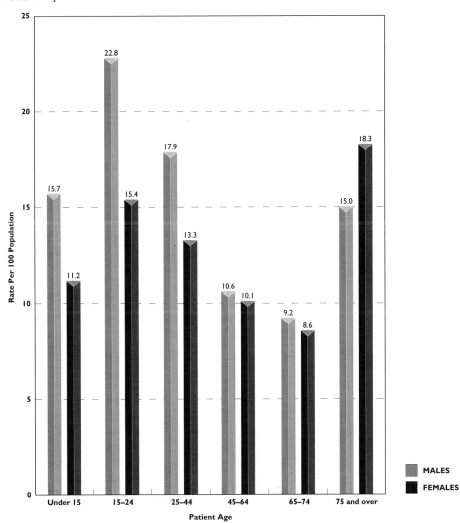

RACE AND HISPANIC ORIGIN

The rank of unintentional-injuries as a cause of death varies with race and Hispanic origin. While ranking fifth overall, following heart disease, cancer, stroke, and chronic lower respiratory diseases, unintentional injuries rank third for Hispanics after heart disease and cancer.

By race, unintentional injuries rank fifth for whites and fourth (after heart disease, cancer, and stroke) for blacks, Asians, Pacific Islanders, American Indians, and Alaskan Natives.

UNINTENTIONAL-INJURY DEATHS RANK, NUMBER, AND RATE BY RACE, HISPANIC ORIGIN, AND SEX, UNITED STATES, 2000

| | | | | Hispanic Origin | | | | | |
| | Total | | | Non-Hispanic Origin | | | Hispanic Origin | | |
Race	Rank	Number	Rate	Rank	Number	Rate	Rank	Number	Rate
All Races	5	97,900	35.6	5	88,558	36.5	3	8,830	27.2
Males	4	63,817	47.4	5	56,736	48.0	3	6,696	41.0
Females	8	34,083	24.2	8	31,822	25.5	5	2,134	13.2
White	5	82,592	36.5	5	73,536	37.4	3	8,649	29.2
Males	5	53,329	48.0	5	46,470	48.3	3	6,558	44.1
Females	8	29,263	25.4	7	27,066	27.0	5	2,091	14.2
Black	4	12,277	34.7	4	12,087	36.1	3	108	5.9
Males	3	8,531	50.8	3	8,380	52.8	3	84	9.2
Females	6	3,746	20.2	6	3,707	21.0	6	24	2.6
Not White or Black[a]	4	3,031	22.1	4	2,935	23.2	3	73	7.0
Males	3	1,957	29.6	3	1,886	31.0	3	54	10.4
Females	4	1,074	15.1	4	1,049	15.9	4	19	3.7

Source: National Center for Health Statistics, Centers for Disease Control and Prevention, and National Safety Council.
Note: Rates are deaths per 100,000 population in each race/sex/Hispanic origin group. Total column includes 512 deaths for which Hispanic origin was not determined.
[a]Includes American Indian, Alaskan Native, Asian, and Pacific Islander.

RANK OF LEADING UNINTENTIONAL-INJURY CAUSES OF DEATH BY RACE, HISPANIC ORIGIN, AND SEX, UNITED STATES, 2000

| | All Races | | | White | | | Black | | | Not White or Black | | |
Cause of Death	Both	Male	Female	Both	Male	Female	Both	Male	Female	Both	Male	Female
Motor Vehicle	1	1	1	1	1	1	1	1	1	1	1	1
Fall	2	3	2	2	3	2	4	4	4	2	2	2
Poisoning	3	2	3	3	2	3	2	2	2	3	4	3
Suffocation by inhalation or ingestion	4	5	4	4	5	4			5	5	5	
Drowning	5	4		5	4		5	5		4	3	4
Fires, flames, smoke			5			5	3	3	3			5

| | Non-Hispanic | | | Hispanic | | |
Cause of Death	Both	Male	Female	Both	Male	Female
Motor Vehicle	1	1	1	1	1	1
Fall	2	3	2	3	3	3
Poisoning	3	2	3	2	2	2
Suffocation by inhalation or ingestion	4	5	4			
Drowning		4		4	4	4
Fires, flames, smoke	5		5	5	5	5

Source: National Safety Council tabulations of National Center for Health Statistics mortality data.

UNINTENTIONAL-INJURY DEATH RATES BY RACE, SEX, AND HISPANIC ORIGIN, UNITED STATES, 2000

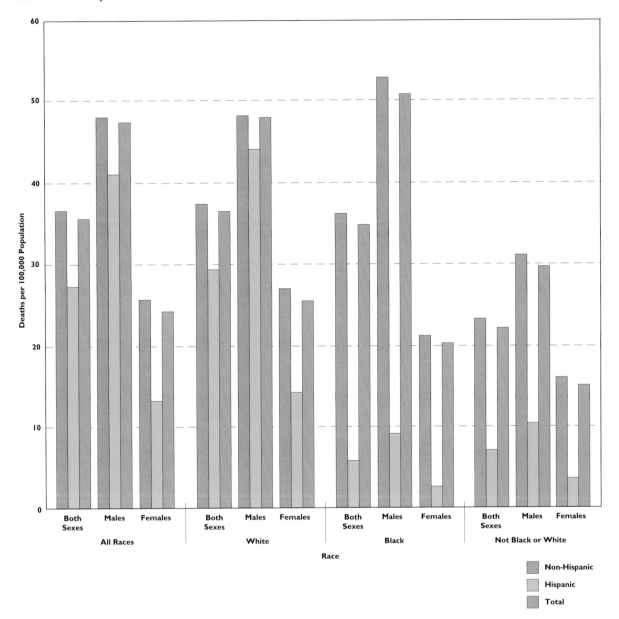

The states listed below participate in the Injury Mortality Tabulations reporting system. Reports from these states are used to make current year estimates. See the Technical Appendix for more information.

The estimated total number of unintentional-injury deaths for 2002 increased 2% from 2001. The number of unintentional-injury deaths in the Work class was down 3%, while the Public Nonmotor-Vehicle class also showed a decrease of 2%. The Motor-Vehicle and Home classes showed increases of 1% and 5%, respectively. The population death rate for the Work class decreased 6%, and the rate for the Public Nonmotor-Vehicle class decreased 3%, while the rates for the Total and Home classes showed increases of 1% and 4%, respectively. The rate for the Motor-Vehicle class remained unchanged.

PRINCIPAL CLASSES OF UNINTENTIONAL-INJURY DEATHS BY STATE, 2002

State	Total[a]		Motor-Vehicle[b]		Work[c]		Home		Public Nonmotor-Vehicle	
	Deaths	Rate[d]	Deaths	Rate[d]	Deaths	Rate[d]	Deaths	Rate[d]	Deaths	Rate[d]
Total U.S.	**99,500**	**35.5**	**44,000**	**15.7**	**4,900**	**1.7**	**33,300**	**11.9**	**19,600**	**7.0**
Colorado	1,814	40.3	781	17.3	86	1.9	456	10.1	539	12.0
Delaware	229	28.4	141	17.5	8	1.0	44	5.4	37	4.6
Florida (9 mos.)	5,497	43.9	2,398	19.1	221	1.8	1,558	12.4	1,242	9.9
Idaho	543	40.5	262	19.5	12	0.9	166	12.4	96	7.2
Kansas	1,030	37.9	492	18.1	60	2.2	275	10.1	221	8.1
Kentucky	1,756	42.9	765	18.7	73	1.8	336	8.2	619	15.1
Missouri	2,339	41.2	1,220	21.5	90	1.6	674	11.9	337	5.9
Virginia	2,347	32.2	925	12.7	106	1.5	609	8.3	333	4.6

Source: Provisional reports of vital statistics registrars; deaths are by place of occurrence. U.S. totals are National Safety Council estimates.
[a] The all-class total may not equal the sum of the separate class totals because Motor-Vehicle and other transportation deaths occurring to persons in the course of their employment are included in the Work death totals as well as the Motor-Vehicle and Public Nonmotor-Vehicle totals and also because unclassified deaths are included in the total.
[b] Differences between these figures and those on pages 162 and 163 are due in most cases to the inclusion of nontraffic deaths in this table.
[c] Work death totals may be too low where incomplete information on death certificates results in the deaths being included in the Public class. The Work totals may include some cases that are not compensable. For compensable cases only, see page 53.
[d] Deaths per 100,000 population, adjusted to annual basis where less than 12 months were reported.

TRAUMATIC BRAIN INJURY

Firearms are the leading cause of traumatic brain injury.

Traumatic brain injury (TBI) is a major cause of morbidity and mortality according to a surveillance summary compiled by the Centers for Disease Control and Prevention. In addition to about 50,000 TBI-related deaths each year in the United States, there are more than one million visits to hospital emergency departments and more than 230,000 hospitalizations. It is estimated that about 5.3 million people have permanent disabilities related to TBI.

TBI includes skull fractures, concussions, cerebral lacerations and contusions, intracranial hemorrhages after injury, other open wounds to the head, and late effects of such injuries (ICD-9 diagnosis codes 800, 801, 803, 804, 850–854, 873, 905.0, and 907.0). These injuries occur as a result of various external causes. Over the period from 1989–1998, the most

common cause of fatal TBI was firearms, which accounted for 40%. Motor-vehicle crashes caused 34% of fatal TBI, and falls caused 10%. Within the firearms category, 68% were due to suicide, 27% to homicide, and 5% to unintentional (accidental), legal intervention, and unknown intentionality.

The death rate from TBI for males was about three times greater than for females — 33.0 compared to 9.8 per 100,000 population.

The graphs on this page show how the causes of TBI deaths vary with age group and the trend in TBI death rates for the principal causes.

Source: Adekoya, N., Thurman, D. J., White, D. D., & Webb, K. W. (2002). Surveillance for traumatic brain injury deaths — United States, 1989–1998. Morbidity and Mortality Weekly Report, 51(SS-10).

AVERAGE ANNUAL DEATH RATES FROM TRAUMATIC BRAIN INJURY BY EXTERNAL CAUSE AND AGE GROUP, UNITED STATES, 1989–1998

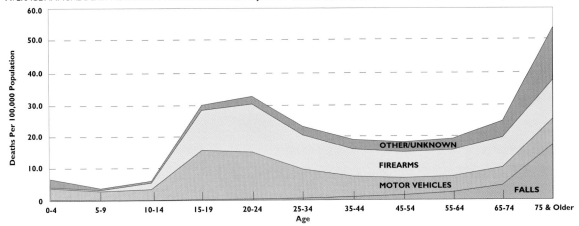

AGE-ADJUSTED DEATH RATES FROM TRAUMATIC BRAIN INJURY BY EXTERNAL CAUSE AND INTENTIONALITY, UNITED STATES, 1989–1998

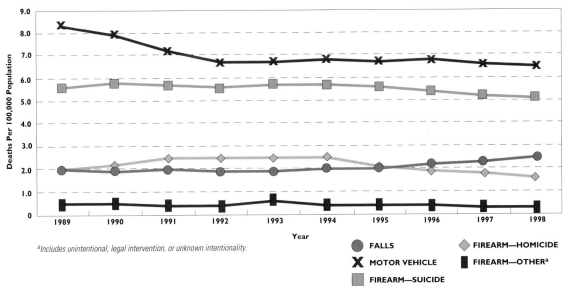

aIncludes unintentional, legal intervention, or unknown intentionality.

FALLS   FIREARM—HOMICIDE
MOTOR VEHICLE FIREARM—OTHER[a]
FIREARM—SUICIDE

MAJOR DISASTERS, 2002

Disasters are front-page news even though the lives lost in the United States are relatively few when compared to the day-to-day life losses from injuries. The National Safety Council tracks major disasters resulting in unintentional-injury deaths. Listed below are the major U.S. disasters taking 25 or more lives during 2002.

Type and Location	No. of Deaths	Date of Disaster
Heat wave in the Midwest and East	48	July 1–2, 2002
Tornadoes in Tennessee and Ohio valleys region	36	November 9–11, 2002
Winter storm in South and Southeast states	29	December 4–5, 2002

Source: National Transportation Safety Board, National Climatic Data Center, and infoplease.com.

LARGEST U.S. DISASTERS, 1983–2002

Year	Date	Type and Location	No. of Deaths
		Air Transportation	
2001	November 12	Crash of scheduled plane near Belle Harbor, N.Y.	265
1996	July 17	Crash of scheduled plane near East Moriches, N.Y.	230
1987	August 16	Crash of scheduled plane in Detroit, Mich.	156
1985	August 2	Crash of scheduled plane in Ft. Worth/Dallas, Texas Airport	135
1994	September 8	Crash of scheduled plane in Aliquippa, Pa.	132
1989	July 19	Crash of scheduled plane in Sioux City, Iowa	112
1996	May 11	Crash of scheduled plane near Miami, Fla.	110
2000	January 31	Crash of scheduled plane near Point Mugu, Calif.	88
1986	August 31	Two-plane collision over Los Angeles, Calif.	82
1990	January 25	Crash of scheduled plane in Cove Neck, N.Y.	73
1994	October 31	Crash of scheduled plane in Indiana	68
1994	July 2	Crash of scheduled plane in Charlotte, N.C.	37
		Weather	
1995	July 11–27	Heat wave in Chicago, Ill.	465
1993	March 12–15	Severe snowstorm in Eastern States	270
1999	July 22–31	Heat wave in the Midwest	232
1998	May–July	Drought and heat wave in South and Southeast	200[a]
1996	January	Snow storm and floods in Appalachians, Mid-Atlantic, and Northeast	187
1996	January–February	Cold wave in eastern two-thirds of the U.S.	100[a]
1993	June–July	Heat wave in Southeast	100[a]
1998	January 5	Winter storm and flooding in South and East	90[a]
1999	September 14–18	Hurricane Floyd, North Carolina and other states	78
1985	May 31	Storm and tornadoes in Pennsylvania and Ohio	74
1997	March	Tornadoes and flooding in South and Southeast	67
1985	November 4–5	Floods in W.Va., Va., Pa., and East Coast	65
1984	March 28–29	Storm and tornadoes in N.C., S.C., and East Coast	62
2001	August	Heat wave in Midwest	56
1999	May 3	Tornadoes in Oklahoma, Kansas, Texas, and Tennessee	54
2002	July 1–2	Heat wave in the Midwest and East	48
1994	March 27	Tornado in Southeast	47
2000	July 8–20	Heat wave in the Southeast	46
1998	February 22	Tornadoes across central Florida	42
2001	June 8–15	Tropical storm Allison from Gulf Coast to southern New England	41
2002	November 9–11	Tornadoes in Tennessee and Ohio valleys region	36
1996	September 5	Hurricane Fran in North Carolina and Virginia	36
1998	April 8	Tornado in central Alabama	34
2002	December 4–5	Winter storm in South and Southeast states	29
1997	May 27	Tornadoes in Texas	29
1994	July 4–17	Floods in Georgia	28
		Work	
1987	April 24	Collapse of apartment building under construction in Bridgeport, Conn.	28
1984	December 21	Mine fire in Orangeville, Utah	27
1991	September 3	Fire at food processing plant in Hamlet, N.C.	25
		Other Disasters	
1994	January 17	Earthquake in San Andreas Fault, Calif.	61
1989	October 17	Earthquake in San Francisco, Calif., and surrounding area	61
1993	September 22	Bridge collapse under train, Mobile, Ala.	47

Source: National Safety Council, Accident Facts, 1984–1998 editions, and Injury Facts, 1999–2002 editions.
[a] Final death toll undetermined.

WHILE YOU SPEAK!

While you make a 10-minute safety speech, 2 persons will be killed and about 390 will suffer a disabling injury. Costs will amount to $11,150,000. On the average, there are 11 unintentional-injury deaths and about 2,330 disabling injuries every hour during the year.

Deaths and disabling injuries by class occurred in the nation at the following rates in 2002:

DEATHS AND DISABLING INJURIES BY CLASS, 2002

| Class | Severity | One Every — | Number per ... | | | 2001 Total |
			Hour	Day	Week	
All	**Deaths**	**5 minutes**	**11**	**273**	**1,910**	**99,500**
	Injuries	**2 seconds**	**2,330**	**55,900**	**392,300**	**20,400,000**
Motor-Vehicle	Deaths	12 minutes	5	121	850	44,000
	Injuries	14 seconds	260	6,300	44,200	2,300,000
Work	Deaths	107 minutes	1	13	90	4,900
	Injuries	9 seconds	420	10,100	71,200	3,700,000
Workers Off-the-Job	Deaths	12 minutes	5	122	860	44,700
	Injuries	4 seconds	810	19,500	136,500	7,100,000
Home	Deaths	16 minutes	4	91	640	33,300
	Injuries	4 seconds	910	21,900	153,800	8,000,000
Public Nonmotor-Vehicle	Deaths	27 minutes	2	54	380	19,600
	Injuries	5 seconds	740	17,800	125,000	6,500,000

Source: National Safety Council estimates.

DEATHS EVERY HOUR ...

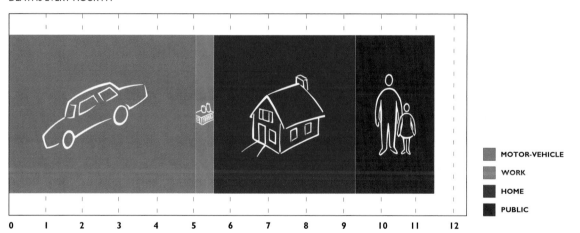

MOTOR-VEHICLE
WORK
HOME
PUBLIC

AN UNINTENTIONAL-INJURY DEATH EVERY FIVE MINUTES ...

Five Minutes

CHILDREN AND YOUTHS

Unintentional-injury deaths increase nearly sevenfold from age 12 to age 19.

For children and youths aged 1 to 24 years, unintentional injuries are the leading cause of death, accounting for 43% of the 43,699 total deaths of these persons in 2000. Overall, motor-vehicle crashes were the leading cause of unintentional-injury deaths for this age group, followed by drowning, poisonings, fires and flames, falls, and firearms.

While unintentional-injury deaths decrease fairly steadily for those aged 1 to 10, they increase markedly for teenagers — from 259 for those age 12 to 1,782 for those age 19. Motor-vehicle crashes account for most of this increase.

For infants under 1 year of age, unintentional injuries are the seventh leading cause of death, following congenital anomalies; short gestation and low birth weight; sudden infant death syndrome; maternal complications of pregnancy; complications involving the placenta, cord, and membranes; and respiratory distress (see page 10). Although unintentional injuries only account for about 3% of deaths for those under age 1, the number of unintentional-injury deaths for this age is greater than for any age from 1 to 15.

UNINTENTIONAL-INJURY DEATHS BY EVENT, AGE 0–24, UNITED STATES, 2000

| Age | Population (000) | Unintentional-Injury Deaths | | | | | | | | | | |
		Total	Rates[a]	Motor-vehicle	Drowning	Poisoning	Fires/ Flames	Falls	Firearms	Choking[b]	Mechanical Suffocation	All Other
<1 year	3,786	881	23.3	168	75	14	37	8	1	77	449	52
1–24 years	92,981	18,918	20.3	12,983	1,514	1,237	748	310	287	161	254	1,424
1 year	3,746	564	15.1	159	184	14	66	18	2	47	26	48
2 years	3,758	531	14.1	189	159	7	80	8	5	25	15	43
3 years	3,763	380	10.1	156	84	6	75	2	8	10	10	29
4 years	3,826	351	9.2	147	66	5	69	8	3	10	8	35
5 years	3,857	303	7.9	165	57	4	44	3	2	3	5	20
6 years	3,912	274	7.0	140	42	4	43	5	3	7	3	27
7 years	3,974	282	7.1	159	35	5	46	2	4	1	5	25
8 years	3,888	269	6.9	159	35	1	25	5	1	0	6	37
9 years	4,212	263	6.2	157	32	3	24	1	8	2	13	23
10 years	4,153	264	6.4	153	32	4	24	4	4	3	8	32
11 years	3,962	291	7.3	160	32	4	22	4	14	2	15	38
12 years	3,896	259	6.6	158	28	5	11	5	9	1	13	29
13 years	3,875	324	8.4	211	35	9	10	3	10	0	11	35
14 years	3,919	450	11.5	310	47	6	17	5	12	5	14	34
15 years	3,895	675	17.3	489	59	23	14	5	12	2	7	64
16 years	3,871	1,177	30.4	923	69	48	10	15	25	4	13	70
17 years	4,029	1,375	34.1	1,099	89	50	13	15	27	2	6	74
18 years	3,929	1,746	44.4	1,364	76	99	28	24	24	4	10	117
19 years	4,141	1,782	43.0	1,376	78	131	14	40	19	8	14	102
20 years	4,029	1,642	40.8	1,244	54	140	15	23	21	6	14	125
21 years	3,783	1,640	43.4	1,216	58	163	26	25	17	4	7	124
22 years	3,623	1,451	40.0	1,041	52	158	27	31	27	3	10	102
23 years	3,476	1,386	39.9	957	58	173	27	28	20	7	12	104
24 years	3,464	1,239	35.8	851	53	175	18	31	10	5	9	87
0–4 years	18,879	2,707	14.3	819	568	46	327	44	19	169	508	207
5–9 years	19,843	1,391	7.0	780	201	17	182	16	18	13	32	132
10–14 years	19,805	1,588	8.0	992	174	28	84	21	49	11	61	168
15–19 years	19,865	6,755	34.0	5,251	371	351	79	99	107	20	50	427
20–24 years	18,375	7,358	40.0	5,309	275	809	113	138	95	25	52	542

Source: National Safety Council tabulations of National Center for Health Statistics mortality data.
Note: Data does not include "age unknown" cases, which totaled 85 in 2000.
[a] Deaths per 100,000 population in each age group.
[b] Suffocation by inhalation or ingestion of food or other object.

ADULTS

Falls account for one third of unintentional-injury deaths of the elderly.

More than 78,000 adults aged 25 and older died as a result of unintentional injuries in 2000, with motor vehicles accounting for about 39% of these deaths. Data for 5-year age groups indicate that motor-vehicle crashes are the most common type of unintentional-injury death through age 79. Poisoning is the second most common type for age groups 25 through 54, and falls are the second most common type from age 55 through age 79, at which point it becomes the primary cause of fatal injury for those aged 80 and older. Falls account for more than one third of the unintentional-injury deaths in this age group.

Death rates per 100,000 population are relatively stable for those aged 25–69, averaging about 33.0. Death rates then increase with age. The death rate for those aged 100 and older is nearly 15 times higher than the average rate for those aged 25–69. All age groups older than 65 have death rates higher than the all-ages rate of 35.6.

UNINTENTIONAL-INJURY DEATHS BY EVENT, AGES 25 AND OLDER, UNITED STATES, 2000

| Age | Population (000) | Unintentional-Injury Deaths | | | | | | | | | | | |
		Total	Rates[a]	Motor-vehicle	Drowning	Poisoning	Fires/ Flames	Falls	Firearms	Choking[b]	Mechanical Suffocation	Natural Heat/Cold	All Other
25–29	17,957	5,898	32.8	3,715	213	980	120	138	74	37	48	20	553
30–34	19,575	5,871	30.0	3,169	206	1,400	121	165	57	57	62	27	607
35–39	22,363	7,471	33.4	3,545	250	2,159	188	238	75	76	88	55	797
40–44	22,534	7,942	35.2	3,382	230	2,504	214	370	78	100	78	78	908
45–49	19,765	6,870	34.8	2,936	182	1,992	214	409	38	140	47	74	838
50–54	17,065	5,408	31.7	2,425	172	1,069	225	462	40	151	58	73	733
55–59	13,248	4,021	30.4	1,917	120	447	187	448	36	156	51	52	607
60–64	10,621	3,484	32.8	1,589	97	241	182	501	14	173	32	55	600
65–69	9,443	3,375	35.7	1,436	80	146	188	595	24	219	25	72	590
70–74	8,752	4,323	49.4	1,602	99	132	213	1,065	17	350	32	85	728
75–79	7,410	5,596	75.5	1,764	71	118	257	1,641	17	573	34	107	1,014
80–84	4,880	6,162	126.3	1,409	85	127	215	2,200	7	662	26	98	1,333
85–89	2,682	5,933	221.2	953	37	109	158	2,352	7	667	23	90	1,537
90–94	1,169	3,939	337.0	285	19	60	78	1,682	4	488	22	56	1,245
95–99	360	1,419	394.2	47	8	14	24	618	0	178	6	17	507
100 and older	63	304	482.5	3	0	1	3	120	0	48	0	1	128
25 and older	177,887	78,016	43.9	30,177	1,869	11,499	2,587	13,004	488	4,075	632	960	12,725
35 and older	140,355	66,247	47.2	23,293	1,450	9,119	2,346	12,701	357	3,981	522	913	11,565
45 and older	95,458	50,834	53.3	16,366	970	4,456	1,944	12,093	204	3,805	356	780	9,860
55 and older	58,628	38,556	65.8	11,005	616	1,395	1,505	11,222	126	3,514	251	633	8,289
65 and older	34,759	31,051	89.3	7,499	399	707	1,136	10,273	76	3,185	168	526	7,082
75 and older	16,564	23,353	141.0	4,461	220	429	735	8,613	35	2,616	111	369	5,764

Source: National Safety Council tabulations of National Center for Health Statistics mortality data.
Note: Data does not include "age unknown" cases, which totaled 85 in 2000.
[a]*Deaths per 100,000 population in each age group.*
[b]*Suffocation by inhalation or ingestion of food or other object.*

Between 1912 and 2002, unintentional-injury deaths per 100,000 population were reduced 55% (after adjusting for the classification change in 1948) from 82.4 to 35.5. The reduction in the overall rate during a period when the nation's population tripled has resulted in 4,700,000 fewer people being killed due to unintentional injuries than there would have been if the rate had not been reduced.

Age-adjusted rates, which eliminate the effect of shifts in the age distribution of the population, have decreased 61% from 1912 to 2002. The adjusted rates, which are shown in the graph on the opposite page, are standardized to the year 2000 standard U.S. population. The break in the lines at 1948 shows the estimated effect of changes in the International Classification of Diseases (ICD). The break in the lines at 1992 resulted from the adoption of the Bureau of Labor Statistics Census of Fatal Occupational Injuries for work-related deaths. Another change in the ICD in 1999 also affects the trends. See the Technical Appendix for comparability.

The table below shows the change in the age distribution of the population since 1910.

The age-adjusted death rate for all unintentional injuries increased and decreased significantly several times during the period from 1910 to 1940. Since 1940, there have been some setbacks, such as in the early 1960s, but the overall trend has been positive. The age-adjusted death rates for unintentional-injury deaths in the work and home classes have declined fairly steadily since they became available in the late 1920s, although the home class rates have increased since the early 1990s. The rates in the public class declined for three decades, rose in the 1960s, and then continued declining. The age-adjusted motor-vehicle death rate rose steadily from 1910 to the late 1930s as the automobile became more widely used. A sharp drop in use occurred during World War II, and a sharp rise in rates occurred in the 1960s, with death rates reflecting economic cycles and a long-term downward trend since then.

UNITED STATES POPULATION, SELECTED YEARS

Year	All Ages	0–14	15–24	25–44	45–64	65 & Older
Number (in thousands)						
1910	91,973[a]	29,499	18,121	26,810	13,424	3,950
2000[b]	274,634	58,964	38,077	81,892	60,991	34,710
2002	280,306	58,883	39,601	81,146	65,374	35,303
Percent						
1910	100.0%	32.1%	19.7%	29.2%	14.6%	4.3%
2000[b]	100.0%	21.5%	13.9%	29.8%	22.2%	12.6%
2002	100.0%	21.0%	14.1%	28.9%	23.3%	12.6%

Source: For 1910: U.S. Bureau of the Census. (1960). Historical Statistics of the United States, Colonial Times to 1957. Series A 71–85. Washington, DC: U.S. Government Printing Office. For 2000: Anderson, R.N., & Rosenberg, H.M. (1998). Age standardization of death rates: Implementation of the year 2000 standard. National Vital Statistics Reports, 47(3), 13. For 2002: Population Projections Program, Population Division. (Internet Release Date: January 2000). Projections of the Total Resident Population by 5-year Age Groups, and Sex with Special Age Categories: Middle Series, 2001 to 2005. Washington, DC: U.S. Bureau of the Census. http://www.census.gov/population/www/projections/natsum-T3.html
[a] Includes 169,000 persons with age unknown.
[b] This is the population used for standardization (age-adjustment) and differs slightly from the actual 2000 population, which totaled 275,306,000.

AGE-ADJUSTED DEATH RATES BY CLASS OF INJURY, UNITED STATES, 1910–2002

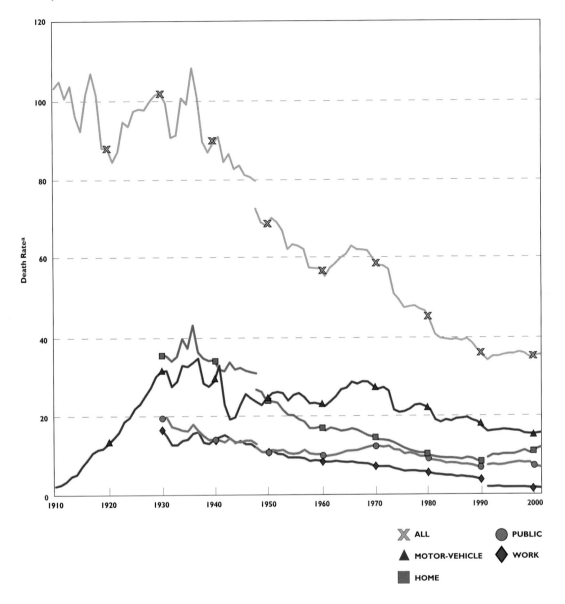

X ALL   ● PUBLIC

▲ MOTOR-VEHICLE   ◆ WORK

■ HOME

[a]Deaths per 100,000 population, adjusted to 2000 standard population. The break at 1948 shows the estimated effect of classification changes.
The break at 1992 is due to the adoption of the Bureau of Labor Statistics' Census of Fatal Occupational Injuries for work-related deaths.

PRINCIPAL CLASSES OF UNINTENTIONAL-INJURY DEATHS

PRINCIPAL CLASSES OF UNINTENTIONAL-INJURY DEATHS, UNITED STATES, 1903–2002

Year	Total[a] Deaths	Rate[b]	Motor-Vehicle Deaths	Rate[b]	Work Deaths	Rate[b]	Home Deaths	Rate[b]	Public Nonmotor-Vehicle Deaths	Rate[b]
1903	70,600	87.2	(c)	—	(c)	—	(c)	—	(c)	—
1904	71,500	86.6	(c)	—	(c)	—	(c)	—	(c)	—
1905	70,900	84.2	(c)	—	(c)	—	(c)	—	(c)	—
1906	80,000	93.2	400	0.5	(c)	—	(c)	—	(c)	—
1907	81,900	93.6	700	0.8	(c)	—	(c)	—	(c)	—
1908	72,300	81.2	800	0.9	(c)	—	(c)	—	(c)	—
1909	72,700	80.1	1,300	1.4	(c)	—	(c)	—	(c)	—
1910	77,900	84.4	1,900	2.0	(c)	—	(c)	—	(c)	—
1911	79,300	84.7	2,300	2.5	(c)	—	(c)	—	(c)	—
1912	78,400	82.5	3,100	3.3	(c)	—	(c)	—	(c)	—
1913	82,500	85.5	4,200	4.4	(c)	—	(c)	—	(c)	—
1914	77,000	78.6	4,700	4.8	(c)	—	(c)	—	(c)	—
1915	76,200	76.7	6,600	6.6	(c)	—	(c)	—	(c)	—
1916	84,800	84.1	8,200	8.1	(c)	—	(c)	—	(c)	—
1917	90,100	88.2	10,200	10.0	(c)	—	(c)	—	(c)	—
1918	85,100	82.1	10,700	10.3	(c)	—	(c)	—	(c)	—
1919	75,500	71.9	11,200	10.7	(c)	—	(c)	—	(c)	—
1920	75,900	71.2	12,500	11.7	(c)	—	(c)	—	(c)	—
1921	74,000	68.4	13,900	12.9	(c)	—	(c)	—	(c)	—
1922	76,300	69.4	15,300	13.9	(c)	—	(c)	—	(c)	—
1923	84,400	75.7	18,400	16.5	(c)	—	(c)	—	(c)	—
1924	85,600	75.6	19,400	17.1	(c)	—	(c)	—	(c)	—
1925	90,000	78.4	21,900	19.1	(c)	—	(c)	—	(c)	—
1926	91,700	78.7	23,400	20.1	(c)	—	(c)	—	(c)	—
1927	92,700	78.4	25,800	21.8	(c)	—	(c)	—	(c)	—
1928	95,000	79.3	28,000	23.4	19,000	15.8	30,000	24.9	21,000	17.4
1929	98,200	80.8	31,200	25.7	20,000	16.4	30,000	24.6	20,000	16.4
1930	99,100	80.5	32,900	26.7	19,000	15.4	30,000	24.4	20,000	16.3
1931	97,300	78.5	33,700	27.2	17,500	14.1	29,000	23.4	20,000	16.1
1932	89,000	71.3	29,500	23.6	15,000	12.0	29,000	23.2	18,000	14.4
1933	90,932	72.4	31,363	25.0	14,500	11.6	29,500	23.6	18,500	14.7
1934	100,977	79.9	36,101	28.6	16,000	12.7	34,000	26.9	18,000	14.2
1935	99,773	78.4	36,369	28.6	16,500	13.0	32,000	25.2	18,000	14.2
1936	110,052	85.9	38,089	29.7	18,500	14.5	37,000	28.9	19,500	15.2
1937	105,205	81.7	39,643	30.8	19,000	14.8	32,000	24.8	18,000	14.0
1938	93,805	72.3	32,582	25.1	16,000	12.3	31,000	23.9	17,000	13.1
1939	92,623	70.8	32,386	24.7	15,500	11.8	31,000	23.7	16,000	12.2
1940	96,885	73.4	34,501	26.1	17,000	12.9	31,500	23.9	16,500	12.5
1941	101,513	76.3	39,969	30.0	18,000	13.5	30,000	22.5	16,500	12.4
1942	95,889	71.6	28,309	21.1	18,000	13.4	30,500	22.8	16,000	12.0
1943	99,038	73.8	23,823	17.8	17,500	13.0	33,500	25.0	17,000	12.7
1944	95,237	71.7	24,282	18.3	16,000	12.0	32,500	24.5	16,000	12.0
1945	95,918	72.4	28,076	21.2	16,500	12.5	33,500	25.3	16,000	12.1
1946	98,033	70.0	33,411	23.9	16,500	11.8	33,000	23.6	17,500	12.5
1947	99,579	69.4	32,697	22.8	17,000	11.9	34,500	24.1	18,000	12.6
1948 (5th Rev.)[d]	98,001	67.1	32,259	22.1	16,000	11.0	35,000	24.0	17,000	11.6
1948 (6th Rev.)[d]	93,000	63.7	32,259	22.1	16,000	11.0	31,000	21.2	16,000	11.0
1949	90,106	60.6	31,701	21.3	15,000	10.1	31,000	20.9	15,000	10.1
1950	91,249	60.3	34,763	23.0	15,500	10.2	29,000	19.2	15,000	9.9
1951	95,871	62.5	36,996	24.1	16,000	10.4	30,000	19.6	16,000	10.4
1952	96,172	61.8	37,794	24.3	15,000	9.6	30,500	19.6	16,000	10.3
1953	95,032	60.1	37,955	24.0	15,000	9.5	29,000	18.3	16,500	10.4
1954	90,032	55.9	35,586	22.1	14,000	8.7	28,000	17.4	15,500	9.6
1955	93,443	56.9	38,426	23.4	14,200	8.6	28,500	17.3	15,500	9.4
1956	94,780	56.6	39,628	23.7	14,300	8.5	28,000	16.7	16,000	9.6
1957	95,307	55.9	38,702	22.7	14,200	8.3	28,000	16.4	17,500	10.3
1958	90,604	52.3	36,981	21.3	13,300	7.7	26,500	15.3	16,500	9.5
1959	92,080	52.2	37,910	21.5	13,800	7.8	27,000	15.3	16,500	9.3
1960	93,806	52.1	38,137	21.2	13,800	7.7	28,000	15.6	17,000	9.4
1961	92,249	50.4	38,091	20.8	13,500	7.4	27,000	14.8	16,500	9.0
1962	97,139	52.3	40,804	22.0	13,700	7.4	28,500	15.3	17,000	9.2
1963	100,669	53.4	43,564	23.1	14,200	7.5	28,500	15.1	17,500	9.3
1964	105,000	54.9	47,700	25.0	14,200	7.4	28,000	14.6	18,500	9.7
1965	108,004	55.8	49,163	25.4	14,100	7.3	28,500	14.7	19,500	10.1
1966	113,563	58.1	53,041	27.1	14,500	7.4	29,500	15.1	20,000	10.2
1967	113,169	57.3	52,924	26.8	14,200	7.2	29,000	14.7	20,500	10.4
1968	114,864	57.6	54,862	27.5	14,300	7.2	28,000	14.0	21,500	10.8
1969	116,385	57.8	55,791	27.7	14,300	7.1	27,500	13.7	22,500	11.2
1970	114,638	56.2	54,633	26.8	13,800	6.8	27,000	13.2	23,500	11.5
1971	113,439	54.8	54,381	26.3	13,700	6.6	26,500	12.8	23,500	11.4
1972	115,448	55.2	56,278	26.9	14,000	6.7	26,500	12.7	23,500	11.2
1973	115,821	54.8	55,511	26.3	14,300	6.8	26,500	12.5	24,500	11.6

See source and footnotes on page 37.

PRINCIPAL CLASSES OF UNINTENTIONAL-INJURY DEATHS, UNITED STATES, 1903–2002, Cont.

Year	Total[a] Deaths	Rate[b]	Motor-Vehicle Deaths	Rate[b]	Work Deaths	Rate[b]	Home Deaths	Rate[b]	Public Nonmotor-Vehicle Deaths	Rate[b]
1974	104,622	49.0	46,402	21.8	13,500	6.3	26,000	12.2	23,000	10.8
1975	103,030	47.8	45,853	21.3	13,000	6.0	25,000	11.6	23,000	10.6
1976	100,761	46.3	47,038	21.6	12,500	5.7	24,000	11.0	21,500	10.0
1977	103,202	47.0	49,510	22.5	12,900	5.9	23,200	10.6	22,200	10.1
1978	105,561	47.5	52,411	23.6	13,100	5.9	22,800	10.3	22,000	9.9
1979	105,312	46.9	53,524	23.8	13,000	5.8	22,500	10.0	21,000	9.4
1980	105,718	46.5	53,172	23.4	13,200	5.8	22,800	10.0	21,300	9.4
1981	100,704	43.9	51,385	22.4	12,500	5.4	21,700	9.5	19,800	8.6
1982	94,082	40.6	45,779	19.8	11,900	5.1	21,200	9.2	19,500	8.4
1983	92,488	39.6	44,452	19.0	11,700	5.0	21,200	9.1	19,400	8.3
1984	92,911	39.4	46,263	19.6	11,500	4.9	21,200	9.0	18,300	7.8
1985	93,457	39.3	45,901	19.3	11,500	4.8	21,600	9.1	18,800	7.9
1986	95,277	39.7	47,865	19.9	11,100	4.6	21,700	9.0	18,700	7.8
1987	95,020	39.2	48,290	19.9	11,300	4.7	21,400	8.8	18,400	7.6
1988	97,100	39.7	49,078	20.1	11,000	4.5	22,700	9.3	18,400	7.5
1989	95,028	38.5	47,575	19.3	10,900	4.4	22,500	9.1	18,200	7.4
1990	91,983	36.9	46,814	18.8	10,100	4.0	21,500	8.6	17,400	7.0
1991	89,347	35.4	43,536	17.3	9,800	3.9	22,100	8.8	17,600	7.0
1992	86,777	34.0	40,982	16.1	4,968[e]	1.9[e]	24,000[e]	9.4[e]	19,000[e]	7.4[e]
1993	90,523	35.1	41,893	16.3	5,035	2.0	26,100	10.1	19,700	7.6
1994	91,437	35.1	42,524	16.3	5,338	2.1	26,300	10.1	19,600	7.5
1995	93,320	35.5	43,363	16.5	5,018	1.9	27,200	10.3	20,100	7.6
1996	94,948	35.8	43,649	16.5	5,058	1.9	27,500	10.4	21,000	7.9
1997	95,644	35.7	43,458	16.2	5,162	1.9	27,700	10.3	21,700	8.1
1998	97,835	36.2	43,501	16.1	5,120	1.9	29,000	10.7	22,600	8.4
1999[f]	97,860	35.9	42,401	15.5	5,185	1.9	30,500	11.2	22,200	8.1
2000[g]	97,900	35.6	43,354	15.7	5,022	1.8	29,200	10.6	22,700	8.2
2001[g]	98,000	35.3	43,700	15.7	5,033	1.8	31,600	11.4	20,000	7.2
2002[h]	99,500	35.5	44,000	15.7	4,900	1.7	33,300	11.9	19,600	7.0
Changes										
1992 to 2002	+15%	+4%	+7%	−2%	−1%	−11%	+39%	+27%	+3%	−5%
2001 to 2002	+2%	+1%	+1%	0%	−3%	−6%	+5%	+4%	−2%	−3%

Source: Total and motor-vehicle deaths, 1903–1932 based on National Center for Health Statistics death registration states; 1933–1948 (5th Rev.), 1949–1963, 1965–2000 are NCHS totals for the U.S. Work deaths for 1992–2001 are from the Bureau of Labor Statistics, Census of Fatal Occupational Injuries. All other figures are National Safety Council estimates.
[a] Duplications between Motor-Vehicle, Work, and Home are eliminated in the Total column.
[b] Rates are deaths per 100,000 population.
[c] Data insufficient to estimate yearly totals.
[d] In 1948 a revision was made in the International Classification of Diseases. The first figures for 1948 are comparable with those for earlier years, the second with those for later years.
[e] Adoption of the Census of Fatal Occupational Injuries figure for the Work class necessitated adjustments to the Home and Public classes. See the Technical Appendix for details.
[f] In 1999 a revision was made in the International Classification of Diseases. See the Technical Appendix for comparability with earlier years.
[g] Revised.
[h] Preliminary.

UNINTENTIONAL-INJURY DEATHS BY AGE

UNINTENTIONAL-INJURY DEATHS BY AGE, UNITED STATES, 1903–2002

Year	All Ages	Under 5 Years	5–14 Years	15–24 Years	25–44 Years	45–64 Years	65–74 Years	75 Years & Over[a]
1903	70,600	9,400	8,200	10,300	20,100	12,600	10,000	
1904	71,500	9,700	9,000	10,500	19,900	12,500	9,900	
1905	70,900	9,800	8,400	10,600	19,600	12,600	9,900	
1906	80,000	10,000	8,400	13,000	24,000	13,600	11,000	
1907	81,900	10,500	8,300	13,400	24,900	14,700	10,100	
1908	72,300	10,100	7,600	11,300	20,500	13,100	9,700	
1909	72,700	9,900	7,400	10,700	21,000	13,300	10,400	
1910	77,900	9,900	7,400	11,900	23,600	14,100	11,000	
1911	79,300	11,000	7,500	11,400	22,400	15,100	11,900	
1912	78,400	10,600	7,900	11,500	22,200	14,700	11,500	
1913	82,500	9,800	7,400	12,200	24,500	16,500	12,100	
1914	77,000	10,600	7,900	11,000	21,400	14,300	11,800	
1915	76,200	10,300	8,200	10,800	20,500	14,300	12,100	
1916	84,800	11,600	9,100	7,700	24,900	17,800	13,700	
1917	90,100	11,600	9,700	11,700	24,400	18,500	14,200	
1918	85,100	10,600	10,100	10,600	21,900	17,700	14,200	
1919	75,500	10,100	10,000	10,200	18,600	13,800	12,800	
1920	75,900	10,200	9,900	10,400	18,100	13,900	13,400	
1921	74,000	9,600	9,500	9,800	18,000	13,900	13,200	
1922	76,300	9,700	9,500	10,000	18,700	14,500	13,900	
1923	84,400	9,900	9,800	11,000	21,500	16,900	15,300	
1924	85,600	10,200	9,900	11,900	20,900	16,800	15,900	
1925	90,000	9,700	10,000	12,400	22,200	18,700	17,000	
1926	91,700	9,500	9,900	12,600	22,700	19,200	17,800	
1927	92,700	9,200	9,900	12,900	22,900	19,700	18,100	
1928	95,000	8,900	9,800	13,100	23,300	20,600	19,300	
1929	98,200	8,600	9,800	14,000	24,300	21,500	20,000	
1930	99,100	8,200	9,100	14,000	24,300	22,200	21,300	
1931	97,300	7,800	8,700	13,500	23,100	22,500	21,700	
1932	89,000	7,100	8,100	12,000	20,500	20,100	21,200	
1933	90,932	6,948	8,195	12,225	21,005	20,819	21,740	
1934	100,977	7,034	8,272	13,274	23,288	24,197	24,912	
1935	99,773	6,971	7,808	13,168	23,411	23,457	24,958	
1936	110,052	7,471	7,866	13,701	24,990	26,535	29,489	
1937	105,205	6,969	7,704	14,302	23,955	24,743	27,532	
1938	93,805	6,646	6,593	12,129	20,464	21,689	26,284	
1939	92,628	6,668	6,378	12,066	20,164	20,842	26,505	
1940	96,885	6,851	6,466	12,763	21,166	21,840	27,799	
1941	101,513	7,052	6,702	14,346	22,983	22,509	27,921	
1942	95,889	7,220	6,340	13,732	21,141	20,764	26,692	
1943	99,038	8,039	6,636	15,278	20,212	20,109	28,764	
1944	95,237	7,912	6,704	14,750	19,115	19,097	27,659	
1945	95,918	7,741	6,836	12,446	19,393	20,097	29,405	
1946	98,033	7,949	6,545	13,366	20,705	20,249	29,219	
1947	99,579	8,219	6,069	13,166	21,155	20,513	30,457	
1948 (5th Rev.)[b]	98,001	8,387	5,859	12,595	20,274	19,809	31,077	
1948 (6th Rev.)[b]	93,000	8,350	5,850	12,600	20,300	19,300	9,800	16,800
1949	90,106	8,469	5,539	11,522	19,432	18,302	9,924	16,918
1950	91,249	8,389	5,519	12,119	20,663	18,665	9,750	16,144
1951	95,871	8,769	5,892	12,366	22,363	19,610	10,218	16,653
1952	96,172	8,871	5,980	12,787	21,950	19,892	10,026	16,667
1953	95,032	8,678	6,136	12,837	21,422	19,479	9,927	16,553
1954	90,032	8,380	5,939	11,801	20,023	18,299	9,652	15,938
1955	93,443	8,099	6,099	12,742	29,911	19,199	9,929	16,464
1956	94,780	8,173	6,319	13,545	20,986	19,207	10,160	16,393
1957	95,307	8,423	6,454	12,973	20,949	19,495	10,076	16,937
1958	90,604	8,789	6,514	12,744	19,658	18,095	9,431	15,373
1959	92,080	8,748	6,511	13,269	19,666	18,937	9,475	15,474
1960	93,806	8,950	6,836	13,457	19,600	19,385	9,689	15,829
1961	92,249	8,622	6,717	13,431	19,273	19,134	9,452	15,620
1962	97,139	8,705	6,751	14,557	19,955	20,335	10,149	16,687
1963	100,669	8,688	6,962	15,889	20,529	21,262	10,194	17,145
1964	100,500	8,670	7,400	17,420	22,080	22,100	10,400	16,930
1965	108,004	8,586	7,391	18,688	22,228	22,900	10,430	17,781
1966	113,563	8,507	7,958	21,030	23,134	24,022	10,706	18,206
1967	113,169	7,825	7,874	21,645	23,255	23,826	10,645	18,099
1968	114,864	7,263	8,369	23,012	23,684	23,896	10,961	17,679
1969	116,385	6,973	8,186	24,668	24,410	24,192	10,643	17,313
1970	114,638	6,594	8,203	24,336	23,979	24,164	10,644	16,718
1971	113,439	6,496	8,143	24,733	23,535	23,240	10,494	16,798
1972	115,448	6,142	8,242	25,762	23,852	23,658	10,446	17,346
1973	115,821	6,037	8,102	26,550	24,750	23,059	10,243	17,080

See source and footnotes on page 39.

UNINTENTIONAL-INJURY DEATHS BY AGE, UNITED STATES, 1903–2002, Cont.

Year	All Ages	Under 5 Years	5–14 Years	15–24 Years	25–44 Years	45–64 Years	65–74 Years	75 Years & Over[a]
1974	104,622	5,335	7,037	24,200	22,547	20,334	9,323	15,846
1975	103,030	4,948	6,818	24,121	22,877	19,643	9,220	15,403
1976	100,761	4,692	6,308	24,316	22,399	19,000	8,823	15,223
1977	103,202	4,470	6,305	25,619	23,460	19,167	9,006	15,175
1978	105,561	4,766	6,118	26,622	25,024	18,774	9,072	15,185
1979	105,312	4,429	5,689	26,574	26,097	18,346	9,013	15,164
1980	105,718	4,479	5,224	26,206	26,722	18,140	8,997	15,950
1981	100,704	4,130	4,866	23,582	26,928	17,339	8,639	15,220
1982	94,082	4,108	4,504	21,306	25,135	15,907	8,224	14,898
1983	92,488	3,999	4,321	19,756	24,996	15,444	8,336	15,636
1984	92,911	3,652	4,198	19,801	25,498	15,273	8,424	16,065
1985	93,457	3,746	4,252	19,161	25,940	15,251	8,583	16,524
1986	95,277	3,843	4,226	19,975	27,201	14,733	8,499	16,800
1987	95,020	3,871	4,198	18,695	27,484	14,807	8,686	17,279
1988	97,100	3,794	4,215	18,507	28,279	15,177	8,971	18,157
1989	95,028	3,770	4,090	16,738	28,429	15,046	8,812	18,143
1990	91,983	3,496	3,650	16,241	27,663	14,607	8,405	17,921
1991	89,347	3,626	3,660	15,278	26,526	13,693	8,137	18,427
1992	86,777	3,286	3,388	13,662	25,808	13,882	8,165	18,586
1993	90,523	3,488	3,466	13,966	27,277	14,434	8,125	19,767
1994	91,437	3,406	3,508	13,898	27,012	15,200	8,279	20,134
1995	93,320	3,067	3,544	13,842	27,660	16,004	8,400	20,803
1996	94,948	2,951	3,433	13,809	27,092	16,717	8,780	22,166
1997	94,644	2,770	3,371	13,367	27,129	17,521	8,578	22,908
1998	97,835	2,689	3,254	13,349	27,172	18,286	8,892	24,193
1999[c]	97,860	2,743	3,091	13,656	27,121	18,924	8,208	24,117
2000[d]	97,900	2,707	2,979	14,113	27,182	19,783	7,698	23,438
2001[d]	98,000	2,600	2,900	14,600	27,500	20,800	6,900	22,700
2002[e]	99,500	2,600	2,500	15,400	28,400	22,100	6,600	21,900
Changes								
1992 to 2002	+15%	−21%	−26%	+13%	+10%	+59%	−19%	+18%
2001 to 2002	+2%	0%	−14%	+5%	+3%	+6%	−4%	−4%

Source: 1903 to 1932 based on National Center for Health Statistics data for registration states; 1933–1948 (5th Rev.), 1949–1963, and 1965–2000 are NCHS totals. All other figures are National Safety Council estimates. See Technical Appendix for comparability.
[a] Includes "age unknown." In 2000, these deaths numbered 85.
[b] In 1948, a revision was made in the International Classification of Diseases. The first figures for 1948 are comparable with those for earlier years, the second with those for later years.
[c] In 1999, a revision was made in the International Classification of Diseases. See the Technical Appendix for comparability with earlier years.
[d] Revised.
[e] Preliminary.

UNINTENTIONAL-INJURY DEATH RATES BY AGE

UNINTENTIONAL-INJURY DEATH RATES[a] BY AGE, UNITED STATES, 1903–2002

Year	Standardized Rate[b]	All Ages	Under 5 Years	5–14 Years	15–24 Years	25–44 Years	45–64 Years	65–74 Years	75 Years & Over[b]
1903	99.4	87.2	98.7	46.8	65.0	87.4	111.7	299.8	
1904	103.4	86.6	99.1	50.9	64.9	84.6	108.1	290.0	
1905	98.4	84.2	98.6	47.0	64.1	81.4	106.2	282.5	
1906	114.2	93.2	99.1	46.5	77.1	97.3	111.7	306.0	
1907	112.4	93.6	102.7	45.5	78.0	98.8	117.8	274.2	
1908	99.7	81.2	97.5	41.2	64.4	79.5	102.2	256.7	
1909	97.4	80.1	94.2	39.6	59.9	79.6	101.0	268.2	
1910	103.0	84.4	92.8	39.1	65.3	87.3	104.0	276.0	
1911	104.7	84.7	101.9	39.3	62.1	81.4	108.7	292.1	
1912	100.4	82.5	97.1	40.5	62.3	79.2	103.2	275.8	
1913	103.5	85.5	88.4	37.4	65.2	85.6	112.5	281.7	
1914	95.9	78.6	94.3	38.9	58.5	73.2	94.6	268.1	
1915	92.1	76.7	90.8	39.7	57.3	69.0	92.1	268.8	
1916	101.4	84.1	101.4	43.3	40.8	82.5	112.1	297.6	
1917	106.7	88.2	108.4	45.3	62.1	79.8	113.8	301.2	
1918	101.2	82.1	91.0	46.5	58.7	72.2	106.3	294.2	
1919	87.7	71.9	87.2	45.9	55.3	60.1	81.8	262.0	
1920	87.8	71.2	87.4	44.9	55.5	56.9	85.6	289.5	
1921	84.3	68.4	80.8	42.4	51.4	55.5	79.4	259.8	
1922	86.9	69.4	80.6	41.5	51.4	57.1	81.4	265.1	
1923	94.5	75.7	82.0	42.4	55.6	64.5	92.6	282.8	
1924	93.3	75.6	82.9	42.4	58.6	61.7	90.2	283.5	
1925	97.2	78.4	78.6	42.3	59.7	64.7	97.8	293.9	
1926	97.7	78.7	77.9	41.4	59.9	65.4	98.2	298.7	
1927	97.5	78.4	75.9	41.0	60.2	65.2	98.0	295.4	
1928	99.6	79.3	74.4	40.4	59.9	65.6	99.9	306.2	
1929	101.2	80.8	73.3	40.0	63.1	67.7	102.1	308.9	
1930	101.8	80.5	71.8	36.9	62.3	67.0	102.9	317.9	
1931	99.2	78.5	69.9	35.2	59.7	63.0	102.1	313.3	
1932	90.5	71.3	65.1	32.8	52.7	55.6	89.3	296.9	
1933	91.1	72.4	65.5	33.4	53.6	56.3	90.8	295.3	
1934	100.5	79.9	68.1	33.9	57.8	61.8	103.3	328.5	
1935	97.9	78.4	68.5	32.2	56.9	61.6	98.0	319.8	
1936	108.1	85.9	74.4	32.9	58.8	65.3	108.6	367.4	
1937	100.7	81.7	69.6	32.7	60.9	62.1	99.3	333.4	
1938	89.4	72.3	65.3	28.5	51.3	52.5	85.4	308.9	
1939	86.7	70.8	62.9	28.2	50.7	51.2	81.0	300.0	
1940	89.1	73.4	64.8	28.8	53.5	53.2	83.4	305.7	
1941	90.7	76.3	65.0	29.7	60.9	57.2	84.8	297.4	
1942	84.3	71.6	63.9	27.9	59.8	52.4	77.1	275.5	
1943	86.3	73.8	66.9	29.0	69.7	50.3	73.6	287.8	
1944	82.5	71.7	63.2	29.1	72.9	48.9	68.9	268.6	
1945	83.4	72.4	59.8	29.5	64.5	50.5	71.6	277.6	
1946	81.0	70.0	60.2	28.1	61.7	48.8	70.9	267.9	
1947	80.5	69.4	57.4	25.8	59.6	49.0	70.6	270.7	
1948 (5th Rev.)[d]	79.5	67.1	56.3	24.6	56.8	46.2	66.8	267.4	
1948 (6th Rev.)[d]	72.5	63.7	56.0	24.5	56.8	46.2	65.1	122.4	464.3
1949	69.0	60.6	54.4	23.0	52.2	43.5	60.6	120.4	450.7
1950	68.1	60.3	51.4	22.6	55.0	45.6	60.5	115.8	414.7
1951	70.1	62.5	50.8	23.6	57.7	49.0	62.7	117.1	413.6
1952	69.0	61.8	51.5	22.5	60.9	47.7	62.7	111.1	399.8
1953	67.0	60.1	49.5	22.1	61.4	46.4	60.5	106.7	383.6
1954	62.2	55.9	46.7	20.5	56.4	43.0	55.9	100.7	354.4
1955	63.4	56.9	43.9	20.7	60.1	44.7	57.7	100.8	350.2
1956	63.0	56.6	43.3	20.2	63.3	44.7	56.7	100.6	335.6
1957	62.2	55.9	43.5	19.9	59.5	44.6	56.6	97.5	333.3
1958	57.5	52.3	44.5	19.6	56.2	42.0	51.7	89.3	292.6
1959	57.4	52.2	43.6	18.9	56.5	42.1	53.2	87.7	284.7
1960	57.3	52.1	44.0	19.1	55.6	42.0	53.6	87.6	281.4
1961	55.4	50.4	42.0	18.1	54.0	41.2	52.1	83.8	267.9
1962	57.5	52.3	42.6	18.0	55.0	42.7	54.6	88.5	277.7
1963	58.6	53.4	42.8	18.2	57.2	44.0	56.3	87.9	277.0
1964	60.0	54.9	43.1	19.1	59.9	47.3	57.6	88.9	263.9
1965	61.9	55.8	43.4	18.7	61.6	47.7	58.8	88.5	268.7
1966	63.0	58.1	44.4	19.9	66.9	49.6	60.7	89.8	267.4
1967	62.1	57.3	42.2	19.4	66.9	49.7	59.2	88.5	257.4
1968	62.0	57.6	40.6	20.5	69.2	50.1	58.5	90.2	244.0
1969	61.8	57.8	40.2	20.0	71.8	51.2	58.4	86.6	232.0
1970	59.8	56.2	38.4	20.1	68.0	49.8	57.6	85.2	219.6
1971	58.1	54.8	37.7	20.1	66.1	48.4	54.7	82.7	213.2
1972	58.0	55.2	35.9	20.6	67.6	47.5	55.2	80.8	214.2
1973	57.1	54.8	35.8	20.6	68.2	48.0	53.3	77.3	206.3

See source and footnotes on page 41.

UNINTENTIONAL-INJURY DEATH RATES[a] BY AGE, UNITED STATES, 1903–2002, Cont.

Year	Standardized Rate[b]	All Ages	Under 5 Years	5–14 Years	15–24 Years	25–44 Years	45–64 Years	65–74 Years	75 Years & Over[c]
1974	50.9	49.0	32.4	18.2	60.9	42.7	46.7	68.7	186.7
1975	49.3	47.8	30.7	17.8	59.5	42.3	44.9	66.2	175.5
1976	47.3	46.3	30.0	16.7	58.9	40.3	43.2	62.0	168.4
1977	47.6	47.0	28.7	17.0	61.3	40.9	43.4	61.5	164.0
1978	47.8	47.5	30.3	16.9	63.1	42.3	42.4	60.5	159.7
1979	47.0	46.9	27.6	16.1	62.6	42.7	41.3	58.8	154.8
1980	46.5	46.5	27.2	15.0	61.7	42.3	40.8	57.5	158.6
1981	44.0	43.9	24.4	14.2	55.9	41.2	39.0	54.4	147.4
1982	40.6	40.6	23.8	13.2	51.2	37.3	35.8	50.9	140.0
1983	39.6	39.6	22.8	12.7	48.2	36.0	34.7	50.8	142.8
1984	39.4	39.4	20.6	12.4	48.9	35.7	34.3	50.7	142.8
1985	39.2	39.3	21.0	12.6	47.9	35.3	34.2	50.9	143.0
1986	39.4	39.7	21.4	12.6	50.5	36.1	33.0	49.6	141.5
1987	39.0	39.2	21.4	12.4	48.1	35.7	33.0	49.8	141.6
1988	39.5	39.7	20.9	12.3	48.5	36.1	33.4	50.9	145.3
1989	38.4	38.5	20.4	11.8	44.8	35.7	32.8	49.3	141.5
1990	36.7	36.9	18.5	10.4	44.0	34.2	31.6	46.4	136.5
1991	35.3	35.4	18.9	10.2	42.0	32.3	29.3	44.5	136.7
1992	34.0	34.0	16.8	9.3	37.8	31.3	28.7	44.2	134.5
1993	35.0	35.1	17.7	9.4	38.8	33.0	29.1	43.6	139.9
1994	35.0	35.1	17.3	9.4	38.4	32.5	29.9	44.3	139.2
1995	35.4	35.5	15.7	9.3	38.2	33.2	30.6	44.8	140.6
1996	35.7	35.8	15.3	8.9	38.1	32.3	31.1	47.0	145.9
1997	35.7	35.7	14.5	8.7	36.5	32.5	31.6	46.3	146.2
1998	36.1	36.2	14.2	8.3	35.9	32.6	31.9	48.3	151.1
1999[e]	35.8	35.9	14.5	7.8	36.1	32.7	32.0	45.0	147.7
2000[f]	34.8	35.6	14.3	7.5	36.7	33.0	32.3	42.3	140.8
2001[f]	35.2	35.3	13.8	7.3	37.4	33.6	32.9	37.9	134.3
2002[g]	35.4	35.5	13.7	6.3	38.9	35.0	33.8	36.4	127.5

Changes									
1992 to 2002		+4%	−18%	−32%	+3%	+12%	+18%	−18%	−5%
2001 to 2002		+1%	−1%	−14%	+4%	+4%	+3%	−4%	−5%

2002 Population (Millions)									
Total		280.306[h]	18.944	39.939	39.601	81.146	65.374	18.129	17.174
Male		137.036	9.677	20.439	20.267	40.224	31.679	8.228	6.520
Female		143.271	9.267	19.498	19.334	40.921	33.695	9.902	10.653

Source: All figures are National Safety Council estimates. See Technical Appendix for comparability.
[a] *Rates are deaths per 100,000 resident population in each age group.*
[b] *Adjusted to the year 2000 standard population to remove the influence of changes in age distribution between 1903 and 2001.*
[c] *Includes "age unknown."*
[d] *In 1948, a revision was made in the International Classification of Diseases. The first figures for 1948 are comparable with those for earlier years, the second with those for later years.*
[e] *In 1999, a revision was made in the International Classification of Diseases. See the Technical Appendix for comparability.*
[f] *Revised.*
[g] *Preliminary.*
[h] *Sum of parts may not equal total due to rounding.*

PRINCIPAL TYPES OF UNINTENTIONAL-INJURY DEATHS

PRINCIPAL TYPES OF UNINTENTIONAL-INJURY DEATHS, UNITED STATES, 1903–1998

Year	Total	Motor-Vehicle	Falls	Drowning[a]	Fires/Burns[b]	Ingest. of Food/Object	Firearms	Poison (Solid, Liquid)	Poison (Gas, Vapor)	All Other
1903	70,600	(c)	(c)	9,200	(c)	(c)	2,500	(c)	(c)	58,900
1904	71,500	(c)	(c)	9,300	(c)	(c)	2,800	(c)	(c)	59,400
1905	70,900	(c)	(c)	9,300	(c)	(c)	2,000	(c)	(c)	59,600
1906	80,000	400	(c)	9,400	(c)	(c)	2,100	(c)	(c)	68,100
1907	81,900	700	(c)	9,000	(c)	(c)	1,700	(c)	(c)	70,500
1908	72,300	800	(c)	9,300	(c)	(c)	1,900	(c)	(c)	60,300
1909	72,700	1,300	(c)	8,500	(c)	(c)	1,600	(c)	(c)	61,300
1910	77,900	1,900	(c)	8,700	(c)	(c)	1,900	(c)	(c)	65,400
1911	79,300	2,300	(c)	9,000	(c)	(c)	2,100	(c)	(c)	65,900
1912	78,400	3,100	(c)	8,600	(c)	(c)	2,100	(c)	(c)	64,600
1913	82,500	4,200	15,100	10,300	8,900	(c)	2,400	3,200	(c)	38,400
1914	77,000	4,700	15,000	8,700	9,100	(c)	2,300	3,300	(c)	33,900
1915	76,200	6,600	15,000	8,600	8,400	(c)	2,100	2,800	(c)	32,700
1916	84,800	8,200	15,200	8,900	9,500	(c)	2,200	2,900	(c)	37,900
1917	90,100	10,200	15,200	7,600	10,800	(c)	2,300	2,800	(c)	41,200
1918	85,100	10,700	13,200	7,000	10,200	(c)	2,500	2,700	(c)	38,800
1919	75,500	11,200	11,900	9,100	9,100	(c)	2,800	3,100	(c)	28,300
1920	75,900	12,500	12,600	6,100	9,300	(c)	2,700	3,300	(c)	29,400
1921	74,000	13,900	12,300	7,800	7,500	(c)	2,800	2,900	(c)	26,800
1922	76,300	15,300	13,200	7,000	8,300	(c)	2,900	2,800	(c)	26,800
1923	84,400	18,400	14,100	6,800	9,100	(c)	2,900	2,800	2,700	27,600
1924	85,600	19,400	14,700	7,400	7,400	(c)	2,900	2,700	2,900	28,200
1925	90,000	21,900	15,500	7,300	8,600	(c)	2,800	2,700	2,800	28,400
1926	91,700	23,400	16,300	7,500	8,800	(c)	2,800	2,600	3,200	27,100
1927	92,700	25,800	16,500	8,100	8,200	(c)	3,000	2,600	2,700	25,800
1928	95,000	28,000	17,000	8,600	8,400	(c)	2,900	2,800	2,800	24,500
1929	98,200	31,200	17,700	7,600	8,200	(c)	3,200	2,600	2,800	24,900
1930	99,100	32,900	18,100	7,500	8,100	(c)	3,200	2,600	2,500	24,200
1931	97,300	33,700	18,100	7,600	7,100	(c)	3,100	2,600	2,100	23,000
1932	89,000	29,500	18,600	7,500	7,100	(c)	3,000	2,200	2,100	19,000
1933	90,932	31,363	18,962	7,158	6,781	(c)	3,014	2,135	1,633	19,886
1934	100,977	36,101	20,725	7,077	7,456	(c)	3,033	2,148	1,643	22,794
1935	99,773	36,369	21,378	6,744	7,253	(c)	2,799	2,163	1,654	21,413
1936	110,052	38,089	23,562	6,659	7,939	(c)	2,817	2,177	1,665	27,144
1937	105,205	39,643	22,544	7,085	7,214	(c)	2,576	2,190	1,675	22,278
1938	93,805	32,582	23,239	6,881	6,491	(c)	2,726	2,077	1,428	18,381
1939	92,623	32,386	23,427	6,413	6,675	(c)	2,618	1,963	1,440	17,701
1940	96,885	34,501	23,356	6,202	7,521	(c)	2,375	1,847	1,583	19,500
1941	101,513	39,969	22,764	6,389	6,922	(c)	2,396	1,731	1,464	19,878
1942	95,889	28,309	22,632	6,696	7,901	(c)	2,678	1,607	1,741	24,325
1943	99,038	23,823	24,701	7,115	8,726	921	2,282	1,745	2,014	27,711
1944	95,237	24,282	22,989	6,511	8,372	896	2,392	1,993	1,860	25,942
1945	95,918	28,076	23,847	6,624	7,949	897	2,385	1,987	2,120	22,033
1946	98,033	33,411	23,109	6,442	7,843	1,076	2,801	1,961	1,821	19,569
1947	99,579	32,697	24,529	6,885	8,033	1,206	2,439	1,865	1,865	14,060
1948 (5th Rev.)[d]	98,001	32,259	24,836	6,428	7,743	1,315	2,191	1,753	2,045	19,611
1948 (6th Rev.)[d]	93,000	32,259	22,000	6,500	6,800	1,299	2,330	1,600	2,020	17,192
1949	90,106	31,701	22,308	6,684	5,982	1,341	2,326	1,634	1,617	16,513
1950	91,249	34,763	20,783	6,131	6,405	1,350	2,174	1,584	1,769	16,290
1951	95,871	36,996	21,376	6,489	6,788	1,456	2,247	1,497	1,627	17,395
1952	96,172	37,794	20,945	6,601	6,922	1,434	2,210	1,440	1,397	17,429
1953	95,032	37,955	20,631	6,770	6,579	1,603	2,277	1,391	1,223	16,603
1954	90,032	35,586	19,771	6,334	6,083	1,627	2,271	1,339	1,223	15,798
1955	93,443	38,426	20,192	6,344	6,352	1,608	2,120	1,431	1,163	15,807
1956	94,780	39,628	20,282	6,263	6,405	1,760	2,202	1,422	1,213	15,605
1957	95,307	38,702	20,545	6,613	6,269	2,043	2,369	1,390	1,143	16,233
1958	90,604	36,981	18,248	6,582[e]	7,291[e]	2,191[e]	2,172	1,429	1,187	14,523
1959	92,080	37,910	18,774	6,434	6,898	2,189	2,258	1,661	1,141	14,815
1960	93,806	38,137	19,023	6,529	7,645	2,397	2,334	1,679	1,253	14,809
1961	92,249	38,091	18,691	6,525	7,102	2,499	2,204	1,804	1,192	14,141
1962	97,139	40,804	19,589	6,439	7,534	1,813	2,092	1,833	1,376	15,659
1963	100,669	43,564	19,335	6,347	8,172	1,949	2,263	2,061	1,489	15,489
1964	105,000	47,700	18,941	6,709	7,379	1,865	2,275	2,100	1,360	16,571
1965	108,004	49,163	19,984	6,799	7,347	1,836	2,344	2,110	1,526	16,895
1966	113,563	53,041	20,066	7,084	8,084	1,831	2,558	2,283	1,648	16,968
1967	113,169	52,924	20,120	7,076	7,423	1,980	2,896	2,506	1,574	16,670
1968	114,864	54,862	18,651	7,372[e]	7,335	3,100[e]	2,394[e]	2,583	1,526	17,041
1969	116,385	55,791	17,827	7,699	7,163	3,712	2,309	2,967	1,549	16,368
1970	114,638	54,633	16,926	7,860	6,718	2,753	2,406	3,679	1,620	18,043
1971	113,439	54,381	16,755	7,396	6,776	2,877	2,360	3,710	1,646	17,538
1972	115,448	56,278	16,744	7,586	6,714	2,830	2,442	3,728	1,690	17,436
1973	115,821	55,511	16,506	8,725	6,503	3,013	2,618	3,683	1,652	17,610

See source and footnotes on page 43.

PRINCIPAL TYPES OF UNINTENTIONAL-INJURY DEATHS, UNITED STATES, 1903–1998, Cont.

Year	Total	Motor-Vehicle	Falls	Drowning[a]	Fires/Burns[b]	Ingest. of Food/Object	Firearms	Poison (Solid, Liquid)	Poison (Gas, Vapor)	All Other
1974	104,622	46,402	16,339	7,876	6,236	2,991	2,513	4,016	1,518	16,731
1975	103,030	45,853	14,896	8,000	6,071	3,106	2,380	4,694	1,577	16,453
1976	100,761	47,038	14,136	6,827	6,338	3,033	2,059	4,161	1,569	15,600
1977	103,202	49,510	13,773	7,126	6,357	3,037	1,982	3,374	1,596	16,447
1978	105,561	52,411	13,690	7,026	6,163	3,063	1,806	3,035	1,737	16,630
1979	105,312	53,524	13,216	6,872	5,991	3,243	2,004	3,165	1,472	15,825
1980	105,718	53,172	13,294	7,257	5,822	3,249	1,955	3,089	1,242	16,638
1981	100,704	51,385	12,628	6,277	5,697	3,331	1,871	3,243	1,280	14,992
1982	94,082	45,779	12,077	6,351	5,210	3,254	1,756	3,474	1,259	14,922
1983	92,488	44,452	12,024	6,353	5,028	3,387	1,695	3,382	1,251	14,916
1984	92,911	46,263	11,937	5,388	5,010	3,541	1,668	3,808	1,103	14,193
1985	93,457	45,901	12,001	5,316	4,938	3,551	1,649	4,091	1,079	14,931
1986	95,277	47,865	11,444	5,700	4,835	3,692	1,452	4,731	1,009	14,549
1987	95,020	48,290	11,733	5,100	4,710	3,688	1,440	4,415	900	14,744
1988	97,100	49,078	12,096	4,966	4,965	3,805	1,501	5,353	873	14,463
1989	95,028	47,575	12,151	4,015	4,716	3,578	1,489	5,603	921	14,980
1990	91,983	46,814	12,313	4,685	4,175	3,303	1,416	5,055	748	13,474
1991	89,347	43,536	12,662	4,818	4,120	3,240	1,441	5,698	736	13,096
1992	86,777	40,982	12,646	3,542	3,958	3,182	1,409	6,449	633	13,976
1993	90,523	41,893	13,141	3,807	3,900	3,160	1,521	7,877	660	14,564
1994	91,437	42,524	13,450	3,942	3,986	3,065	1,356	8,309	685	14,120
1995	93,320	43,363	13,986	4,350	3,761	3,185	1,225	8,461	611	14,378
1996	94,948	43,649	14,986	3,959	3,741	3,206	1,134	8,872	638	14,763
1997	95,644	43,458	15,447	4,051	3,490	3,275	981	9,587	576	14,779
1998	97,835	43,501	16,274	4,406	3,255	3,515	866	10,255	546	15,217

PRINCIPAL TYPES OF UNINTENTIONAL-INJURY DEATHS, UNITED STATES, 1999–2002

Year	Total	Motor-Vehicle	Falls	Poisoning	Ingest. of Food/Object	Drowning[f]	Fires, Flames, Smoke[b]	Mechanical Suffocation	Firearms	All Other
1999[g]	97,860	42,401	13,162	12,186	3,885	3,529	3,348	1,618	824	16,907
2000[h]	97,900	43,354	13,322	12,757	4,313	3,482	3,377	1,335	776	15,184
2001[h]	98,000	43,700	14,300	14,000	4,000	3,300	3,400	1,200	800	13,300
2002[i]	99,500	44,000	14,500	15,700	4,200	3,000	2,900	1,300	800	13,100
Changes										
1992 to 2002	+15%	+7%	(j)	(j)	+32%	(j)	−27%	(j)	−43%	(j)
2001 to 2002	+2%	+1%	+1%	+12%	+5%	−9%	−15%	+8%	0%	−2%

Source: National Center for Health Statistics and National Safety Council. See Technical Appendix for comparability.
[a] *Includes drowning in water transport accidents.*
[b] *Includes burns by fire, and deaths resulting from conflagration regardless of nature of injury.*
[c] *Comparable data not available.*
[d] *In 1948, a revision was made in the International Classification of Diseases. The first figures for 1948 are comparable with those for earlier years, the second with those for later years.*
[e] *Data are not comparable to previous years shown due to classification changes in 1958 and 1968.*
[f] *Excludes water transport drownings.*
[g] *In 1999, a revision was made in the International Classification of Diseases. See the Technical Appendix for comparability.*
[h] *Revised.*
[i] *Preliminary.*
[j] *Comparison not valid because of change in classifications (see footnote "g").*

UNINTENTIONAL-INJURY DEATH RATES FOR PRINCIPAL TYPES

UNINTENTIONAL-INJURY DEATH RATES[a] FOR PRINCIPAL TYPES, UNITED STATES, 1903–1998

Year	Total	Motor-Vehicle	Falls	Drowning[b]	Fires/Burns[c]	Ingest. of Food/Object	Firearms	Poison (Solid, Liquid)	Poison (Gas, Vapor)	All Other
1903	87.2	(d)	(d)	11.4	(d)	(d)	3.1	(d)	(d)	72.7
1904	86.6	(d)	(d)	11.3	(d)	(d)	3.4	(d)	(d)	71.9
1905	84.2	(d)	(d)	11.1	(d)	(d)	2.4	(d)	(d)	70.7
1906	93.2	0.5	(d)	11.0	(d)	(d)	2.4	(d)	(d)	79.3
1907	93.6	0.8	(d)	10.4	(d)	(d)	2.0	(d)	(d)	80.4
1908	81.2	0.9	(d)	10.5	(d)	(d)	2.1	(d)	(d)	67.7
1909	80.1	1.4	(d)	9.4	(d)	(d)	1.8	(d)	(d)	67.5
1910	84.4	2.0	(d)	9.4	(d)	(d)	2.1	(d)	(d)	70.9
1911	84.7	2.5	(d)	9.6	(d)	(d)	2.2	(d)	(d)	70.4
1912	82.5	3.3	(d)	9.0	(d)	(d)	2.2	(d)	(d)	68.0
1913	85.5	4.4	15.5	10.6	9.1	(d)	2.5	3.3	(d)	40.1
1914	78.6	4.8	15.1	8.8	9.1	(d)	2.3	3.3	(d)	35.2
1915	76.7	6.6	14.9	8.6	8.4	(d)	2.1	2.8	(d)	33.3
1916	84.1	8.1	14.9	8.7	9.3	(d)	2.2	2.8	(d)	38.1
1917	88.2	10.0	14.7	7.4	10.5	(d)	2.2	2.7	(d)	40.7
1918	82.1	10.3	12.8	6.8	9.9	(d)	2.4	2.6	(d)	37.3
1919	71.9	10.7	11.4	6.9	8.7	(d)	2.7	3.0	(d)	28.5
1920	71.2	11.7	11.8	5.7	8.7	(d)	2.5	3.1	(d)	27.7
1921	68.4	12.9	11.3	7.2	6.9	(d)	2.6	2.7	(d)	24.8
1922	69.4	13.9	12.0	6.4	7.5	(d)	2.6	2.5	(d)	24.5
1923	75.7	16.5	12.6	6.1	8.1	(d)	2.6	2.5	2.4	24.9
1924	75.6	17.1	12.9	6.5	8.4	(d)	2.5	2.4	2.5	23.3
1925	78.4	19.1	13.4	6.3	7.4	(d)	2.4	2.3	2.4	25.1
1926	78.7	20.1	13.9	6.4	7.5	(d)	2.4	2.2	2.7	23.5
1927	78.4	21.8	13.9	6.8	6.9	(d)	2.5	2.2	2.3	22.0
1928	79.3	23.4	14.1	7.1	7.0	(d)	2.4	2.3	2.3	20.7
1929	80.8	25.7	14.5	6.2	6.7	(d)	2.6	2.1	2.3	20.7
1930	80.5	26.7	14.7	6.1	6.6	(d)	2.6	2.1	2.0	19.7
1931	78.5	27.2	14.6	6.1	5.7	(d)	2.5	2.1	1.7	18.6
1932	71.3	23.6	14.9	6.0	5.7	(d)	2.4	1.8	1.7	15.2
1933	72.4	25.0	15.1	5.7	5.4	(d)	2.4	1.7	1.3	15.8
1934	79.9	28.6	16.4	5.6	5.9	(d)	2.4	1.7	1.3	18.0
1935	78.4	28.6	16.8	5.3	5.7	(d)	2.2	1.7	1.3	16.8
1936	85.9	29.7	18.4	5.2	6.2	(d)	2.2	1.7	1.3	21.2
1937	81.7	30.8	17.5	5.5	5.6	(d)	2.0	1.7	1.3	17.3
1938	72.3	25.1	17.9	5.3	5.0	(d)	2.1	1.6	1.1	14.2
1939	70.8	24.7	17.9	4.9	5.1	(d)	2.0	1.5	1.1	13.6
1940	73.4	26.1	17.7	4.7	5.7	(d)	1.8	1.4	1.2	14.8
1941	76.3	30.0	17.1	4.8	5.2	(d)	1.8	1.3	1.1	15.0
1942	71.6	21.1	16.9	5.0	5.9	(d)	2.0	1.2	1.3	18.2
1943	73.8	17.8	18.4	5.3	6.5	0.7	1.7	1.3	1.5	20.6
1944	71.7	18.3	17.3	4.9	6.3	0.7	1.8	1.5	1.4	19.5
1945	72.4	21.2	18.0	5.0	6.0	0.7	1.8	1.5	1.6	16.6
1946	70.0	23.9	16.5	4.6	5.6	0.8	2.0	1.4	1.3	13.9
1947	69.4	22.8	17.1	4.8	5.6	0.8	1.7	1.3	1.3	14.0
1948 (5th Rev.)[e]	67.1	22.1	17.0	4.4	5.3	0.9	1.5	1.2	1.4	13.3
1948 (6th Rev.)[e]	63.7	22.1	15.1	4.5	4.7	0.9	1.6	1.1	1.4	12.3
1949	60.6	21.3	15.0	4.5	4.0	0.9	1.6	1.1	1.1	11.1
1950	60.3	23.0	13.7	4.1	4.2	0.9	1.4	1.1	1.2	10.7
1951	62.5	24.1	13.9	4.2	4.4	1.0	1.5	1.0	1.1	11.3
1952	61.8	24.3	13.5	4.2	4.5	0.9	1.4	0.9	0.9	11.2
1953	60.1	24.0	13.0	4.3	4.2	1.0	1.4	0.9	0.8	10.2
1954	55.9	22.1	12.3	3.9	3.8	1.0	1.4	0.8	0.8	9.8
1955	56.9	23.4	12.3	3.9	3.9	1.0	1.3	0.9	0.7	9.5
1956	56.6	23.7	12.1	3.7	3.8	1.1	1.3	0.8	0.7	9.4
1957	55.9	22.7	12.1	3.9	3.7	1.2	1.4	0.8	0.7	9.4
1958	52.3	21.3	10.5	3.8[f]	4.2[f]	1.3[f]	1.3	0.8	0.7	8.4
1959	52.2	21.5	10.6	3.7	3.9	1.2	1.3	0.9	0.7	8.4
1960	52.1	21.2	10.6	3.6	4.3	1.3	1.3	0.9	0.7	8.2
1961	50.4	20.8	10.2	3.6	3.9	1.4	1.2	1.0	0.7	7.6
1962	52.3	22.0	10.5	3.5	4.1	1.0	1.1	1.0	0.7	8.4
1963	53.4	23.1	10.3	3.4	4.3	1.0	1.2	1.1	0.8	8.2
1964	54.9	25.0	9.9	3.5	3.9	1.0	1.2	1.1	0.7	8.4
1965	55.8	25.4	10.3	3.5	3.8	1.0	1.2	1.1	0.8	8.7
1966	58.1	27.1	10.3	3.6	4.8	0.9	1.3	1.2	0.8	8.1
1967	57.3	26.8	10.2	3.6	3.8	1.0	1.5	1.3	0.8	8.3
1968	57.6	27.5	9.4	3.7[f]	3.7[f]	1.6[f]	1.2[f]	1.3	0.8	8.4
1969	57.8	27.7	8.9	3.8	3.6	1.8	1.2	1.5	0.8	8.5
1970	56.2	26.8	8.3	3.9	3.3	1.4	1.2	1.8	0.8	8.7
1971	54.8	26.3	8.1	3.6	3.3	1.4	1.1	1.8	0.8	8.4
1972	55.2	26.9	8.0	3.6	3.2	1.4	1.2	1.8	0.8	8.3
1973	54.8	26.3	7.8	4.1	3.1	1.4	1.2	1.7	0.8	8.4

See source and footnotes on page 45.

UNINTENTIONAL-INJURY DEATH RATES[a] FOR PRINCIPAL TYPES, UNITED STATES, 1903–1998, Cont.

Year	Total	Motor-Vehicle	Falls	Drowning[b]	Fires/Burns[c]	Ingest. of Food/Object	Firearms	Poison (Solid, Liquid)	Poison (Gas, Vapor)	All Other
1974	49.0	21.8	7.7	3.7	2.9	1.4	1.2	1.8	0.7	7.8
1975	47.8	21.3	6.9	3.7	2.8	1.4	1.1	2.2	0.7	7.7
1976	46.3	21.6	6.5	3.1	2.9	1.4	0.9	1.9	0.7	7.3
1977	47.0	22.5	6.3	3.2	2.9	1.4	0.9	1.5	0.7	7.6
1978	47.5	23.6	6.2	3.2	2.8	1.4	0.8	1.4	0.8	7.3
1979	46.9	23.8	5.9	3.1	2.7	1.4	0.9	1.4	0.7	7.0
1980	46.5	23.4	5.9	3.2	2.6	1.4	0.9	1.4	0.5	7.2
1981	43.9	22.4	5.5	2.7	2.5	1.5	0.8	1.4	0.6	6.5
1982	40.6	19.8	5.2	2.7	2.2	1.4	0.8	1.5	0.5	6.5
1983	39.6	19.0	5.1	2.7	2.2	1.4	0.7	1.4	0.5	6.6
1984	39.4	19.6	5.1	2.3	2.1	1.5	0.7	1.6	0.5	6.0
1985	39.3	19.3	5.0	2.2	2.1	1.5	0.7	1.7	0.5	6.3
1986	39.7	19.9	4.8	2.4	2.0	1.5	0.6	2.0	0.4	6.1
1987	39.2	19.9	4.8	2.1	1.9	1.5	0.6	1.8	0.4	6.2
1988	39.7	20.1	4.9	2.0	2.0	1.6	0.6	2.2	0.4	5.9
1989	38.5	19.3	4.9	1.9	1.9	1.4	0.6	2.3	0.4	5.8
1990	36.9	18.8	4.9	1.9	1.7	1.3	0.6	2.0	0.3	5.4
1991	35.4	17.3	5.0	1.8	1.6	1.3	0.6	2.3	0.3	5.2
1992	34.0	16.1	5.0	1.4	1.6	1.2	0.6	2.5	0.2	5.4
1993	35.1	16.3	5.1	1.5	1.5	1.2	0.6	3.1	0.3	5.5
1994	35.1	16.3	5.2	1.5	1.5	1.2	0.5	3.2	0.3	5.4
1995	35.5	16.5	5.3	1.7	1.4	1.2	0.5	3.2	0.2	5.5
1996	35.8	16.5	5.6	1.5	1.4	1.2	0.4	3.3	0.2	5.7
1997	35.7	16.2	5.8	1.5	1.3	1.2	0.4	3.6	0.2	5.5
1998	36.2	16.1	6.0	1.6	1.2	1.3	0.3	3.8	0.2	5.7

UNINTENTIONAL-INJURY DEATH RATES[a] FOR PRINCIPAL TYPES, UNITED STATES, 1999-2002

Year	Total	Motor-Vehicle	Falls	Poisoning	Ingest. of Food/Object	Drowning[g]	Fires, Flames, Smoke[c]	Mechanical Suffocation	Firearms	All Other
1999[h]	35.9	15.5	4.8	4.5	1.4	1.3	1.2	0.6	0.3	6.3
2000[i]	35.6	15.7	4.8	4.6	1.6	1.3	1.2	0.5	0.3	5.5
2001[i]	35.3	15.7	5.1	5.0	1.4	1.2	1.2	0.4	0.3	4.8
2002[j]	35.5	15.7	5.2	5.6	1.5	1.1	1.0	0.5	0.3	4.7

Changes										
1992 to 2002	+4%	–2%	(k)	(k)	+25%	(k)	–38%	(k)	–50%	(k)
2001 to 2002	+1%	0%	+2%	+12%	+7%	–8%	–17%	+25%	0%	–2%

Source: National Safety Council estimates. See Technical Appendix for comparability.
[a] Deaths per 100,000 population.
[b] Includes drowning in water transport accidents.
[c] Includes burns by fire, and deaths resulting from conflagration regardless of nature of injury.
[d] Comparable data not available.
[e] In 1948, a revision was made in the International Classification of Diseases. The first figures for 1948 are comparable with those for earlier years, the second with those for later years.
[f] Data are not comparable to previous years shown due to classification changes in 1958 and 1968.
[g] Excludes water transport drownings.
[h] In 1999, a revision was made in the International Classification of Diseases. See the Technical Appendix for comparability.
[i] Revised.
[j] Preliminary.
[k] Comparison not valid because of change in classifications (see footnote "h").

OCCUPATIONAL

INJURY FACTS®

NATIONAL SAFETY COUNCIL

Between 1912 and 2002, unintentional work deaths per 100,000 population were reduced 90%, from 21 to 2. In 1912, an estimated 18,000 to 21,000 workers' lives were lost. In 2002, in a work force nearly quadrupled in size and producing nine times the goods and services, there were only an estimated 4,900 work deaths.

The National Safety Council adopted the Bureau of Labor Statistics' Census of Fatal Occupational Injuries (CFOI) figure, beginning with the 1992 data year, as the authoritative count of work-related deaths. The Technical Appendix discusses the change in the Council's estimating procedures.

The CFOI system counts intentional as well as unintentional work injuries. Each year between 850 and 1,300 homicides and suicides are identified and counted. These fatal intentional injuries are not included in the unintentional-injury estimates below.

Note: The table of fatal occupational injuries by state and event or exposure has been moved to the State Data section, which begins on page 150.

Unintentional-Injury Deaths **4,900**

Unintentional-Injury Deaths per 100,000 Workers **3.6**

Disabling Injuries **3,700,000**

Workers **137,731,000**

Costs . . . . **$146.6 billion**

UNINTENTIONAL INJURIES AT WORK BY INDUSTRY, UNITED STATES, 2002

| Industry Division | Workers[a] (000) | Deaths[a] | | Deaths per 100,000 Workers[a] | | Disabling Injuries |
		2002	Change from 2001	2002	Change from 2001	
All industries	**137,731**	**4,900**	**–3%**	**3.6**	**–4%**	**3,700,000**
Agriculture[b]	3,417	730	+2%	21.0	–4%	150,000
Mining, quarrying[b]	515	150	–11%	29.1	–2%	10,000
Construction	9,162	1,150	–3%	12.6	–3%	460,000
Manufacturing	18,073	510	–7%	2.8	–3%	520,000
Transportation and public utilities	8,060	810	–4%	10.1	–3%	390,000
Trade[b]	27,966	420	–3%	1.5	–4%	710,000
Services[b]	49,668	630	–1%	1.3	–3%	900,000
Government	20,870	500	–1%	2.4	–4%	560,000

Source: National Safety Council estimates based on data from the Bureau of Labor Statistics, National Center for Health Statistics, state vital statistics departments, and state industrial commissions.
[a] *Deaths include persons of all ages. Workers and death rates include persons 16 years and older.*
[b] *Agriculture includes forestry, fishing, and agricultural services. Mining includes oil and gas extraction. Trade includes wholesale and retail trade. Services includes finance, insurance, and real estate.*

UNINTENTIONAL WORK-INJURY DEATHS AND DEATH RATES, UNITED STATES, 1992–2002

Year	Deaths[a]	Workers[b]	Death Rate[c]
1992	4,965	119,168	4.2
1993	5,034	120,778	4.2
1994	5,338	124,470	4.3
1995	5,015	126,248	4.0
1996	5,069	127,997	4.0
1997	5,160	130,810	3.9
1998	5,117	132,772	3.9
1999	5,184	134,688	3.8
2000[d]	5,022	136,402	3.7
2001[d]	5,033	136,246	3.7
2002[e]	4,900	137,731	3.6

Source: Deaths through 2001 are from the Bureau of Labor Statistics, Census of Fatal Occupational Injuries. Employment is from the Bureau of Labor Statistics and is based on the Current Population Survey. All other data are National Safety Council estimates.
[a] *Deaths include persons of all ages. Workers and death rates include persons 16 years and older. Because of adoption of the Census of Fatal Occupational Injuries, deaths and rates from 1992 to the present are not comparable to prior years. See Technical Appendix for change in estimating procedure.*
[b] *In thousands. Workers are persons ages 16 and older gainfully employed, including owners, managers, other paid employees, the self-employed, unpaid family workers, and active duty resident military personnel. Due to changes in procedures, estimates of workers from 1992 to the present are not comparable to prior years.*
[c] *Deaths per 100,000 workers.*
[d] *Revised.*
[e] *Preliminary.*

WORKERS, UNINTENTIONAL-INJURY DEATHS, AND DEATH RATES, UNITED STATES, 1992–2002

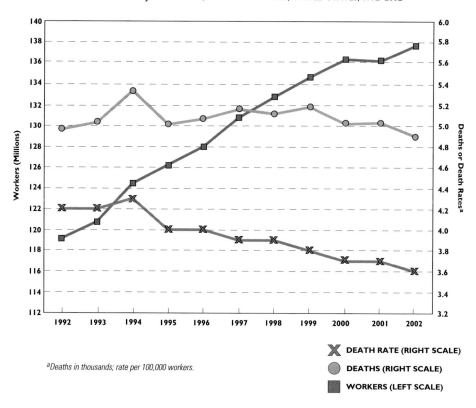

[a]*Deaths in thousands; rate per 100,000 workers.*

✕ **DEATH RATE (RIGHT SCALE)**

● **DEATHS (RIGHT SCALE)**

■ **WORKERS (LEFT SCALE)**

OCCUPATIONAL-INJURY DEATHS AND DEATH RATES, UNITED STATES, 1992–2002

Year	Total	Homicide & Suicide	Unintentional								
			All Industries[a]	Agri-culture[b]	Mining, Quarrying[c]	Construc-tion	Manufac-turing	Transpor-tation & Public Utilities	Trade[d]	Services[e]	Govern-ment
Deaths											
1992	6,217	1,252	4,965	779	175	889	707	767	415	601	586
1993	6,331	1,297	5,034	842	169	895	698	753	450	631	527
1994	6,632	1,294	5,338	814	177	1,000	734	819	492	676	534
1995	6,275	1,260	5,015	769	155	1,021	640	784	461	608	528
1996	6,202	1,133	5,069	762	151	1,025	660	883	451	615	321
1997	6,238	1,078	5,160	799	156	1,075	678	882	451	593	504
1998	6,055	938	5,117	808	143	1,136	631	830	443	634	465
1999	6,054	870	5,184	776	122	1,168	671	918	425	623	451
2000[f]	5,920	898	5,022	693	153	1,114	624	872	447	643	460
2001[f]	5,900	867[h]	5,033	713	169	1,182	547	840	431	634	505
2002[g]	—	—	4,900	730	150	1,150	510	810	420	630	500
Deaths per 100,000 Workers											
1992	5.2	1.0	4.2	23.1	26.4	13.7	3.6	11.5	1.7	1.6	3.0
1993	5.2	1.0	4.2	26.0	25.3	13.3	3.6	11.0	1.8	1.6	2.6
1994	5.3	1.0	4.3	22.8	26.5	14.4	3.7	11.6	1.9	1.7	2.7
1995	4.9	1.0	4.0	21.4	24.8	14.3	3.1	11.0	1.8	1.5	2.7
1996	4.8	0.9	4.0	21.2	26.6	13.7	3.2	12.2	1.7	1.4	1.6
1997	4.8	0.8	3.9	22.5	24.7	13.7	3.3	11.6	1.7	1.3	2.6
1998	4.5	0.7	3.9	22.7	23.1	14.1	3.1	10.8	1.6	1.4	2.4
1999	4.5	0.6	3.8	22.6	21.7	13.8	3.4	11.5	1.5	1.3	2.2
2000[f]	4.3	0.7	3.7	20.1	29.4	12.4	3.1	10.8	1.6	1.4	2.3
2001[f]	4.3	0.6[h]	3.7	22.0	29.9	13.0	2.9	10.3	1.6	1.3	2.5
2002[g]	—	—	3.6	21.0	29.1	12.6	2.8	10.1	1.5	1.3	2.4

Source: Deaths are from Bureau of Labor Statistics, Census of Fatal Occupational Injuries, except 2002 which are National Safety Council estimates. Rates are National Safety Council estimates based on Bureau of Labor Statistics employment data. Deaths include persons of all ages. Death rates include persons 16 years and older. Dashes (—) indicate data not available.
[a] Includes deaths with industry unknown.
[b] Agriculture includes forestry, fishing, and agricultural services.
[c] Mining includes oil and gas extraction.
[d] Trade includes wholesale and retail trade.
[e] Services includes finance, insurance, and real estate.
[f] Revised.
[g] Preliminary.
[h] Excludes 2,886 homicides of workers on September 11, 2001.

OCCUPATIONAL UNINTENTIONAL-INJURY DEATHS AND DEATH RATES BY INDUSTRY, UNITED STATES, 2002

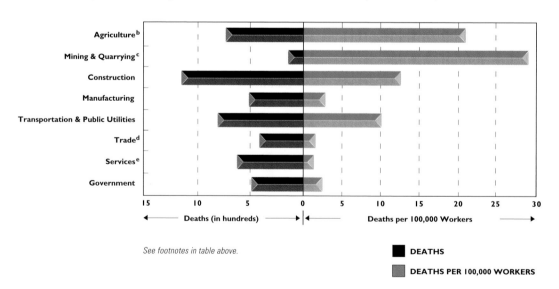

See footnotes in table above.

DEATHS

DEATHS PER 100,000 WORKERS

The true cost to the nation, to employers, and to individuals of work-related deaths and injuries is much greater than the cost of workers' compensation insurance alone. The figures presented below show the National Safety Council's estimates of the total economic costs of occupational deaths and injuries. Cost estimating procedures were revised for the 1993 edition of *Accident Facts*®. In general, cost estimates are not comparable from year to year. As additional or more precise data become available, they are used from that year forward. Previously estimated figures are not revised.

TOTAL COST IN 2002 . . . . **$146.6 billion**
Includes wage and productivity losses of $74.0 billion, medical costs of $27.7 billion, and administrative expenses of $26.3 billion. Includes employer costs of $12.5 billion such as the money value of time lost by

workers other than those with disabling injuries, who are directly or indirectly involved in injuries, and the cost of time required to investigate injuries, write up injury reports, etc. Also includes damage to motor vehicles in work injuries of $2.8 billion and fire losses of $3.3 billion.

Cost per Worker **$1,060**
This figure indicates the value of goods or services each worker must produce to offset the cost of work injuries. It is *not* the average cost of a work injury.

Cost per Death **$1,070,000**

Cost per Disabling Injury **$33,000**
These figures include estimates of wage losses, medical expenses, administrative expenses, and employer costs, and exclude property damage costs except to motor-vehicles.

TIME LOST BECAUSE OF WORK INJURIES

DAYS LOST

TOTAL TIME LOST IN 2002 . . . . **125,000,000**

Due to Injuries in 2002 . . . . **80,000,000**
Includes primarily the actual time lost during the year from disabling injuries, except that it does not include time lost on the day of the injury or time required for further medical treatment or check-up following the injured person's return to work.

Fatalities are included at an average loss of 150 days per case, and permanent impairments are included at actual days lost plus an allowance for lost efficiency resulting from the impairment.

Not included is time lost by persons with nondisabling injuries or other persons directly or indirectly involved in the incidents.

DAYS LOST

Due to Injuries in Prior Years **45,000,000**
This is an indicator of the productive time lost in 2002 due to permanently disabling injuries that occurred in prior years.

DAYS LOST

TIME LOSS IN FUTURE YEARS FROM 2002 INJURIES **65,000,000**
Includes time lost in future years due to on-the-job deaths and permanently disabling injuries that occurred in 2002.

WORKER DEATHS AND INJURIES ON AND OFF THE JOB

Nine out of 10 deaths and about two thirds of the disabling injuries suffered by workers in 2002 occurred off the job. The ratios of off-the-job deaths and injuries to on-the-job were 9.1 to 1 and 1.9 to 1, respectively. Production time lost due to off-the-job injuries totaled about 170,000,000 days in 2002, compared with 80,000,000 days lost by workers injured on the job. Production time lost in future years due to off-the-job injuries in 2002 will total an estimated 430,000,000 days, more than seven times the 60,000,000 days lost in future years from 2002's on-the-job injuries. Off-the-job injuries to workers cost the nation at least $215.1 billion in 2002.

The basis of the rates shown in the table below was changed from 1,000,000 hours to 200,000 hours beginning with the 1998 edition. This change was made so that the rates would be on the same basis as the occupational injury and illness incidence rates shown elsewhere in *Injury Facts*®.

ON- AND OFF-THE-JOB INJURIES, UNITED STATES, 2002

Place	Deaths		Disabling Injuries	
	Number	Rate[a]	Number	Rate[a]
On- and off-the-job	**49,600**	**0.012**	**10,800,000**	**2.7**
On-the-job	4,900	0.003	3,700,000	2.5
Off-the-job	44,700	0.017	7,100,000	2.7
Motor-vehicle	*23,100*	*0.084*	*1,200,000*	*4.4*
Public nonmotor-vehicle	*7,800*	*0.018*	*2,600,000*	*6.1*
Home	*13,800*	*0.007*	*3,300,000*	*1.7*

Source: National Safety Council estimates. Procedures for allocating time spent on and off the job were revised for the 1990 edition. Rate basis changed to 200,000 hours for the 1998 edition. Death and injury rates are not comparable to rate estimates prior to the 1998 edition.
[a] *Per 200,000 hours exposure by place.*

WORKERS' ON- AND OFF-THE-JOB INJURIES, 2002

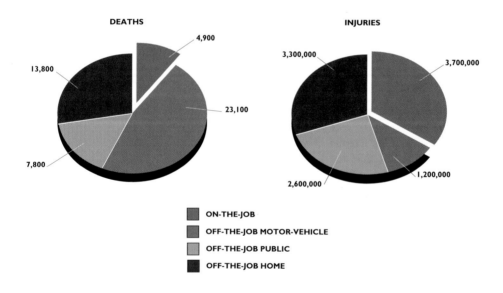

DEATHS

INJURIES

- ON-THE-JOB
- OFF-THE-JOB MOTOR-VEHICLE
- OFF-THE-JOB PUBLIC
- OFF-THE-JOB HOME

According to the National Academy of Social Insurance, an estimated $49.4 billion, including benefits under deductible provisions, was paid out under workers' compensation in 2001 (the latest year for which data were available), an increase of about 3.5% from 2000. Of this total, $27.4 billion was for income benefits and $22.0 billion was for medical and hospitalization costs. Private carriers paid about $27.1 billion of the total workers' compensation benefits in 2001. In 2001,

approximately 127.0 million workers were covered by workers' compensation — a decrease of 0.1% over the 127.1 million in 2000.

The table below shows the trend in the number of compensated or reported cases in each reporting state. Due to the differences in population, industries, and coverage of compensation laws, comparison among states should not be made.

WORKERS' COMPENSATION CASES, UNITED STATES, 2000–2002

State	Deaths[a]			Cases[a]			2001 Compensation Paid ($000)
	2002	2001	2000	2002	2001	2000	
Arizona[b]	109	93	121	126,986	136,403	143,197	392,861
Arkansas	72	73	84	12,305	12,867	13,266	201,136
Colorado[c]	—	—	114	—	—	33,520	581,266
Connecticut	99	61	41	72,982	68,149	82,514	661,471
Delaware	11	10	13	21,334	21,495	22,674	144,588
Georgia[b,d]	—	242	262	—	41,028	44,581	1,067,327
Hawaii[e]	18	34	34	29,974	30,179	31,866	252,041
Indiana	94	96	94	105,929	104,869	92,022	528,005
Iowa	40	69	80	23,587	28,957	29,133	395,981
Kansas	53	44	69	72,825	84,945	90,049	340,343
Kentucky	52	45	61	36,479	39,589	44,092	524,566
Louisiana[b]	53	70	99	13,108	15,754	19,867	501,662
Massachusetts	—	53	67	34,375	40,490	41,162	763,795
Michigan[f]	102	111	106	40,713	43,289	54,307	1,477,986
Minnesota[b]	41	50	46	—	149,850	166,646	908,100
Missouri	128	120	122	147,539	165,109	174,863	1,108,464
Nebraska[g]	58	38	54	61,522	66,011	68,057	237,045
Nevada[b]	40	49	—	83,999	85,303	86,011	380,756
New Mexico[b]	22	26	14	20,534	22,852	19,105	162,022
North Carolina	183	163	227	62,656	63,318	66,871	867,965
North Dakota	14	12	20	19,950	20,320	20,045	79,633
Ohio[f]	147	155	175	236,344	263,911	280,873	2,249,200
Oregon[b,h]	52	34	45	23,482	24,645	25,365	455,625
Pennsylvania[f]	146	134	114	95,206	90,405	80,133	2,440,407
South Dakota[b,d]	15	13	29	26,498	29,204	29,711	74,950
Vermont	—	9	15	—	4,381	4,260	105,017
Washington	84	89	93	217,129	232,706	247,108	1,637,714
West Virginia	239	237	269	56,319	57,261	60,024	712,495

Source: Deaths and Cases — State workers' compensation authorities for calendar or fiscal year. States not listed did not respond to the survey. Compensation Paid — Thompson-Williams, C., Reno, V. P., & Burton, J. F., Jr. (July, 2003). Workers' compensation: benefits, coverage, and costs, 2001. Washington DC: National Academy of Social Insurance.
Note: Dash (—) indicates data not available.

Definitions:
Reported case — a reported case may or may not be work-related and may not receive compensation.
Compensated case — a case determined to be work-related and for which compensation was paid.

[a]Reported cases involving medical and indemnity benefits, unless otherwise noted.
[b]Closed or compensated cases.
[c]Lost-time claims in which the worker misses more than three days or three shifts of work due to the work-related injury.
[d]Cases first closed in the calendar year involving Indemnity benefits only.
[e]Reported cases involving Medical benefits only.
[f]Reported cases involving Indemnity benefits only.
[g]Reported and closed or compensated cases.
[h]Lost-time claims in which the worker misses 3 or more days of work, has a validated hospital admittance, or a fatal injury.

WORKERS' COMPENSATION CLAIMS COSTS, 2000–2001

Motor-vehicle crashes are the most costly workers' compensation claims.

The data in the graphs on this and the next page are from the National Council on Compensation Insurance's (NCCI) Detailed Claim Information (DCI) file, a stratified random sample of lost-time claims in 41 states. Total incurred costs consist of medical and indemnity payments plus case reserves on open claims, and are calculated as of the second report (18 months after the initial report of injury). Injuries that result in medical payments only, without lost time, are not included. For open claims, costs include all payments as of the second report plus case reserves for future payments.

The average cost for all claims combined in 2000–2001 was $13,719, up 14% from the 1999–2000 average of $12,055.

Cause of Injury. The most costly lost-time workers' compensation claims by cause of injury, according to the NCCI data, are for those resulting from motor-vehicle crashes. These injuries averaged more than $22,200 per workers' compensation claim filed in 2000

and 2001. The other causes with above-average costs were those involving a fall or slip ($15,569), miscellaneous causes ($14,401), and cumulative trauma ($13,811).

Nature of Injury. The most costly lost-time workers' compensation claims by the nature of the injury are for those resulting from amputation. These injuries averaged $21,800 per workers' compensation claim filed in 2000 and 2001. The next highest costs were for injuries resulting in fracture ($18,638), carpal tunnel syndrome ($17,301), and other trauma ($16,818).

Part of Body. The most costly lost-time workers' compensation claims are for those involving the head or central nervous system. These injuries averaged $21,523 per workers' compensation claim filed in 2000 and 2001. The next highest costs were for injuries involving the neck ($21,222), multiple body parts ($20,167), and the upper back ($17,672). Injuries to the lower back; hip, thigh, and pelvis; leg; knee; and arm/shoulder also had above-average costs.

AVERAGE TOTAL INCURRED COSTS PER CLAIM BY CAUSE OF INJURY, 2000–2001

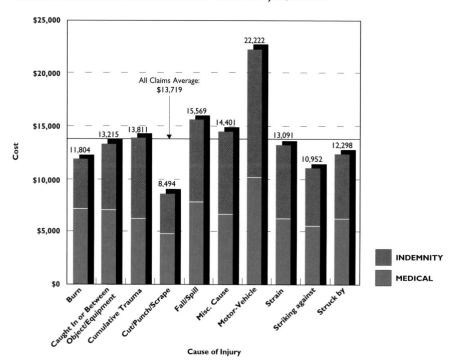

AVERAGE TOTAL INCURRED COSTS PER CLAIM BY NATURE OF INJURY, 2000–2001

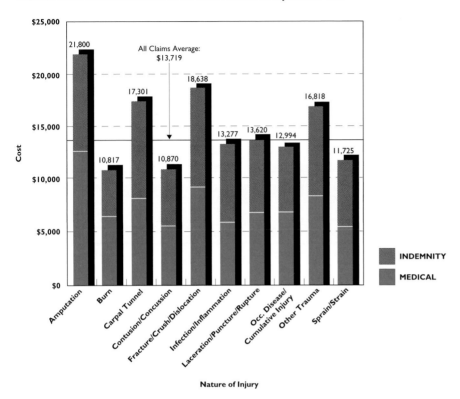

AVERAGE TOTAL INCURRED COSTS PER CLAIM BY PART OF BODY, 2000–2001

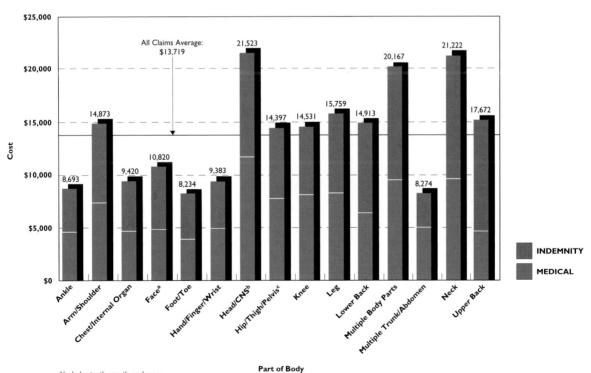

[a] Includes teeth, mouth, and eyes.
[b] Central nervous system.
[c] Includes sacrum and coccyx.

WORK-RELATED TERRORISM DEATHS

More than 3,000 people died as a result of the terrorist attacks on September 11, 2001. Of these, 2,886 were work-related and captured in the Census of Fatal Occupational Injuries. All were classified as work-related homicides.

Eighty percent of the deaths (2,323) were occupants of the World Trade Center or the Pentagon, 14% (412)

were rescue workers, and the remaining 5% (151) were passengers and crew of the four hijacked airplanes.

The table below shows the industry, occupation, and some demographic characteristics of the fatally injured workers.

Source: Bureau of Labor Statistics. (2002, September 25). National Census of Fatal Occupational Injuries in 2001. Press release USDL 02-541.

FATAL OCCUPATIONAL INJURIES DUE TO THE SEPTEMBER 11 TERRORIST ATTACKS, UNITED STATES, 2001

Characteristic	Deaths
Occupation	
Managerial and professional specialty	1,271
Executive, administrative, and managerial	1,072
Professional specialty	199
Technical, sales, and administrative support	**930**
Technicians and related support occupations	92
Health technologists and technicians	8
Airplane pilots and navigators	8
Sales occupations	565
Service occupations	**549**
Protective service occupations	433
Firefighting, including supervisors	336
Police and detectives, including supervisors	64
Guards, including supervisors	33
Food preparation and service occupations	64
Cleaning and building service	25
Personal service occupations	27
Transportation attendants	25
Precision production, craft, and repair	**61**
Mechanics and repairers	20
Construction trades	39
Operators, fabricators, and laborers	**14**
Military occupations	**54**

Characteristic	Deaths
Industry	
Private industry	**2,264**
Construction	**58**
General building contractors	12
Heavy construction, except building	13
Special trade contractors	32
Transportation and public utilities	**78**
Transportation by air	37
Wholesale trade	**27**
Retail trade	**118**
Eating and drinking places	103
Finance, insurance, and real estate	**1,715**
Depository institutions	192
Security and commodity brokers	973
Insurance carriers	202
Insurance agents, brokers, an service	330
Real estate	13
Holding and other investment offices	5
Services	**230**
Business services	141
Government[a]	**622**
Federal government	**124**
National security	118
State government	**49**
Local government	**449**
Police protection	25
Fire protection	344
Administration of economic programs	79

Characteristic	Deaths
State	
New York	2,699
Virginia	165
Pennsylvania	22
Sex	
Men	2,212
Women	674
Age	
20–24 years	112
25–34 years	822
35–44 years	1,068
45–54 years	608
55–64 years	237
65 and older	30
Race or ethnic origin[b]	
White	2,122
Black or African American	261
Hispanic or Latino[c]	259
Asian	149
Native Hawaii or Pacific Islander	29
Other races or not reported	63

Source: U.S. Department of Labor, Bureau of Labor Statistics, Census of Fatal Occupational Injuries.
Note: Totals may include categories not shown separately.
[a]Includes fatalities to workers employed by governmental organizations regardless of industry.
[b]The categories "White" and "Black or African American" do not include "Hispanic or Latino" persons.
[c]Persons identified as Hispanic may be of any race.
Note: Totals for major categories may include subcategories not shown separately.

According to the Bureau of Labor Statistics, the back was the body part most frequently affected in injuries involving days away from work in 2001, accounting for over 24% of the total 1,537,567 injuries in private industry. Multiple-part injuries were the second most common, followed by finger, knee, and head injuries. Overall, the services and manufacturing industries had the highest number of injuries, combining to make up nearly 45% of the total.

NUMBER OF NONFATAL OCCUPATIONAL INJURIES INVOLVING DAYS AWAY FROM WORK[a] BY PART OF BODY AFFECTED AND INDUSTRY DIVISION, PRIVATE INDUSTRY, UNITED STATES, 2001

| Part of Body Affected | Private Industry[b] | Goods Producing | | | | Service Producing | | | | |
		Agri-culture[b,c]	Mining[c]	Construc-tion	Manufac-turing	Trans. & Public Utilities	Wholesale Trade	Retail Trade	Finance, Insurance, & Real Estate	Services
Total[d]	1,537,567	40,153	10,582	185,662	317,326	199,939	111,925	265,700	37,982	368,299
Head	99,523	3,426	562	13,843	22,767	11,734	6,039	16,448	2,734	21,970
Eye	44,811	1,710	257	7,725	13,931	3,875	2,748	6,346	548	7,672
Neck	27,111	445	248	2,252	4,603	3,881	1,978	4,129	481	9,094
Trunk	561,603	13,600	3,466	60,891	108,262	78,155	46,425	93,575	11,223	146,006
Shoulder	88,484	1,755	588	9,412	20,252	13,554	7,083	13,614	1,594	20,632
Back	372,683	8,830	1,968	38,973	66,366	50,765	30,421	64,510	7,579	103,272
Upper extremities	355,344	9,566	2,432	45,983	99,765	32,622	22,306	67,726	9,075	65,870
Wrist	78,857	989	354	7,076	22,362	7,073	4,459	13,636	3,982	18,926
Hand, except finger	63,727	2,453	494	9,863	15,155	5,374	3,878	14,717	1,154	10,640
Finger	123,523	3,814	1,075	19,265	40,181	9,153	7,789	22,396	1,618	18,233
Lower extremities	322,959	9,186	2,813	44,823	56,796	49,430	24,351	55,288	8,378	71,895
Knee	119,670	2,508	1,085	15,584	21,184	17,869	8,427	20,918	2,892	29,203
Foot, except toe	51,721	1,881	425	8,073	10,412	6,473	4,059	8,398	1,408	10,592
Toe	16,396	531	73	2,218	3,611	1,710	1,906	3,389	189	2,770
Body systems	21,657	434	131	2,318	3,796	2,732	811	2,964	1,342	7,129
Multiple parts	139,675	3,250	899	14,571	19,982	20,385	9,320	23,048	4,380	43,841

Source: Bureau of Labor Statistics. (2003). Occupational Injuries and Illnesses in the United States — Profiles Data 1992–2001, CD-ROM Disk 1 (National and Boston, Philadelphia, and Chicago Regions), Version 9.0.

[a]*Days-away-from-work cases include those which result in days away from work with or without restricted work activity.*
[b]*Excludes farms with less than 11 employees.*
[c]*Agriculture includes forestry and fishing; mining includes quarrying and oil and gas extraction.*
[d]*Data may not sum to totals because of rounding and exclusion of nonclassifiable responses.*

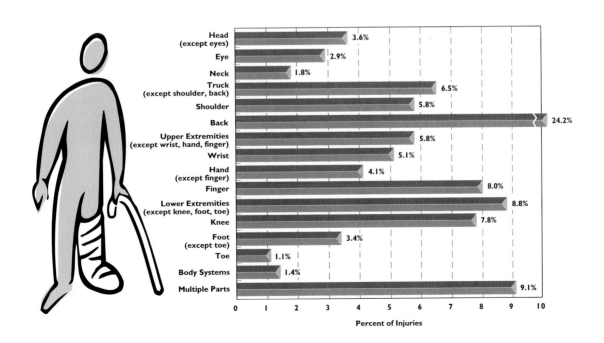

Head (except eyes)	3.6%
Eye	2.9%
Neck	1.8%
Truck (except shoulder, back)	6.5%
Shoulder	5.8%
Back	24.2%
Upper Extremities (except wrist, hand, finger)	5.8%
Wrist	5.1%
Hand (except finger)	4.1%
Finger	8.0%
Lower Extremities (except knee, foot, toe)	8.8%
Knee	7.8%
Foot (except toe)	3.4%
Toe	1.1%
Body Systems	1.4%
Multiple Parts	9.1%

Percent of Injuries

Safety professionals in business and industry often want to compare, or benchmark, the occupational injury and illness incidence rates of their establishments with the national average rates compiled by the U.S. Bureau of Labor Statistics (BLS) through its annual Survey of Occupational Injuries and Illnesses.[a] The incidence rates published on the following pages are for 2001 and were compiled under the OSHA record-keeping requirements in effect at that time. Incidence rates compiled under the revised OSHA record-keeping requirements that went into effect in 2002 will not be published until December 2003 and will appear in the 2004 edition of *Injury Facts®*. *Caution must be used in comparing rates computed for 2002 with rates published for 2001 — keeping in mind the differences in record-keeping requirements.*

Step 1.

The first step in benchmarking is to calculate the incidence rates for the establishment. The basic formula for computing incidence rates is *(N x 200,000)/EH,* or, the number of cases (*N*) multiplied by *200,000* then divided by the number of hours worked (*EH*) by all employees during the time period where *200,000* is the base for 100 full-time workers (working 40 hours per week, 50 weeks per year). Because the BLS rates are based on reports from entire establishments, both the OSHA 300 Log and the number of hours worked should cover the whole establishment being benchmarked. The hours worked and the log also should cover the same time period (e.g., a month, quarter, or full year). The following rates, which are approximately comparable to rates under the old record-keeping system, may be calculated.

Total Cases — the incidence rate of total OSHA-recordable cases per 200,000 hours worked. For this rate, *N* is the total number of cases on the OSHA 300 Log.

Cases with Days Away From Work or Job Transfer or Restriction — the incidence rate of cases with days away from work, or job transfer, or restriction. *N* is the count of cases with a check in column H or column I of the OSHA 300 Log.

Cases With Days Away From Work — the incidence rate of cases with days away from work. *N* is the count of cases with a check in column H of the OSHA 300 Log.

Other Recordable Cases — the incidence rate of recordable cases without days away from work or job transfer or restriction. *N* is the count of cases with a check in column J of the OSHA 300 Log.

Step 2.

After computing one or more of the rates, the next step is to determine the Standard Industrial Classification (SIC) code for the establishment.[b] This code is used to find the appropriate BLS rate for comparison. A convenient way to find an SIC code is to use the search feature on the OSHA Internet site (http://www.osha.gov/oshstats/sicser.html). Otherwise, call a regional BLS office for assistance.

Step 3.

Once the SIC code is known, the national average incidence rates may be found by (a) consulting the table of rates on pages 62–64, (b) visiting the BLS Internet site (www.bls.gov/iif), or (c) calling a regional BLS office. Note that some tables on the Internet site provide incidence rates by size of establishment and rate quartiles within each SIC code. These rates may be useful for a more precise comparison. Note that the incidence rates for 2001 and earlier years were compiled under the old OSHA record-keeping requirements in effect at that time. Caution must be used in comparing rates computed for 2002 with rates published for 2001 — keeping in mind the differences in record-keeping requirements.

An alternative way of benchmarking is to compare the current incidence rates for an establishment to its own prior historical rates to determine if the rates are improving and if progress is satisfactory (using criteria set by the organization).

[a] *Bureau of Labor Statistics. (1997).* BLS Handbook of Methods. *Washington, DC: U.S. Government Printing Office. (Or on the Internet at http://www.bls.gov/opub/hom/home.htm)*
[b] *Executive Office of the President, Office of Management and Budget. (1987).* Standard Industrial Classification Manual. *Springfield, VA: National Technical Information Service.*

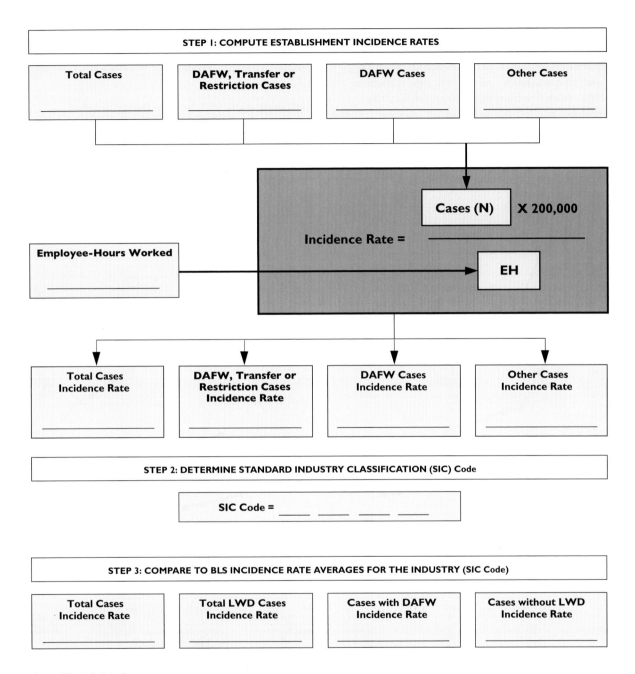

STEP 1: COMPUTE ESTABLISHMENT INCIDENCE RATES

Total Cases	DAFW, Transfer or Restriction Cases	DAFW Cases	Other Cases
_____	_____	_____	_____

$$\text{Incidence Rate} = \frac{\text{Cases (N)} \times 200{,}000}{\text{EH}}$$

Employee-Hours Worked

_____

Total Cases Incidence Rate	DAFW, Transfer or Restriction Cases Incidence Rate	DAFW Cases Incidence Rate	Other Cases Incidence Rate
_____	_____	_____	_____

STEP 2: DETERMINE STANDARD INDUSTRY CLASSIFICATION (SIC) Code

SIC Code = _____ _____ _____ _____

STEP 3: COMPARE TO BLS INCIDENCE RATE AVERAGES FOR THE INDUSTRY (SIC Code)

Total Cases Incidence Rate	Total LWD Cases Incidence Rate	Cases with DAFW Incidence Rate	Cases without LWD Incidence Rate
_____	_____	_____	_____

See page 58 for detailed instructions.
LWD   = Lost Workday
DAFW = Days Away From Work

TRENDS IN OCCUPATIONAL INCIDENCE RATES

Incidence rates continue recent downward trend.

All four occupational injury and illness incidence rates published by the Bureau of Labor Statistics for 2001 decreased from 2000. The incidence rate for total nonfatal cases was 5.7 per 100 full-time workers in 2001, down 7% from the 2000 rate of 6.1. The incidence rate for total lost workday cases was 2.8, also down 7% from the 2000 rate of 3.0. The incidence rate for lost workday cases with days away from work was

1.7 in 2001, down 6% from 1.8 in 2000. The incidence rate in 2001 for nonfatal cases without lost workdays was 2.9, a decrease of 9% from the 2000 rate of 3.2.

Beginning with 1992 data, the Bureau of Labor Statistics revised its annual survey to include only nonfatal cases and stopped publishing the incidence rate of lost workdays.

OCCUPATIONAL INJURY AND ILLNESS INCIDENCE RATES, BUREAU OF LABOR STATISTICS, UNITED STATES, 1973–2001

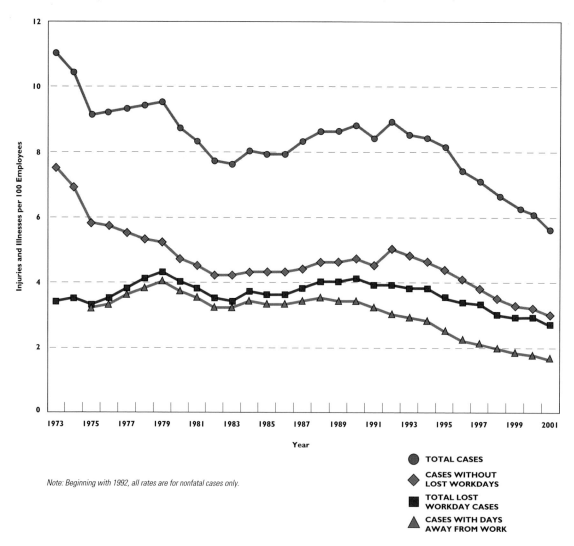

Note: Beginning with 1992, all rates are for nonfatal cases only.

- ● TOTAL CASES
- ◆ CASES WITHOUT LOST WORKDAYS
- ■ TOTAL LOST WORKDAY CASES
- ▲ CASES WITH DAYS AWAY FROM WORK

The tables below and on pages 62–64 present the results of the 2001 Survey of Occupational Injuries and Illnesses conducted by the Bureau of Labor Statistics (BLS), U.S. Department of Labor. The survey collects data on injuries and illnesses (from the OSHA 200 Log) and employee-hours worked from a nationwide sample of about 176,000 establishments representing the private sector of the economy. The survey excludes public employees, private households, the self-employed, and farms with fewer than 11 employees. The incidence rates give the number of cases per 100 full-time workers per year using 200,000 employee-hours as the equivalent. Definitions of the terms are given in the Glossary on page 175.

Beginning with 1992 data, the BLS revised its annual survey to include only nonfatal cases and stopped publishing incidence rates of lost workdays.

BLS ESTIMATES OF NONFATAL OCCUPATIONAL INJURY AND ILLNESS INCIDENCE RATES BY INDUSTRY DIVISION, 2000–2001

	Incidence Rates[c]							
			Lost Workday Cases					
	Total Cases		Total		With Days Away from Work		Cases Without Lost Workdays	
Industry Division	2001	2000	2001	2000	2001	2000	2001	2000
Private Sector[d]	**5.7**	**6.1**	**2.8**	**3.0**	**1.7**	**1.8**	**2.9**	**3.2**
Agriculture, forestry, and fishing[d]	7.3	7.1	3.6	3.6	2.7	2.5	3.7	3.5
Mining	4.0	4.7	2.4	3.0	1.8	2.4	1.6	1.7
Construction	7.9	8.3	4.0	4.1	3.0	3.2	3.9	4.2
Manufacturing	8.1	9.0	4.1	4.5	1.8	2.0	4.0	4.5
Transportation and public utilities	6.9	6.9	4.3	4.3	3.0	3.1	2.6	2.6
Wholesale and retail trade	5.6	5.9	2.5	2.7	1.6	1.7	3.0	3.3
Finance, insurance, and real estate	1.8	1.9	0.7	0.8	0.6	0.6	1.0	1.1
Services	4.6	4.9	2.2	2.2	1.3	1.4	2.5	2.6

Source: Bureau of Labor Statistics.
[a] Industry Division and 2- and 3-digit SIC code totals on pages 62–64 include data for industries not shown separately.
[b] Standard Industrial Classification Manual, 1987 Edition, for industries shown on pages 62–64.
[c] Incidence Rate = $\dfrac{\text{Number of injuries \& illnesses} \times 200{,}000}{\text{Total hours worked by all employees during period covered}}$
where 200,000 is the base for 100 full-time workers (working 40 hours per week, 50 weeks per year). The "Total Cases" rate is based on the number of cases with check marks in columns 2, 6, 9, and 13 of the OSHA 200 Log. The "Total Lost Workday Cases" rate is based on columns 2 and 9. The "Lost Workday Cases With Days Away From Work" rate is based on columns 3 and 10. The "Cases Without Lost Workdays" rate is based on columns 6 and 13.
[d] Excludes farms with less than 11 employees.

BLS ESTIMATES OF NONFATAL OCCUPATIONAL INJURY AND ILLNESS INCIDENCE RATES FOR SELECTED INDUSTRIES, 2001

| Industry[a] | SIC Code[b] | Total Cases | Incidence Rates[c] | | Cases Without Lost Workdays |
| | | | Lost Workday Cases | | |
			Total	With Days Away from Work	
PRIVATE SECTOR[d]	—	**5.7**	**2.8**	**1.7**	**2.9**
Agriculture, Forestry, and Fishing[d]	—	**7.3**	**3.6**	**2.7**	**3.7**
Agricultural production	01–02	7.6	3.7	2.5	4.0
Agricultural services	07	7.1	3.6	2.8	3.5
Forestry	08	6.4	3.3	2.6	3.1
Fishing, hunting, and trapping	09	3.9	2.8	2.4	1.1
Mining	—	**4.0**	**2.4**	**1.8**	**1.6**
Metal mining	10	4.2	2.4	1.3	1.9
Coal mining	12	6.9	4.9	4.5	2.0
Oil and gas extraction	13	3.3	1.7	1.2	1.6
Crude petroleum and natural gas	131	2.5	1.1	0.9	1.4
Oil and gas field services	138	3.8	2.1	1.4	1.7
Nonmetallic minerals, except fuels	14	4.2	2.8	1.7	1.4
Construction	—	**7.9**	**4.0**	**3.0**	**3.9**
General building contractors	15	6.9	3.5	2.6	3.5
Residential building construction	152	6.5	3.5	2.8	2.9
Nonresidential building construction	154	7.6	3.5	2.5	4.1
Heavy construction, except building	16	7.8	4.0	2.9	3.8
Highway and street construction	161	7.7	4.2	3.1	3.5
Heavy construction, except highway	162	7.8	4.0	2.8	3.9
Special trade contractors	17	8.2	4.1	3.2	4.1
Plumbing, heating, air-conditioning	171	9.7	4.6	3.4	5.1
Electrical work	173	6.9	2.9	2.3	3.9
Masonry, stonework, and plastering	174	9.7	5.2	4.2	4.5
Carpentry and floor work	175	9.8	4.9	4.2	4.9
Roofing, siding, and sheet metal work	176	9.1	5.0	4.1	4.1
Miscellaneous special trade contractors	179	7.2	3.8	3.0	3.3
Manufacturing	—	**8.1**	**4.1**	**1.8**	**4.0**
Durable goods	—	8.8	4.3	2.0	4.6
Lumber and wood products	24	10.6	5.5	3.0	5.1
Logging	241	6.5	3.5	3.3	3.1
Sawmills and planing mills	242	10.8	5.9	3.2	4.9
Millwork, plywood, and structural members	243	10.8	5.6	2.9	5.2
Wood containers	244	8.6	5.1	3.5	3.5
Wood buildings and mobile homes	245	16.3	7.8	3.0	8.6
Furniture and fixtures	25	11.0	5.7	2.4	5.3
Household furniture	251	11.1	5.7	2.6	5.4
Office furniture	252	10.0	5.1	1.9	4.9
Public building and related furniture	253	14.4	8.7	2.6	5.7
Stone, clay, and glass products	32	10.1	5.1	2.8	5.0
Flat glass	321	12.3	4.0	1.1	8.3
Glass and glassware, pressed or blown	322	9.2	4.6	2.5	4.6
Products of purchased glass	323	9.2	4.4	1.7	4.8
Cement, hydraulic	324	10.1	4.7	3.3	5.4
Structural clay products	325	11.8	5.1	2.3	6.7
Concrete, gypsum, and plaster products	327	10.7	5.8	3.6	4.9
Miscellaneous nonmetallic mineral products	329	7.5	3.4	1.6	4.1
Primary metal industries	33	10.7	5.3	2.5	5.4
Blast furnace and basic steel products	331	8.4	4.2	2.3	4.2
Iron and steel foundries	332	16.7	7.3	2.8	9.3
Primary nonferrous metals	333	9.9	4.4	1.7	5.5
Nonferrous rolling and drawing	335	7.7	4.1	2.0	3.7
Nonferrous foundries (castings)	336	13.1	7.7	3.5	5.4
Fabricated metal products	34	11.1	5.3	2.6	5.8
Metal cans and shipping containers	341	8.9	3.2	2.0	5.7
Cutlery, hand tools, and hardware	342	9.0	4.2	1.9	4.8
Plumbing and heating, except electric	343	12.5	5.3	1.7	7.2
Fabricated structural metal products	344	12.4	5.7	3.2	6.6
Screw machine products, bolts, etc.	345	9.2	4.3	2.3	4.8
Metal forgings and stampings	346	12.5	6.0	2.3	6.5
Metal services, n.e.c.	347	10.7	5.7	2.9	5.0
Miscellaneous fabricated metal products	349	9.9	5.0	2.3	4.9
Industrial machinery and equipment	35	7.2	3.1	1.6	4.1
Engines and turbines	351	6.4	2.5	1.4	3.8
Farm and garden machinery	352	9.2	4.5	2.1	4.7
Construction and related machinery	353	9.7	4.6	2.6	5.1
Metalworking machinery	354	7.7	3.0	1.7	4.7
Special industry machinery	355	7.3	2.7	1.8	4.6
General industrial machinery	356	8.3	3.8	1.9	4.5
Computer and office equipment	357	2.1	1.0	0.4	1.1
Refrigeration and service machinery	358	9.6	4.4	1.5	5.2

See source and footnotes on page 61.
n.e.c. = not elsewhere classified.

BLS ESTIMATES OF NONFATAL OCCUPATIONAL INJURY AND ILLNESS INCIDENCE RATES FOR SELECTED INDUSTRIES, 2001, Cont.

Industry[a]	SIC Code[b]	Total Cases	Incidence Rates[c]		Cases Without Lost Workdays
			Lost Workday Cases		
			Total	With Days Away from Work	
Industrial machinery, n.e.c.	359	7.5	3.1	1.8	4.4
Electronic and other electric equipment	36	5.0	2.5	1.1	2.5
Electric distribution equipment	361	6.7	3.7	1.5	2.9
Electrical industrial apparatus	362	5.7	2.9	1.1	2.9
Household appliances	363	10.5	4.8	1.8	5.7
Electric lighting and wiring equipment	364	6.5	3.5	1.3	3.0
Communications equipment	366	2.9	1.5	0.8	1.4
Electronic components and accessories	367	3.7	1.8	0.9	1.9
Misc. electrical equipment and supplies	369	8.0	3.8	1.3	4.2
Transportation equipment	37	12.6	6.0	2.2	6.6
Motor vehicles and equipment	371	15.5	7.3	2.4	8.2
Aircraft and parts	372	7.7	3.7	1.5	4.0
Ship and boat building and repairing	373	15.6	7.5	3.6	8.2
Railroad equipment	374	7.9	4.9	2.9	3.0
Motorcycles, bicycles, and parts	375	13.9	6.2	2.8	7.7
Guided missiles, space vehicles, parts	376	2.9	1.6	0.7	1.3
Miscellaneous transportation equipment	379	13.4	6.3	3.1	7.1
Instruments and related products	38	4.0	2.0	0.9	2.0
Search and navigation equipment	381	2.2	1.0	0.4	1.3
Measuring and controlling devices	382	3.7	1.7	1.0	1.9
Medical instruments and supplies	384	4.5	2.3	1.0	2.2
Ophthalmic goods	385	5.9	3.5	1.5	2.4
Miscellaneous manufacturing industries	39	6.4	3.2	1.7	3.3
Musical instruments	393	7.2	3.1	2.4	4.1
Toys and sporting goods	394	6.4	3.0	1.5	3.4
Pens, pencils, office, and art supplies	395	6.3	3.3	1.5	3.1
Costume jewelry and notions	396	5.7	2.4	1.1	3.3
Nondurable goods	—	6.8	3.8	1.6	3.1
Food and kindred products	20	10.9	6.3	2.3	4.6
Meat products	201	14.7	8.5	1.6	6.2
Dairy products	202	11.8	6.9	3.9	4.9
Preserved fruits and vegetables	203	7.9	4.5	1.8	3.4
Grain mill products	204	7.6	3.8	2.1	3.8
Bakery products	205	9.0	5.7	2.3	3.3
Sugar and confectionery products	206	8.7	4.8	1.9	3.9
Fats and oils	207	8.6	5.8	2.6	2.9
Beverages	208	11.4	6.5	3.5	4.9
Miscellaneous foods and kindred products	209	7.5	4.4	2.4	3.1
Tobacco products	21	4.3	1.9	1.4	2.3
Textile mill products	22	5.2	2.7	0.9	2.6
Broadwoven fabric mills, cotton	221	4.6	2.6	0.3	1.9
Broadwoven fabric mills, manmade	222	4.4	2.1	0.6	2.2
Narrow fabric mills	224	6.8	3.0	1.5	3.7
Knitting mills	225	5.0	2.8	1.0	2.3
Textile finishing, except wool	226	4.3	2.3	1.2	2.0
Carpets and rugs	227	4.5	1.9	0.5	2.6
Yarn and thread mills	228	4.9	2.3	0.5	2.6
Miscellaneous textile goods	229	8.6	4.5	1.9	4.1
Apparel and other textile products	23	5.0	2.4	1.2	2.6
Men's and boys' suits and coats	231	5.8	2.3	1.6	3.5
Men's and boys' furnishings	232	6.6	3.3	1.8	3.3
Hats, caps, and millinery	235	6.5	2.6	1.5	3.8
Girls' and children's outerwear	236	4.6	1.8	1.2	2.7
Miscellaneous fabricated textile products	239	6.1	3.1	1.4	3.0
Paper and allied products	26	6.0	3.2	1.7	2.7
Pulp mills	261	4.1	2.1	1.6	2.0
Paper mills	262	4.9	2.5	1.4	2.4
Paperboard mills	263	4.0	1.6	1.0	2.4
Paperboard containers and boxes	265	6.3	3.6	1.8	2.7
Printing and publishing	27	4.6	2.4	1.4	2.2
Newspapers	271	4.9	2.5	1.7	2.5
Periodicals	272	1.8	0.8	0.4	1.0
Books	273	4.0	2.6	1.1	1.4
Commercial printing	275	5.6	2.8	1.6	2.8
Manifold business forms	276	5.7	3.2	1.6	2.5
Blankbooks and bookbinding	278	6.5	3.7	2.2	2.7
Chemicals and allied products	28	4.0	2.1	0.9	1.8
Industrial inorganic chemicals	281	3.6	1.8	0.9	1.8
Plastics materials and synthetics	282	3.8	2.2	1.0	1.6
Drugs	283	3.8	1.9	0.7	1.8
Soap, cleaners, and toilet goods	284	4.1	2.5	0.9	1.7
Paints and allied products	285	5.3	3.1	1.4	2.3
Industrial organic chemicals	286	2.7	1.5	0.6	1.1
Agricultural chemicals	287	4.9	1.9	0.8	3.0

See source and footnotes on page 61.
n.e.c. = not elsewhere classified.

BLS ESTIMATES OF NONFATAL OCCUPATIONAL INJURY AND ILLNESS INCIDENCE RATES FOR SELECTED INDUSTRIES, 2001, Cont.

Industry[a]	SIC Code[b]	Total Cases	Lost Workday Cases Total	Lost Workday Cases With Days Away from Work	Cases Without Lost Workdays
Miscellaneous chemical products	289	5.6	3.0	1.3	2.6
Petroleum and coal products	29	2.9	1.4	0.7	1.5
Asphalt paving and roofing materials	295	6.8	3.1	2.0	3.7
Miscellaneous petroleum and coal products	299	4.0	2.3	—	—
Rubber and miscellaneous plastics products	30	8.7	4.8	2.1	4.0
Tires and inner tubes	301	10.6	6.3	2.5	4.3
Hose and belting and gaskets and packing	305	8.4	4.0	2.1	4.3
Fabricated rubber products, n.e.c.	306	8.5	4.8	2.2	3.8
Miscellaneous plastic products, n.e.c.	308	8.6	4.6	2.1	3.9
Leather and leather products	31	8.7	4.4	1.8	4.3
Footwear, except rubber	314	9.0	4.2	1.8	4.8
Transportation and Public Utilities	**—**	**6.9**	**4.3**	**3.0**	**2.6**
Railroad transportation	40	3.4	2.6	2.3	0.7
Local and interurban passenger transit	41	9.8	5.3	3.8	4.5
Local and suburban transportation	411	13.3	7.4	4.9	5.9
School buses	415	6.3	2.9	2.4	3.4
Trucking and warehousing	42	8.4	5.2	3.9	3.2
Trucking & courier services, except air	421	8.4	5.3	4.1	3.1
Public warehousing and storage	422	8.8	4.9	2.4	—
Water transportation	44	6.0	3.5	3.0	2.5
Transportation by air	45	13.3	9.0	5.9	4.2
Air transportation, scheduled	451	14.4	10.0	6.6	—
Transportation services	47	3.0	1.9	1.4	1.1
Communications	48	2.9	1.8	1.4	1.1
Telephone communications	481	2.6	1.7	1.4	0.9
Cable and other pay television services	484	5.8	3.4	2.0	2.4
Electric, gas, and sanitary services	49	5.7	3.1	1.6	2.6
Electric services	491	5.0	2.5	1.3	2.5
Gas production and distribution	492	5.0	2.6	1.3	2.5
Combination utility services	493	3.5	1.8	0.9	1.7
Water supply	494	5.9	3.3	2.0	2.6
Sanitary services	495	9.0	5.4	3.0	3.6
Wholesale and Retail Trade	**—**	**5.6**	**2.5**	**1.6**	**3.0**
Wholesale trade	—	5.3	2.8	1.7	2.4
Wholesale trade-durable goods	50	4.7	2.3	1.4	2.3
Lumber and construction materials	503	7.3	4.0	2.4	3.3
Electrical goods	506	2.7	1.4	0.7	1.3
Machinery, equipment, and supplies	508	5.5	2.4	1.6	3.1
Wholesale trade-nondurable goods	51	6.2	3.6	2.2	2.6
Groceries and related products	514	8.4	5.3	3.2	3.1
Petroleum and petroleum products	517	5.3	2.8	2.3	2.5
Retail trade	—	5.7	2.4	1.5	3.2
Building materials and garden supplies	52	7.5	3.6	2.0	3.9
General merchandise stores	53	7.8	4.6	2.3	3.1
Food stores	54	7.5	3.3	2.0	4.3
Automotive dealers and service stations	55	5.5	2.2	1.6	3.3
Apparel and accessory stores	56	3.2	1.3	0.8	1.9
Home furniture, furnishings, and equipment	57	4.1	1.9	1.3	2.1
Eating and drinking places	58	5.3	1.6	1.3	3.6
Miscellaneous retail	59	3.7	1.8	1.1	1.9
Finance, Insurance, and Real Estate	**—**	**1.8**	**0.7**	**0.6**	**1.0**
Depository institutions	60	1.4	0.5	0.4	0.9
Insurance agents, brokers, and service	64	0.8	0.3	0.2	0.5
Real estate	65	4.1	2.1	1.5	2.0
Services	**—**	**4.6**	**2.2**	**1.3**	**2.5**
Hotels and other lodging places	70	7.2	3.3	1.8	3.8
Personal services	72	3.1	1.7	1.0	1.4
Business services	73	2.7	1.3	0.8	1.4
Services to buildings	734	4.7	2.4	1.7	2.2
Auto repair, services, and parking	75	4.5	2.1	1.6	2.5
Miscellaneous repair services	76	5.4	2.7	2.0	2.7
Amusement and recreation services	79	7.1	3.2	1.7	3.9
Health services	80	7.2	3.3	1.9	3.8
Nursing and personal care facilities	805	13.5	7.3	3.8	6.2
Hospitals	806	8.8	4.0	2.2	4.9
Legal services	81	0.8	0.3	0.3	0.5
Educational services	82	2.9	1.2	0.8	1.7
Social services	83	5.9	2.9	1.9	3.1
Child day care services	835	3.0	1.5	1.0	1.6
Engineering and management services	87	1.6	0.7	0.5	0.9

See source and footnotes on page 61.
n.e.c. = not elsewhere classified.

BLS ESTIMATES OF NONFATAL OCCUPATIONAL INJURY AND ILLNESS INCIDENCE RATES FOR SELECTED INDUSTRIES, 2001

Incidence Rates per 100 Full-Time Workers

Insurance Agents, Brokers, & Service (SIC 64)
Legal Services (81)
Depository Institutions (60)
Engineering & Management Services (87)
Educational Services (82)
Apparel & Accessory Stores (56)
Business Services (73)
Petroleum & Coal Products (29)
Eating & Drinking Places (58)
Oil & Gas Extraction (13)
Personal Services (72)
Communications (48)
Miscellaneous Retail (59)
Tobacco Products (21)
Transportation Services (47)
Home Furniture, Furnishings, & Equip. (57)
Instruments & Related Products (38)
Chemicals and Allied Products (28)
Real Estate (65)
Auto Repair, Services, & Parking (75)
Automotive Dealers and Service Stations (55)
Wholesale Trade-Durable Goods (50)
Metal Mining (10)
Apparel & Other Textile Products (23)
Printing & Publishing (27)
Electronic & Other Electric Equipment (36)
Railroad Transportation (40)
Textile Mill Products (22)
Miscellaneous Repair Services (76)
Nonmetallic Minerals, Except Fuels (14)
PRIVATE SECTOR
Social Services (83)
Industrial Machinery & Equipment (35)
Electric, Gas, & Sanitary Services (49)
Paper & Allied Products (26)
Misc. Manufacturing Industries (39)
Amusement & Recreation Services (79)
Forestry (8)
Food Stores (54)
Hotels & Other Lodging Places (70)
Health Services (80)
General Building Contractors (15)
Water Transportation (44)
Agricultural Services (7)
Wholesale Trade—Nondurable Goods (51)
Building Materials & Garden Supplies (52)
Agricultural Production (01-02)
Heavy Construction, Except Building (16)
Special Trade Contractors (17)
Leather & Leather Products (31)
General Merchandise Stores (53)
Rubber & Misc. Plastics Products (30)
Coal Mining (12)
Stone, Clay, & Glass Products (32)
Trucking & Warehousing (42)
Primary Metal Industries (33)
Fabricated Metal Products (34)
Local & Interurban Passenger Transit (41)
Lumber & Wood Products (24)
Furniture & Fixtures (25)
Transportation Equipment (37)
Food & Kindred Products (20)
Transportation by Air (45)

■ **LOST WORKDAY CASES**
■ **CASES WITHOUT LOST WORKDAYS**

Note: Industries are shown at the 2-digit SIC level.
Lost workday cases plus cases without lost workdays equals total cases.

The tables on pages 67 through 81 present data on the characteristics of injured and ill workers and the injuries and illnesses that affected them. These data indicate how many workers are killed by on-the-job injuries and how many are affected by nonfatal injuries and illnesses. The data may be used to help set priorities for safety and health programs and for benchmarking.

The fatality information covers only deaths due to injuries and comes from the Bureau of Labor Statistics (BLS) Census of Fatal Occupational Injuries. The data are **10-year totals** for the calendar years 1992–2001. The 10 years were combined because counts for many of the items would be too small to publish if data for a single year were used.

The data on nonfatal cases cover both injuries and illnesses and come from the BLS Survey of Occupational Injuries and Illnesses for the 2001 reference year. The Survey also is used to produce the incidence rates shown on the preceding pages. The estimates on the following pages are the number of cases involving days away from work (with or without days of restricted work activity).

Data are presented for the sex, age, occupation, and race or ethnic origin of the worker and for the nature of injury/illness, the part of body affected, the source of injury/illness, and the event or exposure that produced the injury/illness.

The text at the top of each page describes the kind of establishments that are included in the industry division, the number of workers in the industry division for 2001, and the annual average number of workers for the 1992–2001 period.

Incidence rates, percent distributions, or ranks may be used for benchmarking purposes. For nonfatal cases incidence rates, multiply the number of cases by 1,000 and then divide by the 2001 employment. This will give the number of cases with days away from work per 1,000 employees per year. For fatality rates, multiply the ten-year total fatalities by 100 then divide by the 1992–2001 average annual employment. This will give the number of deaths per 1,000 employees per year. Percent distributions may not add to 100% because of unclassifiable cases not shown.

Major Industry Divisions
Page 67 shows nonfatal injury/illness data for the private sector of the economy (excluding government entities) and fatal injury data for all industries (including government). Pages 68 through 76 present the data for private sector industry divisions. Page 77 presents the fatal injury data for the Government industry division (the BLS Survey does not cover government entities nationwide, so no nonfatal case data are available).

2-Digit SIC Codes
Pages 78 through 81 show fatal and nonfatal data for four Standard Industrial Classification codes that together represent almost one fourth of the National Safety Council membership. The four industries are Chemicals and Allied Products (SIC 28), Electric, Gas, and Sanitary Services (SIC 49), Wholesale Trade — Durable Goods (SIC 50), and Engineering and Management Services (SIC 87). Each of these industries accounts for 5.5% to 6.6% of Council members. Future editions of *Injury Facts®* will present data for other industries that are common among Council members.

The nonfatal occupational injury and illness data cover only the private sector of the economy and exclude employees in federal, state, and local government entities. The fatal injury data cover employees in both the private sector and government.

There were 136,246,000 people employed in 2001, of whom 115,933,000 worked in the private sector and 20,313,000 in government. Over the 10 years from 1992 through 2001, total employment averaged 128,958,000 per year with 109,133,000 in the private sector.

NUMBER OF NONFATAL OCCUPATIONAL INJURIES AND ILLNESSES INVOLVING DAYS AWAY FROM WORK[a] AND FATAL OCCUPATIONAL INJURIES BY SELECTED WORKER AND CASE CHARACTERISTICS, UNITED STATES

Characteristic	Private Industry[b,c] Nonfatal Cases, 2001	All Industries Fatalities, 1992–2001
Total	**1,537,567**	**61,824**
Sex		
Men	1,009,499	56,986
Women	516,842	4,838
Age		
Under 14	—	—
14 to 15	908	263
16 to 19	44,535	1,602
20 to 24	171,659	4,788
25 to 34	389,065	13,456
35 to 44	438,455	15,404
45 to 54	315,794	12,769
55 to 64	135,690	8,257
65 and over	24,541	5,176
Occupation		
Managerial and professional	97,797	6,801
Technical, sales, and administrative support	237,717	7,611
Service	266,346	—
Farming, forestry, and fishing	44,336	8,981
Precision production, craft, and repair	281,027	10,983
Operators, fabricators, and laborers	605,769	20,760
Military occupations	N/A	1,029
Race or ethnic origin[d]		
White, non-Hispanic	765,228	41,513
Black, non-Hispanic	133,785	5,618
Hispanic	191,959	6,849
Asian or Pacific Islander	25,317	1,785
American Indian or Alaskan Native	5,661	348
Not reported	415,616	5,711
Nature of injury, illness		
Sprains, strains	669,889	91
Fractures	108,127	350
Cuts, lacerations, punctures	133,314	9,441
Bruises, contusions	136,361	30
Heat burns	25,078	1,450
Chemical burns	9,451	66
Amputations	8,612	225
Carpal tunnel syndrome	26,794	—
Tendonitis	14,124	—
Multiple injuries	53,211	17,636
Soreness, pain	109,986	11
Back pain	42,679	9
All other	242,621	32,524

Characteristic	Private Industry[b,c] Nonfatal Cases, 2001	All Industries Fatalities, 1992–2001
Part of body affected		
Head	99,523	15,146
Eye	44,811	7
Neck	27,111	1,269
Trunk	561,603	12,350
Back	372,683	791
Shoulder	88,484	27
Upper extremities	355,344	152
Finger	123,523	14
Hand, except finger	63,727	14
Wrist	78,857	9
Lower extremities	322,959	554
Knee	119,670	73
Foot, toe	68,117	28
Body systems	21,657	9,982
Multiple	139,675	21,931
All other	9,695	440
Source of injury, illness		
Chemicals, chemical products	25,125	1,505
Containers	209,078	838
Furniture, fixtures	53,974	182
Machinery	97,634	5,010
Parts and materials	162,475	4,211
Worker motion or position	245,867	29
Floor, ground surfaces	264,677	6,566
Handtools	68,113	1,062
Vehicles	128,534	26,362
Health care patient	67,635	19
All other	214,455	16,040
Event or exposure		
Contact with object, equipment	400,033	9,969
Struck by object	199,855	5,649
Struck against object	101,177	147
Caught in object, equipment, material	68,048	4,137
Fall to lower level	96,359	6,078
Fall on same level	182,641	584
Slips, trips	50,269	16
Overexertion	409,011	67
Overexertion in lifting	227,291	40
Repetitive motion	65,162	—
Exposed to harmful substance	68,269	5,623
Transportation accidents	66,803	25,891
Fires, explosions	3,711	1,948
Assault, violent act	23,694	11,190
by person	17,215	8,702
by other	6,480	2,488
All other	171,615	458

Source: National Safety Council tabulations of Bureau of Labor Statistics data.
Note: Because of rounding and data exclusion of nonclassifiable responses, data may not sum to the totals. Dashes (—) indicate data that do not meet publication guidelines. "N/A" means not applicable.
[a]Days away from work include those that result in days away from work with or without restricted work activity.
[b]Excludes farms with fewer than 11 employees.

[c]Data conforming to OSHA definitions for mining operators in coal, metal, and nonmetal mining and for employees in railroad transportation are provided to BLS by the Mine Safety and Health Administration, U.S. Department of Labor; and the Federal Railroad Administration, U.S. Department of Transportation. Independent mining contractors are excluded from the coal, metal, and nonmetal mining industries.
[d]In the fatalities column, non-Hispanic categories include cases with Hispanic origin not reported.

AGRICULTURE, FORESTRY, AND FISHING

The Agriculture, Forestry, and Fishing industry division includes production of crops and livestock, animal specialties, agricultural services, forestry (but excluding logging, which is in the Manufacturing industry division), and commercial fishing, hunting, and trapping.

Employment in Agriculture, Forestry, and Fishing totaled 3,209,000 in 2001 and averaged 3,385,000 per year from 1992 through 2001. It is the second smallest industry division after Mining.

NUMBER OF NONFATAL OCCUPATIONAL INJURIES AND ILLNESS INVOLVING DAYS AWAY FROM WORK[a] AND FATAL OCCUPATIONAL INJURIES BY SELECTED WORKER AND CASE CHARACTERISTICS, UNITED STATES, AGRICULTURE, FORESTRY, AND FISHING

Characteristic	Nonfatal Cases[b], 2001	Fatalities, 1992–2001
Total	40,153	8,077
Sex		
Men	31,688	7,823
Women	8,356	254
Age		
Under 14	—	—
14 to 15	—	170
16 to 19	1,987	236
20 to 24	6,535	493
25 to 34	11,716	1,173
35 to 44	10,949	1,407
45 to 54	6,158	1,257
55 to 64	1,844	1,300
65 and over	537	2,026
Occupation		
Managerial and professional	940	105
Technical, sales, and administrative support	2,034	168
Service	539	26
Farming, forestry, and fishing	31,940	—
Precision production, craft, and repair	943	53
Operators, fabricators, and laborers	3,706	321
Race or ethnic origin[c]		
White, non-Hispanic	15,703	5,891
Black, non-Hispanic	1,370	301
Hispanic	17,717	1,023
Asian or Pacific Islander	416	106
American Indian or Alaskan Native	70	58
Not reported	4,877	698
Nature of injury, illness		
Sprains, strains	13,758	—
Fractures	3,260	27
Cuts, lacerations, punctures	5,022	350
Bruises, contusions	3,964	—
Heat burns	143	90
Chemical burns	207	—
Amputations	401	48
Carpal tunnel syndrome	168	—
Tendonitis	187	—
Multiple injuries	1,767	1,904
Soreness, pain	2,873	—
Back pain	1,047	—
All other	8,403	5,650

Characteristic	Nonfatal Cases[b], 2001	Fatalities, 1992–2001
Part of body affected		
Head	3,426	1,561
Eye	1,710	—
Neck	445	193
Trunk	13,600	2,082
Back	8,830	86
Shoulder	1,755	—
Upper extremities	9,566	32
Finger	3,814	—
Hand, except finger	2,453	—
Wrist	989	—
Lower extremities	9,186	77
Knee	2,508	—
Foot, toe	2,411	—
Body systems	434	1,982
Multiple	3,250	2,114
All other	246	36
Source of injury, illness		
Chemicals, chemical products	459	122
Containers	3,349	106
Furniture, fixtures	258	—
Machinery	3,026	1,156
Parts and materials	2,910	324
Worker motion or position	5,645	—
Floor, ground surfaces	5,760	537
Handtools	2,844	80
Vehicles	3,227	4,160
Health care patient	—	—
All other	12,638	1,590
Event or exposure		
Contact with object, equipment	13,433	1,876
Struck by object	7,034	996
Struck against object	2,582	18
Caught in object, equipment, material	2,261	857
Fall to lower level	2,950	538
Fall on same level	3,242	30
Slips, trips	1,347	—
Overexertion	7,073	—
Overexertion in lifting	4,152	—
Repetitive motion	674	—
Exposed to harmful substance	1,522	800
Transportation accidents	2,041	4,125
Fires, explosions	48	108
Assault, violent act	2,745	554
by person	—	151
by other	2,708	403
All other	5,077	45

Source: National Safety Council tabulations of Bureau of Labor Statistics data.
Note: Because of rounding and data exclusion of nonclassifiable responses, data may not sum to the totals. Dashes (—) indicate data that do not meet publication guidelines.
[a]Days away from work include those that result in days away from work with or without restricted work activity.

[b]Excludes farms with fewer than 11 employees.
[c]In the fatalities column, non-Hispanic categories include cases with Hispanic origin not reported.

MINING, QUARRYING, AND OIL AND GAS EXTRACTION

The Mining industry division includes metal mining, coal mining, oil and gas extraction, and mining and quarrying of nonmetallic minerals such as stone, sand, and gravel.

Mining is the smallest industry division. Mining employment in 2001 amounted to 566,000 workers.

Over the 10 years from 1992 through 2001, employment in Mining averaged 609,000 per year. Oil and gas extraction accounts for about three fifths of employment in this division.

NUMBER OF NONFATAL OCCUPATIONAL INJURIES AND ILLNESS INVOLVING DAYS AWAY FROM WORK[a] AND FATAL OCCUPATIONAL INJURIES BY SELECTED WORKER AND CASE CHARACTERISTICS, UNITED STATES, MINING, QUARRYING, AND OIL AND GAS EXTRACTION

Characteristic	Nonfatal Cases[b], 2001	Fatalities, 1992–2001
Total	**10,582**	**1,597**
Sex		
Men	10,315	1,578
Women	268	19
Age		
Under 14	—	—
14 to 15	—	—
16 to 19	110	32
20 to 24	1,095	141
25 to 34	2,373	401
35 to 44	3,103	471
45 to 54	2,858	353
55 to 64	775	139
65 and over	78	59
Occupation		
Managerial and professional	206	81
Technical, sales, and administrative support	105	36
Service	12	13
Farming, forestry, and fishing	8	—
Precision production, craft, and repair	5,620	881
Operators, fabricators, and laborers	4,577	581
Race or ethnic origin[c]		
White, non-Hispanic	2,720	1,203
Black, non-Hispanic	286	57
Hispanic	721	188
Asian or Pacific Islander	7	5
American Indian or Alaskan Native	19	19
Not reported	6,829	125
Nature of injury, illness		
Sprains, strains	4,026	—
Fractures	1,505	5
Cuts, lacerations, punctures	914	31
Bruises, contusions	1,127	—
Heat burns	101	58
Chemical burns	44	5
Amputations	64	10
Carpal tunnel syndrome	61	—
Tendonitis	21	—
Multiple injuries	559	535
Soreness, pain	405	—
Back pain	140	—
All other	1,755	952

Characteristic	Nonfatal Cases[b], 2001	Fatalities, 1992–2001
Part of body affected		
Head	562	347
Eye	257	—
Neck	248	28
Trunk	3,466	313
Back	1,968	13
Shoulder	588	—
Upper extremities	2,432	5
Finger	1,075	—
Hand, except finger	494	—
Wrist	354	—
Lower extremities	2,813	12
Knee	1,085	—
Foot, toe	498	—
Body systems	131	280
Multiple	899	607
All other	31	5
Source of injury, illness		
Chemicals, chemical products	863	87
Containers	489	37
Furniture, fixtures	56	7
Machinery	1,147	305
Parts and materials	1,855	194
Worker motion or position	582	—
Floor, ground surfaces	1,819	103
Handtools	633	8
Vehicles	815	454
Health care patient	—	—
All other	2,323	401
Event or exposure		
Contact with object, equipment	4,425	611
Struck by object	2,456	294
Struck against object	929	7
Caught in object, equipment, material	985	309
Fall to lower level	900	114
Fall on same level	899	8
Slips, trips	144	—
Overexertion	2,777	—
Overexertion in lifting	1,008	—
Repetitive motion	114	—
Exposed to harmful substance	414	162
Transportation accidents	304	479
Fires, explosions	35	179
Assault, violent act	7	29
by person	7	14
by other	—	15
All other	562	12

Source: National Safety Council tabulations of Bureau of Labor Statistics data.
Note: Because of rounding and data exclusion of nonclassifiable responses, data may not sum to the totals. Dashes (—) indicate data that do not meet publication guidelines.
[a]Days away from work include those that result in days away from work with or without restricted work activity.

[b]Data conforming to OSHA definitions for mining operators in coal, metal, and nonmetal mining are provided to BLS by the Mine Safety and Health Administration, U.S. Department of Labor. Independent mining contractors are excluded from the coal, metal, and nonmetal mining industries.
[c]In the fatalities column, non-Hispanic categories include cases with Hispanic origin not reported.

CONSTRUCTION

The Construction industry division includes establishments engaged in construction of buildings, heavy construction other than buildings, and special trade contractors such as plumbing, electrical, and carpentry.

In 2001, employment in the Construction industry division totaled 9,125,000 workers. Employment over the 1992-2001 period averaged 7,724,000 workers per year.

NUMBER OF NONFATAL OCCUPATIONAL INJURIES AND ILLNESS INVOLVING DAYS AWAY FROM WORK[a] AND FATAL OCCUPATIONAL INJURIES BY SELECTED WORKER AND CASE CHARACTERISTICS, UNITED STATES, CONSTRUCTION

Characteristic	Nonfatal Cases, 2001	Fatalities, 1992–2001
Total	**185,662**	**10,833**
Sex		
Men	180,527	10,680
Women	4,904	153
Age		
Under 14	—	—
14 to 15	—	17
16 to 19	4,484	345
20 to 24	24,453	1,038
25 to 34	58,947	2,749
35 to 44	52,842	3,009
45 to 54	29,219	2,056
55 to 64	10,663	1,163
65 and over	1,440	440
Occupation		
Managerial and professional	2,437	693
Technical, sales, and administrative support	2,698	115
Service	386	22
Farming, forestry, and fishing	470	—
Precision production, craft, and repair	113,326	5,521
Operators, fabricators, and laborers	65,875	4,425
Race or ethnic origin[b]		
White, non-Hispanic	110,593	7,194
Black, non-Hispanic	10,135	753
Hispanic	29,749	1,749
Asian or Pacific Islander	1,520	109
American Indian or Alaskan Native	1,095	66
Not reported	32,570	962
Nature of injury, illness		
Sprains, strains	71,225	8
Fractures	19,786	46
Cuts, lacerations, punctures	27,107	285
Bruises, contusions	12,689	7
Heat burns	2,453	194
Chemical burns	1,032	5
Amputations	949	26
Carpal tunnel syndrome	1,224	—
Tendonitis	1,230	—
Multiple injuries	6,298	3,243
Soreness, pain	9,526	—
Back pain	4,103	—
All other	32,143	7,018

Characteristic	Nonfatal Cases, 2001	Fatalities, 1992–2001
Part of body affected		
Head	13,843	2,967
Eye	7,725	—
Neck	2,252	163
Trunk	60,891	1,657
Back	38,973	91
Shoulder	9,412	—
Upper extremities	45,983	17
Finger	19,265	5
Hand, except finger	9,863	—
Wrist	7,076	—
Lower extremities	44,823	65
Knee	15,584	7
Foot, toe	10,291	—
Body systems	2,318	2,366
Multiple	14,571	3,555
All other	982	43
Source of injury, illness		
Chemicals, chemical products	1,954	195
Containers	8,093	131
Furniture, fixtures	2,922	47
Machinery	11,867	1,253
Parts and materials	44,110	1,526
Worker motion or position	25,778	—
Floor, ground surfaces	34,285	3,385
Handtools	17,374	129
Vehicles	10,284	2,529
Health care patient	—	—
All other	28,984	1,636
Event or exposure		
Contact with object, equipment	63,937	2,077
Struck by object	35,620	1,029
Struck against object	13,939	20
Caught in object, equipment, material	8,349	1,019
Fall to lower level	23,826	3,385
Fall on same level	13,780	51
Slips, trips	5,896	—
Overexertion	38,505	8
Overexertion in lifting	20,510	6
Repetitive motion	3,741	—
Exposed to harmful substance	6,242	1,836
Transportation accidents	6,817	2,780
Fires, explosions	846	296
Assault, violent act	664	329
by person	187	170
by other	477	159
All other	21,408	69

Source: National Safety Council tabulations of Bureau of Labor Statistics data.
Note Because of rounding and data exclusion of nonclassifiable responses, data may not sum to the totals. Dashes (—) indicate data that do not meet publication guidelines.

[a] Days away from work include those that result in days away from work with or without restricted work activity.
[b] In the fatalities column, non-Hispanic categories include cases with Hispanic origin not reported.

MANUFACTURING

The Manufacturing industry division includes establishments engaged in the mechanical or chemical transformation of materials or substances into new products. It includes durable and nondurable goods such as food, textiles, apparel, lumber, wood products, paper and paper products, printing, chemicals and pharmaceuticals, petroleum and coal products, rubber and plastics products, metals and metal products, machinery, electrical equipment, and transportation equipment.

Manufacturing employment in 2001 was 18,898,000 workers. Average annual employment from 1992 through 2001 was 20,034,000 workers.

NUMBER OF NONFATAL OCCUPATIONAL INJURIES AND ILLNESS INVOLVING DAYS AWAY FROM WORK[a] AND FATAL OCCUPATIONAL INJURIES BY SELECTED WORKER AND CASE CHARACTERISTICS, UNITED STATES, MANUFACTURING

Characteristic	Nonfatal Cases, 2001	Fatalities, 1992–2001
Total	**317,326**	**7,186**
Sex		
Men	238,220	6,770
Women	78,412	416
Age		
Under 14	15	—
14 to 15	11	16
16 to 19	4,976	158
20 to 24	27,924	519
25 to 34	77,269	1,508
35 to 44	93,898	1,950
45 to 54	74,241	1,596
55 to 64	32,511	1,080
65 and over	3,809	348
Occupation		
Managerial and professional	6,117	700
Technical, sales, and administrative support	19,056	507
Service	6,389	118
Farming, forestry, and fishing	1,831	—
Precision production, craft, and repair	59,313	1,379
Operators, fabricators, and laborers	223,252	3,345
Race or ethnic origin[b]		
White, non-Hispanic	171,491	4,904
Black, non-Hispanic	26,492	774
Hispanic	42,782	674
Asian or Pacific Islander	5,461	119
American Indian or Alaskan Native	1,080	36
Not reported	70,021	679
Nature of injury, illness		
Sprains, strains	123,041	19
Fractures	22,493	39
Cuts, lacerations, punctures	32,526	531
Bruises, contusions	25,506	5
Heat burns	4,709	297
Chemical burns	3,047	35
Amputations	4,239	42
Carpal tunnel syndrome	11,240	—
Tendonitis	5,567	—
Multiple injuries	10,199	1,897
Soreness, pain	18,189	—
Back pain	*6,906*	—
All other	56,571	4,318

Characteristic	Nonfatal Cases, 2001	Fatalities, 1992–2001
Part of body affected		
Head	22,767	1,843
Eye	*13,931*	—
Neck	4,603	132
Trunk	108,262	1,550
Back	*66,366*	*102*
Shoulder	*20,252*	—
Upper extremities	99,765	29
Finger	*40,181*	—
Hand, except finger	*15,155*	—
Wrist	*22,362*	—
Lower extremities	56,796	89
Knee	*21,184*	*17*
Foot, toe	*14,023*	*6*
Body systems	3,796	1,061
Multiple	19,982	2,439
All other	1,356	43
Source of injury, illness		
Chemicals, chemical products	7,081	286
Containers	41,748	221
Furniture, fixtures	8,829	27
Machinery	36,878	1,183
Parts and materials	55,371	727
Worker motion or position	64,511	7
Floor, ground surfaces	34,599	531
Handtools	16,482	82
Vehicles	15,200	2,163
Health care patient	—	—
All other	36,617	1,959
Event or exposure		
Contact with object, equipment	105,023	2,689
Struck by object	*45,768*	*1,671*
Struck against object	*22,966*	*29*
Caught in object, equipment, material	*27,497*	*985*
Fall to lower level	11,863	476
Fall on same level	25,009	91
Slips, trips	9,220	7
Overexertion	80,628	20
Overexertion in lifting	*42,983*	*13*
Repetitive motion	28,607	—
Exposed to harmful substance	16,079	680
Transportation accidents	6,168	2,115
Fires, explosions	520	452
Assault, violent act	638	598
by person	*379*	*359*
by other	*259*	*239*
All other	33,571	58

Source: National Safety Council tabulations of Bureau of Labor Statistics data.
Note: Because of rounding and data exclusion of nonclassifiable responses, data may not sum to the totals. Dashes (—) indicate data that do not meet publication guidelines.

[a]*Days away from work include those that result in days away from work with or without restricted work activity.*
[b]*In the fatalities column, non-Hispanic categories include cases with Hispanic origin not reported.*

TRANSPORTATION AND PUBLIC UTILITIES

This industry division includes transportation by rail, highway, air, water, or pipeline and associated transportation services; communications by telephone, radio, television, cable, or satellite; and electric, gas, and sanitary services.

Employment in the Transportation and Public Utilities industry division totaled 8,131,000 in 2001 and averaged 7,448,000 workers per year from 1992 through 2001.

NUMBER OF NONFATAL OCCUPATIONAL INJURIES AND ILLNESS INVOLVING DAYS AWAY FROM WORK[a] AND FATAL OCCUPATIONAL INJURIES BY SELECTED WORKER AND CASE CHARACTERISTICS, UNITED STATES, TRANSPORTATION AND PUBLIC UTILITIES[b]

Characteristic	Nonfatal Cases, 2001	Fatalities, 1992–2001
Total	**199,939**	**9,404**
Sex		
Men	155,509	8,964
Women	38,917	440
Age		
Under 14	—	—
14 to 15	—	—
16 to 19	2,771	86
20 to 24	15,925	462
25 to 34	52,026	2,014
35 to 44	64,837	2,639
45 to 54	44,866	2,431
55 to 64	16,129	1,329
65 and over	1,755	427
Occupation		
Managerial and professional	3,788	337
Technical, sales, and administrative support	31,503	910
Service	11,059	140
Farming, forestry, and fishing	298	—
Precision production, craft, and repair	29,274	787
Operators, fabricators, and laborers	123,588	7,190
Race or ethnic origin[c]		
White, non-Hispanic	68,221	6,269
Black, non-Hispanic	16,778	1,204
Hispanic	12,324	812
Asian or Pacific Islander	2,141	237
American Indian or Alaskan Native	373	32
Not reported	100,103	850
Nature of injury, illness		
Sprains, strains	96,770	9
Fractures	13,758	28
Cuts, lacerations, punctures	9,733	945
Bruises, contusions	18,742	—
Heat burns	1,143	331
Chemical burns	841	7
Amputations	305	47
Carpal tunnel syndrome	1,666	—
Tendonitis	1,128	—
Multiple injuries	7,888	3,605
Soreness, pain	19,569	—
Back pain	*7,531*	—
All other	28,398	4,429

Characteristic	Nonfatal Cases, 2001	Fatalities, 1992–2001
Part of body affected		
Head	11,734	1,955
Eye	*3,875*	—
Neck	3,881	164
Trunk	78,155	1,657
Back	*50,765*	*104*
Shoulder	*13,554*	—
Upper extremities	32,622	9
Finger	*9,153*	—
Hand, except finger	*5,374*	—
Wrist	*7,073*	—
Lower extremities	49,430	56
Knee	*17,869*	*8*
Foot, toe	*8,183*	—
Body systems	2,732	1,231
Multiple	20,385	4,255
All other	1,000	77
Source of injury, illness		
Chemicals, chemical products	1,788	154
Containers	41,812	101
Furniture, fixtures	4,129	8
Machinery	4,711	242
Parts and materials	14,046	436
Worker motion or position	32,153	—
Floor, ground surfaces	34,015	319
Handtools	3,459	75
Vehicles	36,049	6,769
Health care patient	1,941	—
All other	25,836	1,297
Event or exposure		
Contact with object, equipment	41,146	771
Struck by object	*19,548*	*490*
Struck against object	*13,073*	*11*
Caught in object, equipment, material	*5,641*	*266*
Fall to lower level	16,332	293
Fall on same level	18,544	35
Slips, trips	7,200	—
Overexertion	57,524	—
Overexertion in lifting	*31,163*	—
Repetitive motion	5,059	—
Exposed to harmful substance	6,909	539
Transportation accidents	18,096	6,510
Fires, explosions	418	152
Assault, violent act	2,110	1,056
by person	*867*	*901*
by other	*1,243*	*155*
All other	26,602	45

Source: National Safety Council tabulations of Bureau of Labor Statistics data.
Note: Because of rounding and data exclusion of nonclassifiable responses, data may not sum to the totals. Dashes (—) indicate data that do not meet publication guidelines.
[a] Days away from work include those that result in days away from work with or without restricted work activity.

[b] Data conforming to OSHA definitions for employees in railroad transportation are provided to BLS by the Federal Railroad Administration, U.S. Department of Transportation.
[c] In the fatalities column, non-Hispanic categories include cases with Hispanic origin not reported.

WHOLESALE TRADE

Establishments in Wholesale Trade generally sell merchandise to retailers; to industrial, commercial, institutional, farm, construction contractors, or professional business users; to other wholesalers; or to agents or brokers.

Wholesale Trade employed 5,085,000 people in 2001 and an average of 4,960,000 people annually from 1992 through 2001.

NUMBER OF NONFATAL OCCUPATIONAL INJURIES AND ILLNESS INVOLVING DAYS AWAY FROM WORK[a] AND FATAL OCCUPATIONAL INJURIES BY SELECTED WORKER AND CASE CHARACTERISTICS, UNITED STATES, WHOLESALE TRADE

Characteristic	Nonfatal Cases, 2001	Fatalities, 1992–2001
Total	**111,925**	**2,460**
Sex		
Men	94,471	2,341
Women	17,394	119
Age		
Under 14	—	—
14 to 15	61	—
16 to 19	1,863	48
20 to 24	12,241	189
25 to 34	31,178	515
35 to 44	32,109	610
45 to 54	22,093	514
55 to 64	9,004	370
65 and over	1,547	206
Occupation		
Managerial and professional	4,030	203
Technical, sales, and administrative support	18,661	645
Service	1,227	32
Farming, forestry, and fishing	1,153	—
Precision production, craft, and repair	14,380	247
Operators, fabricators, and laborers	72,061	1,268
Race or ethnic origin[b]		
White, non-Hispanic	63,198	1,702
Black, non-Hispanic	11,215	186
Hispanic	14,101	260
Asian or Pacific Islander	1,689	67
American Indian or Alaskan Native	299	5
Not reported	21,423	240
Nature of injury, illness		
Sprains, strains	52,261	9
Fractures	7,181	17
Cuts, lacerations, punctures	8,059	253
Bruises, contusions	11,461	—
Heat burns	948	80
Chemical burns	432	—
Amputations	641	10
Carpal tunnel syndrome	1,675	—
Tendonitis	954	—
Multiple injuries	3,983	772
Soreness, pain	7,514	—
Back pain	3,169	—
All other	16,817	1,317

Characteristic	Nonfatal Cases, 2001	Fatalities, 1992–2001
Part of body affected		
Head	6,039	582
Eye	2,748	—
Neck	1,978	45
Trunk	46,425	505
Back	30,421	23
Shoulder	7,083	—
Upper extremities	22,306	6
Finger	7,789	—
Hand, except finger	3,878	—
Wrist	4,459	—
Lower extremities	24,351	31
Knee	8,427	5
Foot, toe	5,965	—
Body systems	811	318
Multiple	9,320	953
All other	695	20
Source of injury, illness		
Chemicals, chemical products	1,258	57
Containers	25,973	69
Furniture, fixtures	3,196	—
Machinery	7,068	179
Parts and materials	13,081	134
Worker motion or position	16,440	—
Floor, ground surfaces	15,223	173
Handtools	3,014	27
Vehicles	15,323	1,402
Health care patient	128	—
All other	11,221	416
Event or exposure		
Contact with object, equipment	29,550	430
Struck by object	14,590	236
Struck against object	6,942	6
Caught in object, equipment, material	5,708	187
Fall to lower level	6,488	154
Fall on same level	10,219	26
Slips, trips	3,272	—
Overexertion	34,665	—
Overexertion in lifting	20,292	—
Repetitive motion	3,695	—
Exposed to harmful substance	2,376	134
Transportation accidents	7,697	1,299
Fires, explosions	652	93
Assault, violent act	283	307
by person	164	209
by other	119	98
All other	13,029	13

Source: National Safety Council tabulations of Bureau of Labor Statistics data.
Note: Because of rounding and data exclusion of nonclassifiable responses, data may not sum to the totals. Dashes (—) indicate data that do not meet publication guidelines.

[a]*Days away from work include those that result in days away from work with or without restricted work activity.*
[b]*In the fatalities column, non-Hispanic categories include cases with Hispanic origin not reported.*

RETAIL TRADE

Establishments in Retail Trade generally sell merchandise for personal or household consumption. Retail Trade is the second largest industry division after Services.

Retail Trade employed 22,478,000 people in 2001 and an average of 21,379,000 people annually from 1992 through 2001.

NUMBER OF NONFATAL OCCUPATIONAL INJURIES AND ILLNESS INVOLVING DAYS AWAY FROM WORK[a] AND FATAL OCCUPATIONAL INJURIES BY SELECTED WORKER AND CASE CHARACTERISTICS, UNITED STATES, RETAIL TRADE

Characteristic	Nonfatal Cases, 2001	Fatalities, 1992–2001
Total	**265,700**	**6,589**
Sex		
Men	144,131	5,462
Women	117,422	1,127
Age		
Under 14	—	—
14 to 15	499	22
16 to 19	18,427	317
20 to 24	40,777	649
25 to 34	63,301	1,438
35 to 44	67,603	1,494
45 to 54	43,782	1,285
55 to 64	21,301	841
65 and over	6,930	533
Occupation		
Managerial and professional	10,562	888
Technical, sales, and administrative support	87,599	3,337
Service	69,639	775
Farming, forestry, and fishing	1,313	—
Precision production, craft, and repair	27,364	316
Operators, fabricators, and laborers	68,558	1,210
Race or ethnic origin[b]		
White, non-Hispanic	136,766	3,740
Black, non-Hispanic	16,394	715
Hispanic	28,735	785
Asian or Pacific Islander	5,033	740
American Indian or Alaskan Native	878	29
Not reported	77,894	580
Nature of injury, illness		
Sprains, strains	113,662	6
Fractures	15,296	41
Cuts, lacerations, punctures	29,219	3,866
Bruises, contusions	27,689	—
Heat burns	10,082	94
Chemical burns	1,671	—
Amputations	1,303	5
Carpal tunnel syndrome	3,445	—
Tendonitis	2,013	—
Multiple injuries	7,835	867
Soreness, pain	17,918	—
Back pain	6,596	—
All other	35,566	1,705

Characteristic	Nonfatal Cases, 2001	Fatalities, 1992–2001
Part of body affected		
Head	16,448	2,070
Eye	6,346	—
Neck	4,129	207
Trunk	93,575	1,837
Back	64,510	149
Shoulder	13,614	8
Upper extremities	67,726	10
Finger	22,396	—
Hand, except finger	14,717	—
Wrist	13,636	—
Lower extremities	55,288	57
Knee	20,918	8
Foot, toe	11,787	—
Body systems	2,964	427
Multiple	23,048	1,929
All other	2,522	52
Source of injury, illness		
Chemicals, chemical products	3,969	100
Containers	55,545	44
Furniture, fixtures	14,636	21
Machinery	16,468	80
Parts and materials	16,804	205
Worker motion or position	36,492	—
Floor, ground surfaces	53,440	282
Handtools	14,558	360
Vehicles	19,603	1,505
Health care patient	205	—
All other	33,981	3,988
Event or exposure		
Contact with object, equipment	71,628	264
Struck by object	39,545	158
Struck against object	19,022	9
Caught in object, equipment, material	9,083	94
Fall to lower level	11,772	170
Fall on same level	44,567	86
Slips, trips	9,866	—
Overexertion	67,771	—
Overexertion in lifting	45,097	—
Repetitive motion	7,591	—
Exposed to harmful substance	15,316	198
Transportation accidents	7,646	1,416
Fires, explosions	801	118
Assault, violent act	2,715	4,287
by person	2,410	3,953
by other	305	334
All other	26,028	45

Source: National Safety Council tabulations of Bureau of Labor Statistics data.
Note: Because of rounding and data exclusion of nonclassifiable responses, data may not sum to the totals. Dashes (—) indicate data that do not meet publication guidelines.

[a] Days away from work include those that result in days away from work with or without restricted work activity.
[b] In the fatalities column, non-Hispanic categories include cases with Hispanic origin not reported.

FINANCE, INSURANCE, AND REAL ESTATE

Establishments in the Finance, Insurance, and Real Estate industry division include banks and other savings institutions; securities and commodities brokers, dealers, exchanges, and services; insurance carriers, brokers, and agents; real estate operators, developers, agents, and brokers; and holding and other investment offices.

Finance, Insurance, and Real Estate had 8,615,000 workers in 2001 and an annual average of 8,105,000 from 1992 through 2001.

NUMBER OF NONFATAL OCCUPATIONAL INJURIES AND ILLNESS INVOLVING DAYS AWAY FROM WORK[a] AND FATAL OCCUPATIONAL INJURIES BY SELECTED WORKER AND CASE CHARACTERISTICS, UNITED STATES, FINANCE, INSURANCE, AND REAL ESTATE

Characteristic	Nonfatal Cases, 2001	Fatalities, 1992–2001
Total	**37,982**	**1,055**
Sex		
Men	17,446	817
Women	20,472	238
Age		
Under 14	—	—
14 to 15	—	—
16 to 19	456	—
20 to 24	2,926	43
25 to 34	8,275	174
35 to 44	11,360	243
45 to 54	9,441	278
55 to 64	4,072	175
65 and over	1,018	137
Occupation		
Managerial and professional	4,931	383
Technical, sales, and administrative support	15,491	388
Service	8,954	131
Farming, forestry, and fishing	1,950	—
Precision production, craft, and repair	4,497	53
Operators, fabricators, and laborers	2,014	49
Race or ethnic origin[b]		
White, non-Hispanic	17,765	746
Black, non-Hispanic	3,845	70
Hispanic	4,785	101
Asian or Pacific Islander	794	30
American Indian or Alaskan Native	156	—
Not reported	10,637	105
Nature of injury, illness		
Sprains, strains	14,937	—
Fractures	3,017	8
Cuts, lacerations, punctures	2,546	325
Bruises, contusions	2,814	—
Heat burns	183	12
Chemical burns	138	—
Amputations	43	—
Carpal tunnel syndrome	2,204	—
Tendonitis	581	—
Multiple injuries	1,635	280
Soreness, pain	2,761	—
Back pain	898	—
All other	7,123	423

Characteristic	Nonfatal Cases, 2001	Fatalities, 1992–2001
Part of body affected		
Head	2,734	273
Eye	548	—
Neck	481	23
Trunk	11,223	210
Back	7,579	18
Shoulder	1,594	—
Upper extremities	9,075	—
Finger	1,618	—
Hand, except finger	1,154	—
Wrist	3,982	—
Lower extremities	8,378	12
Knee	2,892	—
Foot, toe	1,597	—
Body systems	1,342	144
Multiple	4,380	377
All other	369	14
Source of injury, illness		
Chemicals, chemical products	635	29
Containers	3,359	—
Furniture, fixtures	2,212	5
Machinery	2,292	35
Parts and materials	1,431	47
Worker motion or position	8,683	—
Floor, ground surfaces	11,129	118
Handtools	1,233	33
Vehicles	1,867	373
Health care patient	381	—
All other	4,759	413
Event or exposure		
Contact with object, equipment	6,268	50
Struck by object	3,091	29
Struck against object	1,878	—
Caught in object, equipment, material	792	18
Fall to lower level	3,979	104
Fall on same level	7,288	17
Slips, trips	1,401	—
Overexertion	7,337	—
Overexertion in lifting	4,231	—
Repetitive motion	4,161	—
Exposed to harmful substance	1,449	79
Transportation accidents	1,296	369
Fires, explosions	—	10
Assault, violent act	784	419
by person	728	322
by other	57	97
All other	3,988	6

Source: National Safety Council tabulations of Bureau of Labor Statistics data.
Note: Because of rounding and data exclusion of nonclassifiable responses, data may not sum to the totals. Dashes (—) indicate data that do not meet publication guidelines.

[a]Days away from work include those that result in days away from work with or without restricted work activity.
[b]In the fatalities column, non-Hispanic categories include cases with Hispanic origin not reported.

SERVICES

Establishments in the Services industry division provide services, rather than merchandise, for individuals, businesses, government agencies, and other organizations. Broad categories in this industry division include lodging places, personal and business services, automobile services, repair services, motion pictures, amusement and recreation services, health, legal, education, social services, etc.

Services is the largest industry division with 39,826,000 workers in 2001 and an annual average of 35,489,000 from 1992 through 2001.

NUMBER OF NONFATAL OCCUPATIONAL INJURIES AND ILLNESS INVOLVING DAYS AWAY FROM WORK[a] AND FATAL OCCUPATIONAL INJURIES BY SELECTED WORKER AND CASE CHARACTERISTICS, UNITED STATES, SERVICES

Characteristic	Nonfatal Cases, 2001	Fatalities, 1992–2001
Total	**368,299**	**7,671**
Sex		
Men	137,194	6,389
Women	230,697	1,282
Age		
Under 14	—	—
14 to 15	289	22
16 to 19	9,462	196
20 to 24	39,784	628
25 to 34	83,981	1,730
35 to 44	101,745	1,910
45 to 54	83,136	1,524
55 to 64	39,391	1,007
65 and over	7,427	646
Occupation		
Managerial and professional	64,785	2,381
Technical, sales, and administrative support	60,572	916
Service	168,141	1,603
Farming, forestry, and fishing	5,373	—
Precision production, craft, and repair	26,310	1,168
Operators, fabricators, and laborers	42,138	1,372
Race or ethnic origin[b]		
White, non-Hispanic	178,772	5,078
Black, non-Hispanic	47,270	795
Hispanic	41,045	812
Asian or Pacific Islander	8,256	261
American Indian or Alaskan Native	1,692	45
Not reported	91,263	680
Nature of injury, illness		
Sprains, strains	180,209	14
Fractures	21,832	79
Cuts, lacerations, punctures	18,187	1,612
Bruises, contusions	32,370	5
Heat burns	5,316	154
Chemical burns	2,041	—
Amputations	668	19
Carpal tunnel syndrome	5,110	—
Tendonitis	2,443	—
Multiple injuries	13,046	2,184
Soreness, Pain	31,231	—
Back pain	12,289	—
All other	55,846	3,598

Characteristic	Nonfatal Cases, 2001	Fatalities, 1992–2001
Part of body affected		
Head	21,970	1,891
Eye	7,672	—
Neck	9,094	168
Trunk	146,006	1,400
Back	103,272	94
Shoulder	20,632	—
Upper extremities	65,870	25
Finger	18,233	—
Hand, except finger	10,640	—
Wrist	18,926	—
Lower extremities	71,895	80
Knee	29,203	11
Foot, toe	13,362	5
Body systems	7,129	1,277
Multiple	43,841	2,813
All other	2,495	67
Source of injury, illness		
Chemicals, chemical products	7,118	351
Containers	28,710	74
Furniture, fixtures	17,737	42
Machinery	14,176	316
Parts and materials	12,866	380
Worker motion or position	55,582	6
Floor, ground surfaces	74,407	726
Handtools	8,516	199
Vehicles	26,165	3,293
Health care patient	64,924	12
All other	58,098	2,272
Event or exposure		
Contact with object, equipment	64,623	722
Struck by object	32,205	449
Struck against object	19,846	32
Caught in object, equipment, material	7,733	235
Fall to lower level	18,247	557
Fall on same level	59,093	147
Slips, trips	11,925	—
Overexertion	112,732	13
Overexertion in lifting	57,855	9
Repetitive motion	11,521	—
Exposed to harmful substance	17,961	724
Transportation accidents	16,737	3,068
Fires, explosions	362	261
Assault, violent act	13,749	2,090
by person	12,437	1,506
by other	1,312	584
All other	41,349	89

Source: National Safety Council tabulations of Bureau of Labor Statistics data.
Note: Because of rounding and data exclusion of nonclassifiable responses, data may not sum to the totals. Dashes (—) indicate data that do not meet publication guidelines.

[a] Days away from work include those that result in days away from work with or without restricted work activity.
[b] In the fatalities column, non-Hispanic categories include cases with Hispanic origin not reported.

GOVERNMENT

Government includes workers at all levels from federal civilian and military to state, county, and municipal.

Government employment totaled 20,313,000 in 2001. From 1992 through 2001, Government employment averaged 19,835,000 per year.

NUMBER OF NONFATAL OCCUPATIONAL INJURIES AND ILLNESS INVOLVING DAYS AWAY FROM WORK[a] AND FATAL OCCUPATIONAL INJURIES BY SELECTED WORKER AND CASE CHARACTERISTICS, UNITED STATES, GOVERNMENT

Characteristic	Nonfatal Cases, 2001	Fatalities, 1992–2001
Total	(b)	6,457
Sex		
Men		5,696
Women		761
Age		
Under 14		—
14 to 15		9
16 to 19		159
20 to 24		598
25 to 34		1,662
35 to 44		1,554
45 to 54		1,390
55 to 64		784
65 and over		278
Occupation		
Managerial and professional		984
Technical, sales, and administrative support		549
Service		2,201
Farming, forestry, and fishing		—
Precision production, craft, and repair		548
Operators, fabricators, and laborers		870
Military occupations		1,029
Race or ethnic origin[c]		
White, non-Hispanic		4,546
Black, non-Hispanic		713
Hispanic		391
Asian or Pacific Islander		96
American Indian or Alaskan Native		52
Not reported		659
Nature of injury, illness		
Sprains, strains		20
Fractures		52
Cuts, lacerations, punctures		1,168
Bruises, contusions		—
Heat burns		126
Chemical burns		—
Amputations		15
Carpal tunnel syndrome		—
Tendonitis		—
Multiple injuries		2,228
Soreness, pain		—
Back pain		—
All other		2,839

Characteristic	Nonfatal Cases, 2001	Fatalities, 1992–2001
Part of body affected	(b)	
Head		1,530
Eye		—
Neck		134
Trunk		1,044
Back		96
Shoulder		—
Upper extremities		15
Finger		—
Hand, except finger		—
Wrist		—
Lower extremities		68
Knee		12
Foot, toe		5
Body systems		864
Multiple		2,730
All other		72
Source of injury, illness		
Chemicals, chemical products		103
Containers		49
Furniture, fixtures		20
Machinery		236
Parts and materials		215
Worker motion or position		5
Floor, ground surfaces		344
Handtools		64
Vehicles		3,483
Health care patient		7
All other		1,931
Event or exposure		
Contact with object, equipment		423
Struck by object		257
Struck against object		11
Caught in object, equipment, material		153
Fall to lower level		244
Fall on same level		87
Slips, trips		—
Overexertion		12
Overexertion in lifting		7
Repetitive motion		—
Exposed to harmful substance		426
Transportation accidents		3,507
Fires, explosions		270
Assault, violent act		1,426
by person		1,059
by other		367
All other		59

Source: National Safety Council tabulations of Bureau of Labor Statistics data.
Note: Because of rounding and data exclusion of nonclassifiable responses, data may not sum to the totals. Dashes (—) indicate data that do not meet publication guidelines.
[a]Days away from work include those that result in days away from work with or without restricted work activity.

[b]Data for government entities not collected in the national BLS Survey of Occupational Injuries and Illnesses.
[c]In the fatalities column, non-Hispanic categories include cases with Hispanic origin not reported.

CHEMICALS AND ALLIED PRODUCTS

The Chemicals industry (SIC 28) includes production of basic chemicals and manufacture of products by predominantly chemical processes. It includes basic chemicals such as acids alkalies, salts, and organic chemicals; intermediate products such as synthetic fibers, plastics materials, colors, and pigments; and finished products such as drugs, cosmetics, soaps, paints, and fertilizers.

Employment in the Chemicals industry totaled 1,022,000 in 2001. From 1992 through 2001, Chemicals employment averaged 1,046,000 per year.

NUMBER OF NONFATAL OCCUPATIONAL INJURIES AND ILLNESS INVOLVING DAYS AWAY FROM WORK[a] AND FATAL OCCUPATIONAL INJURIES BY SELECTED WORKER AND CASE CHARACTERISTICS, UNITED STATES, CHEMICALS AND ALLIED PRODUCTS (SIC 28)

Characteristic	Nonfatal Cases, 2001	Fatalities, 1992–2001
Total	**8,980**	**376**
Sex		
Men	6,295	335
Women	2,669	41
Age		
Under 14	—	—
14 to 15	—	—
16 to 19	46	9
20 to 24	503	21
25 to 34	1,979	92
35 to 44	2,868	115
45 to 54	2,429	85
55 to 64	969	48
65 and over	62	6
Occupation		
Managerial and professional	512	49
Technical, sales, and administrative support	1,239	48
Service	295	8
Farming, forestry, and fishing	22	—
Precision production, craft, and repair	1,007	70
Operators, fabricators, and laborers	5,868	200
Race or ethnic origin[b]		
White, non-Hispanic	4,397	240
Black, non-Hispanic	962	57
Hispanic	1,321	31
Asian or Pacific Islander	147	10
American Indian or Alaskan Native	—	—
Not reported	2,153	35
Nature of injury, illness		
Sprains, strains	3,337	—
Fractures	573	—
Cuts, lacerations, punctures	580	20
Bruises, contusions	721	—
Heat burns	470	54
Chemical burns	369	19
Amputations	85	—
Carpal tunnel syndrome	276	—
Tendonitis	145	—
Multiple injuries	326	104
Soreness, pain	468	—
Back pain	209	—
All other	1,629	177

Characteristic	Nonfatal Cases, 2001	Fatalities, 1992–2001
Part of body affected		
Head	669	64
Eye	381	—
Neck	122	—
Trunk	3,035	34
Back	1,911	—
Shoulder	510	—
Upper extremities	2,167	—
Finger	817	—
Hand, except finger	320	—
Wrist	570	—
Lower extremities	1,742	—
Knee	669	—
Foot, toe	379	—
Body systems	211	84
Multiple	947	188
All other	87	—
Source of injury, illness		
Chemicals, chemical products	729	90
Containers	1,728	18
Furniture, fixtures	147	—
Machinery	676	32
Parts and materials	620	14
Worker motion or position	1,777	—
Floor, ground surfaces	1,270	20
Handtools	365	—
Vehicles	485	102
Health care patient	—	—
All other	1,183	100
Event or exposure		
Contact with object, equipment	2,042	37
Struck by object	939	12
Struck against object	421	—
Caught in object, equipment, material	574	25
Fall to lower level	351	22
Fall on same level	939	—
Slips, trips	308	—
Overexertion	2,034	—
Overexertion in lifting	970	—
Repetitive motion	646	—
Exposed to harmful substance	1,321	61
Transportation accidents	251	101
Fires, explosions	51	130
Assault, violent act	13	21
by person	10	13
by other	—	8
All other	1,025	—

Source: National Safety Council tabulations of Bureau of Labor Statistics data.
Note: Because of rounding and data exclusion of nonclassifiable responses, data may not sum to the totals. Dashes (—) indicate data that do not meet publication guidelines.

[a] Days away from work include those that result in days away from work with or without restricted work activity.
[b] In the fatalities column, non-Hispanic categories include cases with Hispanic origin not reported.

ELECTRIC, GAS, AND SANITARY SERVICES

The Electric, Gas, and Sanitary Services industry (SIC 49) includes, primarily, the generation, transmission, and distribution of electricity; the transmission and distribution of gas; and the operation of water and sewerage systems. Establishments in this industry may be either publicly or privately owned. The data below for nonfatal injuries and illnesses covers only privately owned establishments. The fatal injury data covers both public and private establishments.

Employment in the Electric, Gas, and Sanitary Services industry totaled 852,000 in 2001 and averaged 892,000 annually from 1992 through 2001.

NUMBER OF NONFATAL OCCUPATIONAL INJURIES AND ILLNESS INVOLVING DAYS AWAY FROM WORK[a] AND FATAL OCCUPATIONAL INJURIES BY SELECTED WORKER AND CASE CHARACTERISTICS, UNITED STATES, ELECTRIC, GAS, AND SANITARY SERVICES (SIC 49)

Characteristic	Nonfatal Cases, 2001	Fatalities, 1992–2001
Total	**13,871**	**1,130**
Sex		
Men	12,657	1,098
Women	1,208	32
Age		
Under 14	—	—
14 to 15	—	—
16 to 19	95	12
20 to 24	684	54
25 to 34	3,118	245
35 to 44	4,916	341
45 to 54	3,789	311
55 to 64	1,166	138
65 and over	66	28
Occupation		
Managerial and professional	284	83
Technical, sales, and administrative support	2,038	56
Service	191	14
Farming, forestry, and fishing	47	—
Precision production, craft, and repair	5,100	488
Operators, fabricators, and laborers	6,174	479
Race or ethnic origin[b]		
White, non-Hispanic	6,973	735
Black, non-Hispanic	1,207	153
Hispanic	1,247	119
Asian or Pacific Islander	156	10
American Indian or Alaskan Native	48	—
Not reported	4,239	109
Nature of injury, illness		
Sprains, strains	6,800	—
Fractures	1,060	—
Cuts, lacerations, punctures	790	34
Bruises, contusions	1,214	—
Heat burns	215	48
Chemical burns	61	—
Amputations	38	8
Carpal tunnel syndrome	174	—
Tendonitis	53	—
Multiple injuries	401	309
Soreness, pain	906	—
Back pain	391	—
All other	2,160	723

Characteristic	Nonfatal Cases, 2001	Fatalities, 1992–2001
Part of body affected		
Head	750	199
Eye	367	—
Neck	289	7
Trunk	5,201	175
Back	3,204	5
Shoulder	1,033	—
Upper extremities	2,354	—
Finger	843	—
Hand, except finger	450	—
Wrist	435	—
Lower extremities	3,621	8
Knee	1,314	—
Foot, toe	569	—
Body systems	197	346
Multiple	1,435	386
All other	25	7
Source of injury, illness		
Chemicals, chemical products	207	53
Containers	1,785	27
Furniture, fixtures	152	—
Machinery	476	91
Parts and materials	1,430	225
Worker motion or position	3,040	—
Floor, ground surfaces	2,298	69
Handtools	589	11
Vehicles	1,806	475
Health care patient	—	—
All other	2,087	174
Event or exposure		
Contact with object, equipment	2,858	153
Struck by object	1,324	81
Struck against object	910	—
Caught in object, equipment, material	474	72
Fall to lower level	1,122	64
Fall on same level	1,223	6
Slips, trips	678	—
Overexertion	3,083	—
Overexertion in lifting	1,437	—
Repetitive motion	470	—
Exposed to harmful substance	775	304
Transportation accidents	1,007	463
Fires, explosions	63	82
Assault, violent act	194	50
by person	54	23
by other	140	27
All other	2,398	8

Source: National Safety Council tabulations of Bureau of Labor Statistics data.
Note: Because of rounding and data exclusion of nonclassifiable responses, data may not sum to the totals. Dashes (—) indicate data that do not meet publication guidelines.

[a]Days away from work include those that result in days away from work with or without restricted work activity.
[b]In the fatalities column, non-Hispanic categories include cases with Hispanic origin not reported.

WHOLESALE TRADE — DURABLE GOODS

The Wholesale Trade-Durable Goods industry (SIC 50) includes establishments primarily engaged in the wholesale distribution of goods such as motor vehicles, furniture and home furnishings, lumber and other construction materials, professional and commercial equipment, metals and minerals (except petroleum), electrical goods, hardware, plumbing and heating equipment, machinery, and other durable goods and associated supplies.

Employment in the Wholesale Trade-Durable Goods industry totaled 4,024,000 in 2001 and averaged 3,822,000 each year from 1992 through 2001.

NUMBER OF NONFATAL OCCUPATIONAL INJURIES AND ILLNESS INVOLVING DAYS AWAY FROM WORK[a] AND FATAL OCCUPATIONAL INJURIES BY SELECTED WORKER AND CASE CHARACTERISTICS, UNITED STATES, WHOLESALE TRADE-DURABLE GOODS (SIC 50)

Characteristic	Nonfatal Cases, 2001	Fatalities, 1992–2001
Total	**54,638**	**1,418**
Sex		
Men	47,073	1,365
Women	7,540	53
Age		
Under 14	—	—
14 to 15	—	—
16 to 19	998	30
20 to 24	5,772	110
25 to 34	15,655	305
35 to 44	15,787	351
45 to 54	10,440	309
55 to 64	4,447	200
65 and over	929	108
Occupation		
Managerial and professional	1,718	118
Technical, sales, and administrative support	10,477	401
Service	615	15
Farming, forestry, and fishing	—	—
Precision production, craft, and repair	12,022	206
Operators, fabricators, and laborers	29,457	664
Race or ethnic origin[b]		
White, non-Hispanic	30,454	952
Black, non-Hispanic	4,547	115
Hispanic	6,849	159
Asian or Pacific Islander	832	44
American Indian or Alaskan Native	110	—
Not reported	11,846	146
Nature of injury, illness		
Sprains, strains	23,749	6
Fractures	3,696	10
Cuts, lacerations, punctures	4,748	153
Bruises, contusions	5,225	—
Heat burns	640	36
Chemical burns	198	—
Amputations	386	7
Carpal tunnel syndrome	874	—
Tendonitis	400	—
Multiple injuries	2,001	440
Soreness, pain	3,670	—
Back pain	1,476	—
All other	9,053	765

Characteristic	Nonfatal Cases, 2001	Fatalities, 1992–2001
Part of body affected		
Head	3,571	350
Eye	1,894	—
Neck	969	27
Trunk	21,399	303
Back	13,979	12
Shoulder	2,999	—
Upper extremities	12,251	—
Finger	4,803	—
Hand, except finger	2,110	—
Wrist	2,092	—
Lower extremities	10,956	16
Knee	3,956	—
Foot, toe	2,554	—
Body systems	468	178
Multiple	4,743	533
All other	282	7
Source of injury, illness		
Chemicals, chemical products	664	32
Containers	8,726	47
Furniture, fixtures	1,802	—
Machinery	4,567	135
Parts and materials	10,679	118
Worker motion or position	7,506	—
Floor, ground surfaces	6,959	91
Handtools	1,851	16
Vehicles	5,493	741
Health care patient	128	—
All other	6,263	234
Event or exposure		
Contact with object, equipment	16,517	320
Struck by object	8,628	197
Struck against object	3,643	5
Caught in object, equipment, material	2,934	118
Fall to lower level	3,445	79
Fall on same level	4,715	17
Slips, trips	1,314	—
Overexertion	15,801	—
Overexertion in lifting	9,282	—
Repetitive motion	1,734	—
Exposed to harmful substance	1,338	85
Transportation accidents	3,154	662
Fires, explosions	418	63
Assault, violent act	76	181
by person	61	126
by other	—	55
All other	6,125	9

Source: National Safety Council tabulations of Bureau of Labor Statistics data.
Note: Because of rounding and data exclusion of nonclassifiable responses, data may not sum to the totals. Dashes (—) indicate data that do not meet publication guidelines.

[a] Days away from work include those that result in days away from work with or without restricted work activity.
[b] In the fatalities column, non-Hispanic categories include cases with Hispanic origin not reported.

The Engineering, Accounting, Research, Management, and Related Services industry (SIC 87) includes engineering, architectural and surveying services; accounting, auditing, and bookkeeping services; research, development, and testing services; and management and public relations services.

Employment in the Engineering, Accounting, Research, Management, and Related Services industry totaled 3,593,000 in 2001 and averaged 2,956,000 annually from 1992 through 2001.

NUMBER OF NONFATAL OCCUPATIONAL INJURIES AND ILLNESS INVOLVING DAYS AWAY FROM WORK[a] AND FATAL OCCUPATIONAL INJURIES BY SELECTED WORKER AND CASE CHARACTERISTICS, UNITED STATES, ENGINEERING AND MANAGEMENT SERVICES (SIC 87)

Characteristic	Nonfatal Cases, 2001	Fatalities, 1992–2001
Total	**16,183**	**493**
Sex		
Men	11,018	446
Women	5,150	47
Age		
Under 14	—	—
14 to 15	—	—
16 to 19	137	6
20 to 24	1,405	36
25 to 34	4,292	103
35 to 44	4,413	138
45 to 54	3,918	91
55 to 64	1,552	84
65 and over	414	34
Occupation		
Managerial and professional	3,308	278
Technical, sales, and administrative support	5,680	106
Service	1,361	7
Farming, forestry, and fishing	131	—
Precision production, craft, and repair	1,867	43
Operators, fabricators, and laborers	3,613	54
Race or ethnic origin[b]		
White, non-Hispanic	8,265	392
Black, non-Hispanic	1,236	21
Hispanic	1,515	26
Asian or Pacific Islander	314	15
American Indian or Alaskan Native	—	—
Not reported	4,831	38
Nature of injury, illness		
Sprains, strains	7,090	—
Fractures	1,461	—
Cuts, lacerations, punctures	978	43
Bruises, contusions	1,413	—
Heat burns	135	16
Chemical burns	110	—
Amputations	45	—
Carpal tunnel syndrome	450	—
Tendonitis	148	—
Multiple injuries	598	203
Soreness, pain	754	—
Back pain	359	—
All other	3,002	228

Characteristic	Nonfatal Cases, 2001	Fatalities, 1992–2001
Part of body affected		
Head	1,591	117
Eye	442	—
Neck	544	10
Trunk	5,366	59
Back	3,393	—
Shoulder	776	—
Upper extremities	3,088	—
Finger	806	—
Hand, except finger	418	—
Wrist	954	—
Lower extremities	3,268	—
Knee	1,147	—
Foot, toe	584	—
Body systems	355	70
Multiple	1,756	231
All other	216	5
Source of injury, illness		
Chemicals, chemical products	457	11
Containers	1,708	6
Furniture, fixtures	526	—
Machinery	1,095	13
Parts and materials	1,207	17
Worker motion or position	2,892	—
Floor, ground surfaces	3,431	40
Handtools	737	—
Vehicles	1,769	306
Health care patient	108	—
All other	2,251	94
Event or exposure		
Contact with object, equipment	3,044	16
Struck by object	1,674	11
Struck against object	701	—
Caught in object, equipment, material	418	5
Fall to lower level	1,071	31
Fall on same level	2,550	11
Slips, trips	429	—
Overexertion	3,536	—
Overexertion in lifting	2,003	—
Repetitive motion	1,027	—
Exposed to harmful substance	870	40
Transportation accidents	1,533	311
Fires, explosions	—	18
Assault, violent act	208	64
by person	149	34
by other	59	30
All other	1,899	—

Source: National Safety Council tabulations of Bureau of Labor Statistics data.
Note: Because of rounding and data exclusion of nonclassifiable responses, data may not sum to the totals. Dashes (—) indicate data that do not meet publication guidelines.

[a]Days away from work include those that result in days away from work with or without restricted work activity.
[b]In the fatalities column, non-Hispanic categories include cases with Hispanic origin not reported.

OCCUPATIONAL HEALTH

Disorders associated with repeated trauma were the most common illness with over 216,000 new cases in 2001.

Approximately 333,800 occupational illnesses were recognized or diagnosed by employers in 2001 according to the Bureau of Labor Statistics (BLS). Disorders associated with repeated trauma were the most common illness with 216,400 new cases, followed by skin diseases and disorders (nearly 39,000), disorders due to physical agents (14,600), and respiratory conditions due to toxic agents (14,500).

The overall incidence rate of occupational illness for all workers was 36.7 per 10,000 full-time workers. Of the major industry divisions, manufacturing had the highest rate in 2001, 105.0 per 10,000 full-time workers. Workers in manufacturing also had the highest rates for disorders associated with repeated trauma, respiratory conditions due to toxic agents, disorders due to physical

agents, and poisoning. Agriculture had the second highest incidence rate, 32.3, although agricultural workers had the highest rate of all the industry divisions for skin diseases and disorders. Mining had the highest incidence rate for dust diseases of the lungs.

The table below shows the number of occupational illnesses and the incidence rate per 10,000 full-time workers as measured by the 2001 BLS survey. To convert these to incidence rates per 100 full-time workers, which are comparable to other published BLS rates, divide the rates in the table by 100. The BLS survey records illnesses only for the year in which they are recognized or diagnosed as work-related. Since only recognized cases are included, the figures underestimate the incidence of occupational illness.

NUMBER OF OCCUPATIONAL ILLNESSES AND INCIDENCE RATES BY INDUSTRY AND TYPE OF ILLNESS, UNITED STATES, 2001

Occupational Illness	Private Sector[a]	Agricul-ture[a,b]	Mining[b]	Con-struction	Manu-facturing	Trans. & Pub. Util.	Trade[b]	Finance[b]	Services
Number of Illnesses (in thousands)									
All Illnesses	**333.8**	**4.9**	**0.9**	**7.0**	**181.3**	**19.2**	**33.6**	**15.8**	**71.2**
Disorders associated with repeated trauma	216.4	0.7	0.6	2.6	141.0	10.1	18.4	12.4	30.6
Skin diseases, disorders	38.9	2.6	(c)	1.4	16.1	1.6	3.2	0.6	13.4
Disorders due to physical agents	14.6	0.4	0.1	0.9	6.7	0.8	3.0	0.2	2.5
Respiratory conditions due to toxic agents	14.5	0.1	(c)	0.5	4.1	1.4	1.9	0.7	5.9
Poisoning	2.8	0.1	(c)	0.1	1.4	0.2	0.4	0.1	0.6
Dust diseases of the lungs	1.3	(c)	0.1	0.1	0.4	0.1	0.2	(c)	0.3
All other occupational diseases	45.1	1.0	0.1	1.4	11.6	4.9	6.4	1.8	17.9
Incidence Rate per 10,000 Full-Time Workers									
All Illnesses	**36.7**	**32.3**	**15.9**	**11.4**	**105.0**	**29.1**	**14.1**	**23.0**	**25.3**
Disorders associated with repeated trauma	23.8	4.6	10.2	4.3	81.6	15.4	7.7	18.1	10.8
Skin diseases, disorders	4.3	17.5	0.2	2.3	9.3	2.4	1.4	0.9	4.8
Respiratory conditions due to toxic agents	1.6	0.4	0.3	0.8	2.4	2.1	0.8	1.0	2.1
Disorders due to physical agents	1.6	2.4	2.3	1.5	3.9	1.3	1.3	0.3	0.9
Poisoning	0.3	0.6	0.1	0.2	0.8	0.2	0.2	0.2	0.2
Dust diseases of the lungs	0.1	0.1	1.7	0.1	0.2	0.2	0.1	(d)	0.1
All other occupational diseases	5.0	6.8	1.1	2.2	6.7	7.5	2.7	2.6	6.4

Source: Bureau of Labor Statistics, U.S. Department of Labor. Components may not add to totals due to rounding.
[a] Private sector includes all industries except government, but excludes farms with less than 11 employees.
[b] Agriculture includes forestry and fishing; mining includes quarrying and oil and gas extraction; trade includes wholesale and retail; finance includes insurance and real estate.
[c] Fewer than 50 cases.
[d] Incidence rate less than 0.05.

NONFATAL OCCUPATIONAL ILLNESS INCIDENCE RATES, U.S. PRIVATE INDUSTRY, 1995–2001

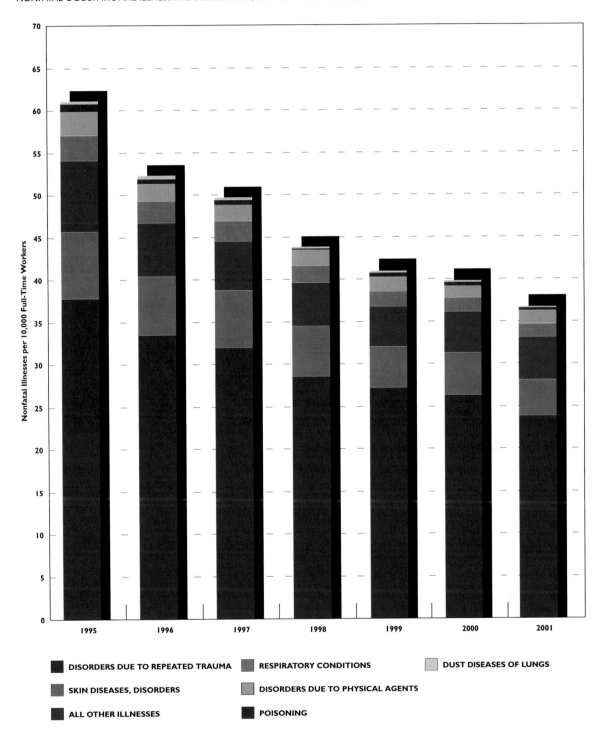

DISORDERS DUE TO REPEATED TRAUMA   **RESPIRATORY CONDITIONS**   **DUST DISEASES OF LUNGS**

SKIN DISEASES, DISORDERS   **DISORDERS DUE TO PHYSICAL AGENTS**

ALL OTHER ILLNESSES   **POISONING**

MOTOR VEHICLE

INJURY FACTS®

NATIONAL SAFETY COUNCIL

Between 1912 and 2002, motor-vehicle deaths per 10,000 registered vehicles were reduced 94%, from 33 to about 2. In 1912, there were 3,100 fatalities when the number of registered vehicles totaled only 950,000. In 2002, there were 44,000 fatalities, but registrations soared to 243 million.

While mileage data were not available in 1912, the 2002 mileage death rate of 1.56 per 100,000,000 vehicle miles was down 1% from 2001 and the lowest rate on record. Disabling injuries in motor-vehicle accidents totaled 2,300,000 in 2002, and total motor-vehicle costs were estimated at $242.7 billion. Costs include wage and productivity losses, medical expenses, administrative expenses, motor-vehicle property damage, and employer costs.

Motor-vehicle deaths increased 1% from 2001 to 2002 and also increased 1% from 2000. Miles traveled was up about 2%, the number of registered vehicles increased 3%, and the population increased 1%. As a result, the mileage death rate was down 1%, the registration death rate was down 3%, and the population death rate was down slightly from 2001 to 2002.

Compared with 1992, motor-vehicle deaths in 2002 increased by about 7%. However, mileage, registration, and population death rates were all sharply lower in 2002 compared to 1992 (see chart on next page).

The word "accident" may be used in this section as well as the word "crash." When used, "accident" has a specific meaning as defined in the *Manual on Classification of Motor Vehicle Traffic Accidents, ANSI D16.2-1996.* "Crash" is generally used by the National Highway Traffic Safety Administration to mean the same as accident, but it is not formally defined.

Deaths 44,000
Disabling injuries 2,300,000
Cost . . . . $242.7 billion
Motor-vehicle mileage . . . . 2,829 billion
Registered vehicles in the United States 242,500,000
Licensed drivers in the United States 193,300,000
Death rate per 100,000,000 vehicle miles 1.56
Death rate per 10,000 registered vehicles 1.81
Death rate per 100,000 population 15.7

ACCIDENT AND VEHICLE TOTALS, 2002

Severity of Accident	Number of Accidents	Drivers (Vehicles) Involved
Fatal	39,200	52,700
Disabling injury	1,600,000	2,600,000
Property damage and nondisabling injury[a]	16,700,000	28,000,000
Total (rounded)	18,300,000	30,700,000

[a]Estimating procedures for these figures were revised beginning with the 1990 edition.

TRAVEL, DEATHS, AND DEATH RATES, UNITED STATES, 1925–2002

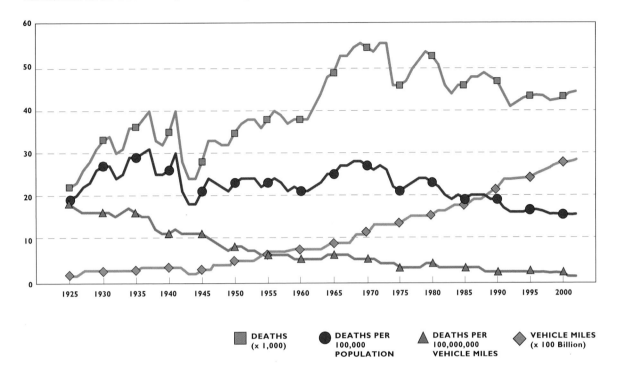

■ DEATHS (x 1,000)	● DEATHS PER 100,000 POPULATION	▲ DEATHS PER 100,000,000 VEHICLE MILES	◆ VEHICLE MILES (x 100 Billion)

DEATHS DUE TO MOTOR-VEHICLE ACCIDENTS, 2002

TYPE OF EVENT AND AGE OF VICTIM

All Motor-Vehicle Accidents
Includes deaths involving mechanically or electrically powered highway-transport vehicles in motion (except those on rails), both on and off the highway or street.

	Total	Change from 2001	Death Rate[a]
Deaths	44,000	+1%	15.7
Nonfatal injuries	2,300,000		

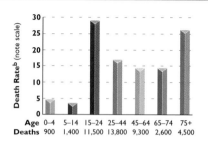

Collision Between Motor Vehicles
Includes deaths from collisions of two or more motor vehicles. Motorized bicycles and scooters, trolley buses, and farm tractors or road machinery traveling on highways are motor vehicles.

	Total	Change from 2001	Death Rate[a]
Deaths	18,200	−1%	6.5
Nonfatal injuries	1,520,000		

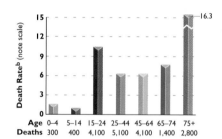

Collision with Fixed Object
Includes deaths from collisions in which the first harmful event is the striking of a fixed object such as a guardrail, abutment, impact attenuator, etc.

	Total	Change from 2001	Death Rate[a]
Deaths	13,500	+5%	4.8
Nonfatal injuries	460,000		

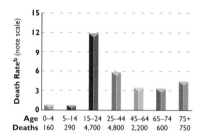

Pedestrian Accidents
Includes all deaths of persons struck by motor vehicles, either on or off a street or highway, regardless of the circumstances of the accident.

	Total	Change from 2001	Death Rate[a]
Deaths	5,700	−7%	2.0
Nonfatal injuries	80,000		

See footnotes on page 89.

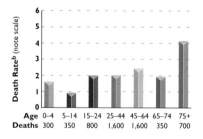

Noncollision Accidents

Includes deaths from accidents in which the first injury or damage-producing event was an overturn, jacknife, or other type of noncollision.

	Total	Change from 2001	Death Rate[a]
Deaths	5,500	+6%	2.0
Nonfatal injuries	170,000		

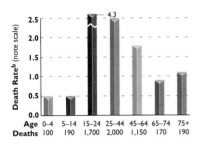

Collision with Pedalcycle

Includes deaths of pedalcyclists and motor-vehicle occupants from collisions between pedalcycles and motor vehicles on streets, highways, private driveways, parking lots, etc.

	Total	Change from 2001	Death Rate[a]
Deaths	700	−13%	0.2
Nonfatal injuries	55,000		

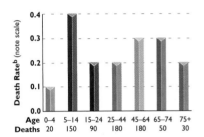

Collision with Railroad Train

Includes deaths from collisions of motor vehicles (moving or stalled) and railroad vehicles at public or private grade crossings. In other types of accidents, classification requires motor vehicle to be in motion.

	Total	Change from 2001	Death Rate[a]
Deaths	300	0%	0.1
Nonfatal injuries	2,000		

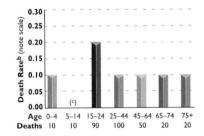

Other Collision

Includes deaths from motor-vehicle collisions not specified in other categories above. Most of the deaths arose out of accidents involving animals or animal-drawn vehicles.

	Total	Change from 2001	Death Rate[a]
Deaths	100	0%	([c])
Nonfatal Injuries	13,000		

Note: Procedures and benchmarks for estimating deaths by type of accident and age were changed in 1990. Estimates for 1987 and later years are not comparable to earlier years. The noncollision and fixed object categories were most affected by the changes.
[a]*Deaths per 100,000 population.*
[b]*Deaths per 100,000 population in each age group.*
[c]*Death rate was less than 0.05.*

TYPE OF MOTOR-VEHICLE ACCIDENT

Although motor-vehicle deaths occur more often in collisions between motor vehicles than any other type of accident, this type represents only about 41% of the total. Collisions between a motor vehicle and a fixed object were the next most common type, with about 31% of the deaths, followed by pedestrian accidents and noncollisions (rollovers, etc.).

While collisions between motor vehicles accounted for less than half of motor-vehicle fatalities, this accident type represented 66% of injuries, 64% of injury accidents, and 68% of all accidents. Single-vehicle accidents involving collisions with fixed objects, pedestrians, and noncollisions, on the other hand,

accounted for a greater proportion of fatalities and fatal accidents compared to less serious accidents. These three accident types made up 56% of fatalities and 58% of fatal accidents, but 32% or less of injuries, injury accidents, or all accidents.

Of collisions between motor vehicles, angle collisions cause the greatest number of deaths, about 8,700 in 2002 and the greatest number of nonfatal injuries as well as fatal and injury accidents. The table below shows the estimated number of motor-vehicle deaths, injuries, fatal accidents, injury accidents, and all accidents, for various types of accidents.

MOTOR-VEHICLE DEATHS AND INJURIES AND NUMBER OF ACCIDENTS BY TYPE OF ACCIDENT, 2002

Type of Accident	Deaths	Nonfatal Injuries	Fatal Accidents	Injury Accidents	All Accidents
Total	44,000	2,300,000	39,200	1,600,000	18,300,000
Collision with —					
Pedestrian	5,700	80,000	5,600	65,000	210,000
Other motor vehicle	18,200	1,520,000	15,300	1,020,000	12,380,000
Angle collision	8,700	755,000	7,700	490,000	5,480,000
Head-on collision	6,700	85,000	5,100	45,000	320,000
Rear-end collision	2,000	615,000	1,800	440,000	5,400,000
Sideswipe and other two-vehicle collisions	800	65,000	700	45,000	1,180,000
Railroad train	300	2,000	300	2,000	3,000
Pedalcycle	700	5,500	700	50,000	140,000
Animal, animal-drawn vehicle	100	13,000	100	13,000	820,000
Fixed object	13,500	460,000	12,300	330,000	4,120,000
Noncollision	5,500	170,000	4,700	120,000	630,000

Source: National Safety Council estimates, based on reports from state traffic authorities. Procedures for estimating the number of accidents by type were changed for the 1998 edition and are not comparable to estimates in previous editions (see Technical Appendix).

There are two methods commonly used to measure the costs of motor-vehicle crashes. One is the *economic cost* framework and the other is the *comprehensive cost* framework.

Economic costs may be used by a community or state to estimate the economic impact of motor-vehicle crashes that occurred within its jurisdiction in a given time period. It is a measure of the productivity lost and expenses incurred because of the crashes. Economic costs, however, should not be used for cost-benefit analysis because they do not reflect what society is willing to pay to prevent a statistical fatality or injury.

There are five economic cost components: (a) wage and productivity losses, which include wages, fringe benefits, household production, and travel delay; (b) medical expenses, including emergency service costs; (c) administrative expenses, which include the administrative cost of private and public insurance plus police and legal costs; (d) motor-vehicle damage, including the value of damage to property; and (e) employer costs for crashes involving workers.

The information below shows the average economic costs in 2002 per death (*not* per fatal crash), per injury (*not* per injury crash), and per property-damage crash.

ECONOMIC COSTS, 2002

Death **$1,090,000**

Nonfatal disabling injury **$39,900**

Incapacitating injury[a] *$52,100*

Nonincapacitating evident injury[a] *$17,200*

Possible injury[a] *$9,800*

Property-damage crash (including minor injuries) **$6,200**

Comprehensive costs include not only the economic cost components, but also a measure of the value of lost quality of life associated with the deaths and injuries, that is, what society is willing to pay to prevent them. The values of lost quality of life were obtained through empirical studies of what people actually pay to reduce their safety and health risks, such as through the purchase of air bags or smoke detectors. Comprehensive costs should be used for cost-benefit analysis, but because the lost quality of life represents only a dollar equivalence of intangible qualities, they do not represent real economic losses and should not be used to determine the economic impact of past crashes.

The information below shows the average comprehensive costs in 2002 on a per-person basis.

COMPREHENSIVE COSTS, 2002

Death **$3,470,000**

Incapacitating injury[a] *$172,000*

Nonincapacitating evident injury[a] *$44,200*

Possible injury[a] *$21,000*

No injury **$2,000**

Source: National Safety Council estimates (see the Technical Appendix) and Children's Safety Network Economics and Insurance Resource Center, Pacific Institute for Research and Evaluation.
[a] Committee on Motor Vehicle Traffic Accident Classification. (1997). Manual on Classification of Motor Vehicle Traffic Accidents, ANSI D16.1-1996 (6th ed.). Itasca, IL: National Safety Council.
Note: The National Safety Council's cost estimating procedures were extensively revised for the 1993 edition. New components were added, new benchmarks adopted, and a new discount rate assumed. The costs are not comparable to those of prior years.

All states and the District of Columbia have 21-year-old drinking age and child safety seat laws. Breath alcohol ignition interlock device laws are in effect in 41 states. Mandatory belt use laws are in effect in 49 states plus the District of Columbia, of which 19 states and D.C. are standard enforcement. Graduated licensing is in effect in some form in 44 states and the District of Columbia.

STATE LAWS

	Alcohol Laws				Mandatory Belt Use Law		Graduated Licensing Laws				
State	Administrative License Revocation[a]	BAC Limit[b]	Zero Tolerance Limit[c] for Minors	Alcohol Ignition Interlock Device[d]	Enforcement	Seating Positions Covered by Law	Minimum Instructional Permit Period[e]	Minimum Hours of Supervised Driving[f]	Passenger Restrictions	Nighttime Driving Restrictions	Unrestricted License Minimum Age[g]
Alabama	1996	0.08	0.02	no	standard	front	6 mo.	30/–	yes	yes	16yrs.
Alaska	1983	0.08	0.00	yes	secondary	all	6 mo.	none	no	no	16yrs.
Arizona	1992	0.10	0.00	yes	secondary	front	6 mo.	25/5	no	no	16yrs.
Arkansas	1995	0.08	0.02	yes	secondary	front	6 mo.	none	no	no	18yrs.
California	1989	0.08	0.01	yes[h]	standard	all	6 mo.	50/10	yes	yes	17yrs.
Colorado	1983	0.10	0.02	yes[h]	secondary	front	6 mo.	50/10	yes	yes	17yrs.
Connecticut	1990	0.08	0.02	no	standard	front[i]	6 mo.	none	no	no	16yrs, 4 mo.
Delaware	yes	0.10	0.02	yes[h]	secondary	front	12 mo.	none[j]	yes	yes	16yrs, 10mo.
Dist. of Columbia	yes	0.08	0.00	no	standard	all	6 mo.	40+10[k]	yes	yes	18yrs.
Florida	1990	0.08	0.02	yes[h]	secondary	front	12 mo.	50/10	no	yes	18yrs.
Georgia	1995	0.08	0.02	yes[h]	standard	front[i]	12 mo.	40/6	yes	yes	18yrs.
Hawaii	1990	0.08	0.02	no	standard	front[i]	3 mo.	none	no	no	16yrs.
Idaho	1994	0.08	0.02	yes	secondary	front	4 mo.	50/10	no	yes	16yrs.
Illinois	1986	0.08	0.00	yes[h]	secondary	front	3 mo.	25/–	yes	yes	18yrs.
Indiana	yes	0.08	0.02	yes	standard	front	2 mo.	none	yes	yes	18yrs.
Iowa	1982	0.10	0.02	yes	standard	front	6 mo.	20/2	no	yes	17yrs.
Kansas	1988	0.08	0.02	yes	secondary	front	6 mo.	50/10	no	no	16yrs.
Kentucky	no	0.08	0.02	yes[h]	secondary	all	6 mo.	none	no	yes[n]	16yrs, 6 mo.
Louisiana	1984	0.08	0.02	yes	standard	front[i]	3 mo.	none	no	yes	17yrs.
Maine	1984	0.08	0.00	yes[h]	secondary	all	3 mo.	35/5	no	no	16yrs, 3 mo.
Maryland	1989	0.08[m]	0.00	yes	standard	front[i]	4 mo.	40/–	no	yes	17yrs., 7 mo.
Massachusetts	1994	0.08	0.02	no	secondary	all	6 mo.	12/–	yes	yes	18yrs.
Michigan	no	0.10	0.02	yes[h]	standard	front[i]	6 mo.	50/10	no	yes	17yrs.
Minnesota	1976	0.10	0.01	no	secondary	front[i]	6 mo.	30/10	no	no	17yrs.
Mississippi	1983	0.10	0.02	yes[h]	secondary	front	6 mo.	none	no	yes	16yrs.
Missouri	1987	0.10	0.02	yes[h]	secondary	front[i]	6 mo.	20/–	no	yes	18yrs.
Montana	no	0.10	0.02	yes	secondary	all	none	none	no	no	15yrs.
Nebraska	1993	0.08	0.02	yes	secondary	front[i]	none	50/–	no	yes	17yrs.
Nevada	1983	0.10	0.02	yes[h]	secondary	all	30–90 days	50/–	yes	no	18yrs.
New Hampshire	1993	0.08	0.02	no	(l)	(l)	6 mo.	20/–	yes	yes	18yrs.
New Jersey	no	0.10	0.01	yes[h]	standard	front	12 mo.	1 year	yes	yes	18yrs.
New Mexico	1984	0.08	0.02	yes	standard	all	6 mo.	50/10	yes	yes	16yrs., 6mo.
New York	1994[o]	0.10[m]	0.02	yes[h]	standard	front[i]	6 mo.	20/–	no	yes	18yrs.
North Carolina	1983	0.08	0.00	yes[h]	standard	front[i]	12 mo.	none	yes	yes	16yrs., 6mo.
North Dakota	1983	0.10	0.02	yes[h]	secondary	front	6 mo.	none	no	no	16yrs.
Ohio	1993	0.10	0.02	yes	secondary	front	6 mo.	50/10	no	yes	17yrs.
Oklahoma	1983	0.08	0.00	yes	standard	front	none	none	no	no	16yrs.
Oregon	1983	0.08	0.00	yes	standard	all	6 mo.	100/–	yes	yes	18yrs.
Pennsylvania	no	0.10	0.02	yes[h]	secondary	front[i]	6 mo.	50/–	yes	yes	17yrs., 6mo.
Rhode Island	no	0.08	0.02	yes[h]	secondary	all	6 mo.	none	no	yes	17yrs., 6mo.
South Carolina	1998	0.10	0.02	yes	secondary	front[q]	180 days	40/10	yes	yes	17yrs.
South Dakota	no	0.08	0.02	no	secondary	front	6 mo.	none	no	yes	16yrs.
Tennessee	no	0.08	0.02	yes	secondary	front[i]	180 days	50/10	yes	yes	18yrs.
Texas	1995	0.08	0.00	yes[h]	standard	front[i]	6 mo.	none	yes	yes	18yrs.
Utah	1983	0.08	0.00	yes	secondary[q]	all	none	30/10	yes	yes	17yrs.
Vermont	1969[o]	0.08	0.02	no	secondary	all	12 mo.	40/10	yes	no	16yrs., 6 mo.
Virginia	1995	0.08	0.02	yes	secondary	front[i]	9 mo.	40/10	yes	yes	18yrs.
Washington	1998	0.08	0.02	yes[h]	standard	all	6 mo.	50/10	yes	yes	18yrs.
West Virginia	1981	0.10	0.02	yes	secondary	front[i]	6 mo.	30/–[k]	yes	yes	17yrs.
Wisconsin	1988	0.10[r]	0.00	yes[h]	secondary	front[p]	12 mo.	30/10	yes	yes	18yrs.
Wyoming	1973	0.08	0.02	no	secondary	all	10 days	none	no	no	16yrs.

Source: Offices of State Governor's Highway Safety Representatives (survey of state laws as of April 2003).

[a] Year original law became effective, not when grandfather clauses expired.
[b] Blood alcohol concentration that constitutes the threshold of legal intoxication.
[c] Blood alcohol concentration that constitutes "zero tolerance" threshold for minors (<21 years of age unless otherwise noted).
[d] Instruments designed to prevent drivers from starting their cars when breath alcohol content is at or above a set point.
[e] Minimum instructional periods often include time spent in driver's education classes.
[f] Figures shown as follows: Total hours/Nighttime hours. For example, 25/5 means 25 hours of supervised driving, 5 of which must be at night.
[g] Minimum age to obtain unrestricted license provided driver is crash and violation free. Alcohol restrictions still apply at least until 21.
[h] Primarily for repeat offenders (CA, CO, DE, FL, GA, IL, KY, ME, MI, MS, MO, NV, NJ, NY, NC, ND, PA, RI, TX, WA, WI).

[i] Required for certain ages at all seating positions.
[j] No minimum amount of supervised driving but with level 1 permit driving has to be supervised at all times for the first 6 months.
[k] DC: 40 hours of supervised driving during learner's stage; 10 hours at night during intermediate stage. WV: none if driver's education course completed.
[l] Standard enforcement law in effect for ages under 18 only.
[m] BAC of 0.07 is prima facia evidence of DUI (MD). BAC of 0.05–0.08 constitutes driving while ability impaired (NY).
[n] During permit period only.
[o] Revocation by judicial action (NY) or Department of Motor Vehicles (VT).
[p] Belt use required in rear seat if lap/shoulder belt is available.
[q] Secondary for 19 and older, standard for under 19.
[r] 0.08 after second DUI conviction.

Motor-vehicle crashes are the leading cause of death and the second leading cause of serious injuries among teenagers 15–19 years old. The combination of immaturity, inexperience, and risk-taking behavior produces high crash risks for teenage drivers. Graduated driver licensing (GDL) addresses these factors by allowing beginners to get their initial driving experience under lower-risk conditions.

GDL is a three-phase licensing system consisting of a learner's permit, a provisional license, and a full license. The essential features of GDL are that a learner's permit allows driving only while supervised by a fully licensed person, a provisional license allows unsupervised driving with certain restrictions, and both the learner's permit and the provisional license must be held for a specified minimum period of time. Successful completion of the provisional license phase results in full licensure.

The following facts about teenage drivers and GDL were taken from 13 papers, published in the *Journal of Safety Research* (Vol. 34, No. 1, January 2003), that summarized current GDL research. GDL is effective in helping beginning teenage drivers gain driving knowledge and experience while reducing their risks of crashes and injuries.

Risks
Compared to older drivers, teenagers are less able to assess driving hazards and think that their crash risk is lower. Without GDL, teenage driver crash risk is greatest in the first few months after full licensure. The crash rate is highest in the first month after licensure, drops quickly over the next few months of licensure, and then drops more slowly.

Late-night driving increases the risk of fatal crashes per mile of travel for teenage drivers. The hours of 9 p.m. to midnight have both high fatal crash risk and high miles of teenage driving.

Passengers, especially teenage passengers, increase crash rates substantially for 16- to 17-year-old drivers, and the risk increases as the number of passengers increases.

Effectiveness
Many GDL programs in the United States and abroad have been evaluated and all evaluations show positive results — crash reductions of 4% to 60%. Because of the differences in GDL programs and the evaluation methods in various studies, it is not possible to combine results into a single numerical measure of GDL effectiveness.

The learner's permit phase
Under GDL, the learner's permit must be held for a specified minimum time to allow the beginning driver to acquire on-the-road experience. Some GDL jurisdictions also require a minimum amount of supervised driving during the learner's permit phase, typically 20–50 hours of which part must be at night. Crash risk is low for teenage drivers with a learner's permit. Crashes typically occur when drivers violate the requirements of their permit and drive unsupervised.

The provisional license phase
Under GDL, teenage drivers must successfully complete their learner's permit requirements, reach the minimum age required in their jurisdiction, and pass a road test to receive a provisional license. This license allows unsupervised driving under certain conditions. Provisional licenses typically prohibit unsupervised driving at night, may limit the number or type of passengers, and may have other restrictions.

Research has established conclusive evidence that nighttime driving restrictions reduce crashes. Passenger restrictions may have contributed to the overall GDL effects, but research to date cannot separate the effects of passenger restrictions from other GDL requirements.

The roles of teens and parents
With or without GDL, most parents are involved in managing their teenage drivers by teaching, supervising, and imposing restrictions. GDL can support parents in these activities. Parents also are in the best position to enforce GDL requirements.

Young drivers generally support GDL programs and restrictions, and report that they generally comply. Parents strongly support GDL, which establishes norms for and supports many restrictions on their teenage drivers that parents themselves impose. Parents are critical to enforcing compliance with GDL provisions.

ALCOHOL

According to studies conducted by the National Highway Traffic Safety Administration (NHTSA), about 41% of all traffic fatalities in 2001 involved an intoxicated or alcohol-impaired driver or nonmotorist. In 2001, 35% of all traffic fatalities occurred in crashes where at least one driver or nonoccupant was intoxicated (blood alcohol concentration [BAC] of 0.08 or greater). Of the 14,933 people killed in such crashes, 67% were themselves intoxicated. The other 33% were passengers, nonintoxicated drivers, or nonintoxicated nonoccupants. The following data summarize the extent of alcohol involvement in motor-vehicle crashes:

• Traffic fatalities in alcohol-related crashes rose by 0.4% from 2000 to 2001 and declined by 13% from 1991 to 2001. (See corresponding chart.) In 1991, alcohol-related fatalities accounted for 49% of all traffic deaths.

• According to NHTSA, alcohol was involved in 41% of fatal crashes and 7% of all crashes, both fatal and nonfatal, in 2001.

• Approximately 1.5 million drivers were arrested in 2000 for driving under the influence of alcohol or narcotics.

• There were 17,448 alcohol-related traffic fatalities in 2001, an average of one alcohol-related fatality every 30 minutes. An average of one person every 2 minutes is injured in a crash where alcohol is present.

• In 2001, alcohol was present in 32% of all fatal crashes on weekdays, compared to 54% on weekends. The rate of alcohol involvement in fatal crashes during the day is 19%, compared to 63% at night.

PERCENT OF TOTAL TRAFFIC FATALITIES WITH ALCOHOL PRESENT, BY STATE, 2001

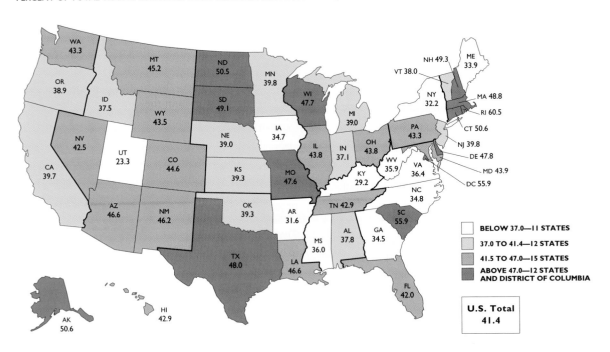

ALCOHOL (CONT.)

- From 1991 to 2001, intoxication rates decreased for drivers of all age groups. The greatest decrease was for 25-to-34-year-old drivers (22%). NHTSA estimates that 20,970 lives have been saved by 21-year-old minimum drinking age laws since 1975. All states and the District of Columbia now have such laws.

- Safety belts were used by about 23% of fatally injured intoxicated drivers, compared to 33% of fatally injured alcohol-impaired drivers and 53% of fatally injured sober drivers.

- The driver, pedestrian, or both were intoxicated in 41% of all fatal pedestrian crashes in 2001. In these crashes, the intoxication rate for pedestrians was more than double the rate for drivers.

- The cost of alcohol-related motor-vehicle crashes is estimated by the National Safety Council at $34.1 billion in 2002.

Source: National Center for Statistics and Analysis. (2002). Traffic Safety Facts 2001 — Alcohol. Washington, DC: National Highway Traffic Safety Administration.

PERCENT OF ALL TRAFFIC FATALITIES THAT OCCURRED IN ALCOHOL-RELATED CRASHES, 1991–2001

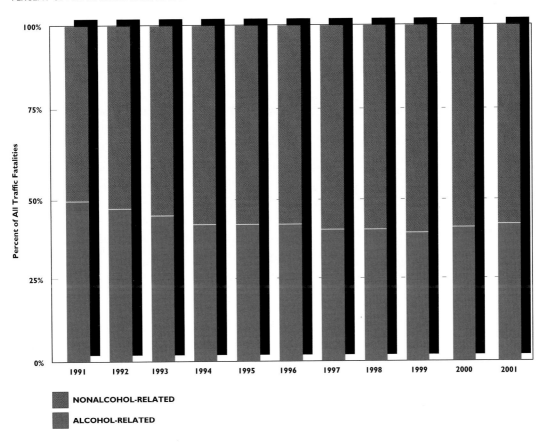

Safety Belts

- When used, lap/shoulder safety belts reduce the risk of fatal injury to front seat passenger car occupants by 45% and reduce the risk of moderate-to-critical injury by 50%.

- For light truck occupants, safety belts reduce the risk of fatal injury by 60% and moderate-to-critical injury by 65%.

- Forty-nine states and the District of Columbia have mandatory belt use laws in effect, the only exception being New Hampshire. Thirty-two of the states with belt use laws in effect in 2001 specified secondary enforcement (i.e., police officers are permitted to write a citation only after a vehicle is stopped for some other traffic infraction). Seventeen states and the District of Columbia had laws that allowed primary enforcement, enabling officers to stop vehicles and write citations whenever they observe violations of the belt law.

- Safety belts saved an estimated 12,144 lives in 2001 among passenger vehicle occupants over 4 years old. An *additional* 9,167 lives could have been saved in 2001 if all passenger vehicle occupants over age 4 wore safety belts. From 1975 through 2000, an estimated 147,246 lives were saved by safety belts.

- Safety belts provide the greatest protection against occupant ejection. Among crashes in which a fatality occurred in 2001, only 1% of restrained passenger car occupants were ejected, compared to 24% of unrestrained occupants.

- The results of a 1995 study by the National Highway Traffic Safety Administration suggest that belt use among fatally injured occupants was at least 15% higher in states with primary enforcement laws.

Air Bags

- Air bags, combined with lap/shoulder belts, offer the best available protection for passenger vehicle occupants. The overall fatality-reducing effectiveness for air bags is estimated at 12% over and above the benefits from using safety belts alone.

- Lap/shoulder belts should always be used, even in a vehicle with an air bag. Air bags are a supplemental form of protection and are not designed to deploy in crashes that are not severe.

- Children in rear-facing child seats should not be placed in the front seat of vehicles equipped with passenger-side air bags. The impact of the deploying air bag could result in injury to the child.

- An estimated 1,816 lives were saved by air bags in 2001, and a total of 8,369 lives were saved from 1987 through 2001.

- Beginning September 1997, all new passenger cars were required to have driver and passenger side air bags. In 1998, the same requirement went into effect for light trucks.

Child Restraints

- Child restraints saved an estimated 269 lives in 2001 among children under the age of 5. Of the 269 lives saved, 235 were attributed to the use of child safety seats, while 34 lives were spared with the use of adult belts.

- At 100% child safety seat use for children under the age of 5, an estimated additional 138 lives could have been saved in 2001.

- All states and the District of Columbia have had child restraint use laws in effect since 1985.

- Research has shown that child safety seats reduce fatal injury in passenger cars by 71% for infants (less than 1 year old), and by 54% for toddlers (1–4 years old). For infants and toddlers in light trucks, the corresponding reductions are 58% and 59%, respectively.

- In 2001, there were 497 occupant fatalities among children less than 5 years of age. Of these, an estimated 49% were totally unrestrained.

- An estimated 5,085 lives have been saved by child restraints from 1975 through 2001.

ESTIMATED NUMBER OF LIVES SAVED BY RESTRAINT SYSTEMS, 1975–2001

Restraint Type	1975–93	1994	1995	1996	1997	1998	1999	2000	2001
Seat Belts	60,838	9,206	9,790	10,414	10,750	11,018	11,197	11,889	12,144
Air Bags	389	276	470	686	842	1,043	1,263	1,584	1,816
Child Restraints	2,630	308	279	365	312	299	307	316	269

Motorcycle Helmets

- Motorcycle helmets are estimated to be 29% effective in preventing fatal injuries to motorcyclists.

- Helmets saved the lives of 674 motorcyclists in 2001. An additional 444 lives could have been saved if all motorcyclists had worn helmets.

- Reported helmet use rates for fatally injured motorcyclists in 2001 were 53% for operators and 41% for passengers, compared with 54% and 47%, respectively, in 2000.

- In 2001, 20 states, the District of Columbia, and Puerto Rico required helmet use by all motorcycle operators and passengers. In another 27 states, only persons under 18 were required to wear helmets. Three states had no laws requiring helmet use.

Safety Belt and Helmet Use

- According to the latest observational survey by the National Highway Traffic Safety Administration, the national safety belt use rate was 75% in 2002, the highest rate yet observed and a continuation of the relatively steady pattern of increased use since belt use was first measured by a national survey at 58% in 1994.

- States with primary enforcement of belt laws reached a milestone of 80% belt use in 2002, while use in states with secondary enforcement was significantly lower at 69%.

- The Northeast experienced a 7 percentage point increase in belt use from 2001 to 2002 to reach 69%, eliminating all statistically significant regional differences except for that between the Northeast and the West, which had the highest use rate of 79%.

- Belt use increased a significant 3 percentage points among vans and SUVs from 2001 to 2002 to reach 78%. The use rates for these vehicles continue to be similar to those of passenger cars (77%), while the use rate for pickups continues to lag significantly behind at 64%.

- Helmet use declined by 13 percentage points over 2 years, from 71% in 2000 to 58% in 2002. This drop is statistically significant and corresponds to a 45% increase in nonuse.

Source: National Center for Statistics and Analysis. (2002). Traffic Safety Facts 2001—Occupant Protection; Traffic Safety Facts 2001—Motorcycles; Safety Belt and Helmet Use in 2002—Overall Results (DOT HS 809 500, September). Washington, DC: National Highway Traffic Safety Administration.

BELT USE BY ENFORCEMENT LAW AND VEHICLE TYPE

| | Belt Use | | | | | | |
| | Use in June 2002 | | Use in June 2001 | | 2001–2002 Change | | |
Category	Estimate (%)	Std. Error (%)	Estimate (%)	Std. Error (%)	Estimate (%)	Std. Error (%)	Conversion Rate[a] (%)
Primary	**80**	**1.7**	**78**	**1.9**	**2**	**1.2**	**9**
Passenger Cars	82	1.7	81	1.7	1	1.1	5
Vans and SUVs	83	1.3	79	1.8	4[b]	1.3	19
Pickup Trucks	71	2.7	70	3.5	1	2.8	3
Secondary	**69**	**1.1**	**67**	**2.3**	**2**	**1.9**	**6**
Passenger Cars	71	1.1	71	1.9	0	1.4	0
Vans and SUVs	73	1.4	70	2.2	3	2.3	10
Pickup Trucks	55	2.0	50	3.6	5	3.8	10

[a] The rate of decrease of belt nonuse from one year to the next.
[b] Significant at the 95% confidence level.

DEATHS AND DEATH RATES BY DAY AND NIGHT

About 54% of all motor-vehicle deaths in 2002 occurred during the day, while the remainder occurred at night. Death rates based on mileage, however, were over 2.5 times higher at night than during the day, with vehicle miles traveled by night representing only 25% of the total.

Source: State traffic authorities and the Federal Highway Administration.

DEATH RATES BY DAY AND NIGHT, 2002

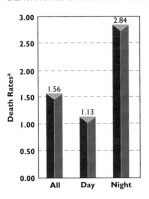

[a]Per 100,000,000 vehicle miles.

DEATHS AND MILEAGE DEATH RATES BY MONTH

Motor-vehicle deaths in 2002 were at their lowest level in February and increased to their highest level in July. In 2002, the highest monthly mileage death rate of 1.66 deaths per 100,000,000 vehicle miles occurred in July, September, and December. The overall rate for the year was 1.56.

Source: Deaths — National Safety Council estimates. Mileage — Federal Highway Administration, Traffic Volume Trends.

MOTOR-VEHICLE DEATHS AND MILEAGE DEATH RATES BY MONTH, 2002

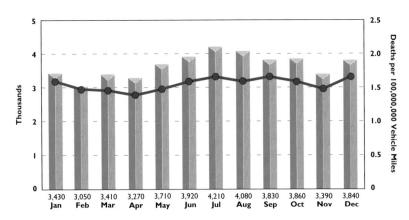

MOTOR-VEHICLE DEATHS (LEFT SCALE)

MILEAGE DEATH RATE (RIGHT SCALE)

Jan	Feb	Mar	Apr	May	Jun	Jul	Aug	Sep	Oct	Nov	Dec
3,430	3,050	3,410	3,270	3,710	3,920	4,210	4,080	3,830	3,860	3,390	3,840

MOTOR-VEHICLE ACCIDENTS
BY TIME OF DAY AND DAY OF WEEK

More fatal accidents occurred on Saturday than any other day of the week in 2002, according to reports from state traffic authorities. Over 19% of fatal accidents occurred on Saturday, compared to about 16% on Fridays and over 15% on Sundays. For all accidents, Friday had the highest percentage with about 17%.

Patterns by hour of day for fatal accidents show peaks during afternoon rush hour for weekdays and, especially, late night for weekends. For all accidents, peaks occur during both morning and afternoon rush hour.

PERCENT OF WEEKLY ACCIDENTS BY HOUR OF DAY AND DAY OF WEEK, UNITED STATES, 2002

Time of Day	Fatal Accidents								All Accidents							
	Total	Mon.	Tues.	Wed.	Thurs.	Fri.	Sat.	Sun.	Total	Mon.	Tues.	Wed.	Thurs.	Fri.	Sat.	Sun.
All Hours	100.0%	11.9%	12.2%	13.6%	11.9%	15.8%	19.3%	15.3%	100.0%	14.4%	14.7%	14.8%	14.9%	17.1%	13.6%	10.5%
Midnight–3:59 A.M.	16.7%	1.2%	1.2%	1.8%	1.7%	2.0%	4.5%	4.3%	6.5%	0.6%	0.6%	0.6%	0.7%	0.8%	1.5%	1.6%
4:00–7:59 A.M.	12.4%	2.0%	1.5%	1.7%	1.6%	1.8%	2.5%	1.4%	10.9%	1.8%	1.9%	1.9%	1.9%	1.7%	1.0%	0.8%
8:00–11:59 A.M.	12.6%	1.9%	1.8%	1.8%	1.6%	2.0%	2.0%	1.5%	16.9%	2.7%	2.7%	2.6%	2.6%	2.7%	2.3%	1.4%
Noon–3:59 P.M.	18.4%	2.5%	2.7%	2.6%	2.2%	3.0%	2.7%	2.6%	25.1%	3.9%	3.7%	3.7%	3.7%	4.5%	3.3%	2.5%
4:00–7:59 P.M.	22.2%	2.5%	2.9%	3.5%	2.6%	3.2%	4.0%	3.5%	27.0%	3.8%	4.1%	4.2%	4.2%	4.9%	3.2%	2.5%
8:00–11:59 P.M.	17.7%	1.8%	2.0%	2.4%	2.1%	3.8%	3.7%	2.0%	13.5%	1.5%	1.7%	1.8%	1.9%	2.5%	2.4%	1.7%

Source: Based on reports from 8 state traffic authorities.
Note: Column and row totals may not equal sums of parts due to rounding.

PERCENT OF ACCIDENTS BY TIME OF DAY AND DAY OF WEEK, 2002

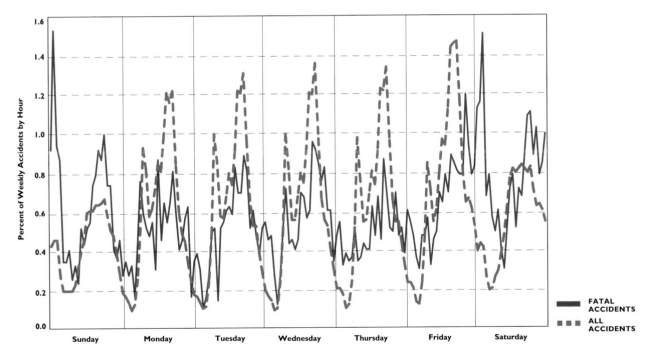

TYPE OF MOTOR VEHICLE

The types of vehicles listed in the table below are classified by body style, not by vehicle use. The light truck category includes both commercial and noncommercial trucks under 10,000 pounds gross vehicle weight. It also includes minivans and sport-utility vehicles. The medium/heavy truck category includes truck tractors with or without semi-trailers.

Passenger Cars

In 2002, passenger cars comprised about 58% of the registered vehicles and were involved in more than their share of motor-vehicle accidents (59.1%). Approximately 55% of all motor-vehicle occupant fatalities are passenger car occupants. (see corresponding chart.)

Trucks

Light trucks represent about 35% of all motor-vehicle registrations and an equivalent percentage of vehicles involved in fatal accidents. Medium and heavy trucks account for nearly 4% of registered vehicles and over 8% of vehicles involved in fatal accidents. Medium and heavy truck occupants as well as light truck occupants are slightly under-represented in motor-vehicle occupant fatalities compared to their proportion of registrations. Medium and heavy truck occupants account for only about 2% of all motor-vehicle occupant fatalities, and light truck occupants account for 31%.

There were 861,000 light truck occupants and 29,000 large truck occupants injured in 2001, according to the National Highway Traffic Safety Administration.

Motorcycles

The number of registered motorcycles in the United States totaled about 4,903,000 in 2002, compared to approximately 4,081,000 a decade earlier. Although motorcycles accounted for about 2% of the total 242,500,000 vehicle registrations in 2002, they were over represented in the distribution of fatalities by type of vehicle. Of the 37,500 occupant deaths in motor-vehicle accidents in 2002, about 3,200 (9%) were motorcycle riders. Approximately 60,000 riders and passengers were injured in 2001 according to the National Highway Traffic Safety Administration.

Motorcycles traveled an estimated 8.7 billion miles in 2002. The 2002 mileage death rate for motorcycle riders is estimated to be about 37 occupant deaths per 100,000,000 miles of motorcycle travel, about 31 times the mileage death rate for occupants of other types of vehicles (passenger autos, trucks, buses, etc.).

TYPES OF MOTOR VEHICLES INVOLVED IN ACCIDENTS, 2002

Type of Vehicle	In Fatal Accidents		In All Accidents		Percent of Total Vehicle Registrations[a]	No. of Occupant Fatalities
	Number	Percent	Number	Percent		
All Types	52,700	100.0%	30,700,000	100.0%	100.0%	37,500[b]
Passenger cars	24,800	47.1	18,140,000	59.1	58.5	20,500
Trucks	23,100	43.8	12,180,000	39.7	39.1	12,460
Light trucks	18,600	35.3	11,170,000	36.4	35.2	11,700
Medium/heavy trucks	4,500	8.5	1,010,000	3.3	3.9	760
Farm tractor, equipment	100	0.2	9,000	(c)	(d)	70
Buses, commercial	200	0.4	68,000	0.2	0.1	40
Buses, school	100	0.2	65,000	0.2	0.3	30
Motorcycles	3,200	6.1	190,000	0.6	} 2.1	3,200
Motor scooters, motor bikes	100	0.2	6,000	(c)		100
Other	1,100	2.0	42,000	0.1	(d)	1,100

Source: Based on reports from 9 state traffic authorities. Vehicle registrations based on data from Federal Highway Administration. Estimating procedures were changed for the 1998 edition and are not comparable to estimates in previous editions.
[a]Percentage figures are based on numbers of vehicles and do not reflect miles traveled or place of travel, both of which affect accident experience. Percents may not add due to rounding.
[b]In addition to these occupant fatalities, there were 5,700 pedestrian, 700 pedalcyclist, and 100 other deaths.
[c]Less than 0.05%.
[d]Data not available.

REGISTRATIONS, INVOLVEMENTS, AND OCCUPANT FATALITIES BY TYPE OF VEHICLE, 2002

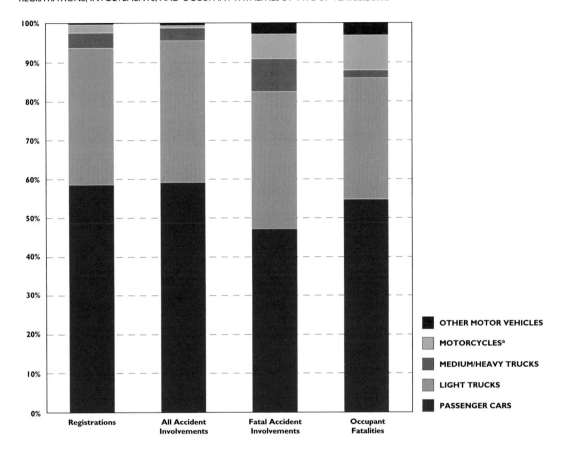

aIncludes motor scooters and motorbikes.

SCHOOL BUS TRANSPORTATION, 2001

School bus–related crashes killed 141 persons and injured an estimated 13,000 persons nationwide in 2001, according to data from the National Highway Traffic Safety Administration's Fatality Analysis Reporting System (FARS) and General Estimates System (GES).

A school bus–related crash is defined by NHTSA to be any crash in which a vehicle, regardless of body design, used as a school bus is directly or indirectly involved, such as a crash involving school children alighting from a vehicle.

Over the period from 1996–2001, about 72% of the deaths in fatal school bus–related crashes were occupants of vehicles other than the school bus and 16% were pedestrians. About 5% were school bus passengers and 4% were school bus drivers.

Of the pedestrians killed in school bus–related crashes over this period, approximately 77% were struck by the school bus.

Out of the people injured in school bus–related crashes from 1996 through 2001, about 44% were school bus passengers, 9% were school bus drivers, and another 43% were occupants of other vehicles. The remainder were pedestrians, pedalcyclists, and other or unknown type persons.

Characteristics of school bus transportation.
School Bus Fleet (vol. 48, no. 1) found that in the 2000–2001 school year, 47 states reported about 22.6 million public school pupils were transported at public expense and 31 states reported another 1.0 million private school pupils were transported at public expense. This compares to estimates from the U.S. Department of Education of enrollments in fall 2000 in grades K–12 of about 47.2 million public school pupils and 5.9 million private school pupils nationwide. About 457,000 school buses were reported in use in 50 states, and the buses in 41 states traveled about 4.1 billion route miles.

FATALITIES IN SCHOOL BUS–RELATED CRASHES, UNITED STATES, 1992–2001

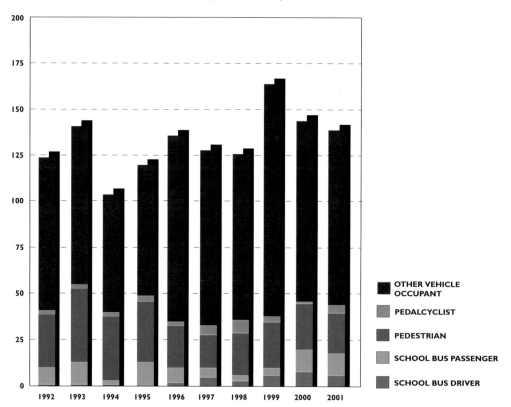

DEATHS AND INJURIES IN SCHOOL BUS–RELATED CRASHES, UNITED STATES, 1996–2001

	1996	1997	1998	1999	2000	2001
Deaths						
Total	**136**	**128**	**126**	**164**	**144**	**141**
School bus driver	2	5	3	6	8	6
School bus passenger	8	5	3	4	12	12
Pedestrian	23	18	23	25	25	22
Pedalcyclist	2	5	7	3	1	4
Occupant of other vehicle	101	95	90	126	98	95
Other or Unknown	0	0	0	0	0	2
Injuries						
Total	**15,000**	**19,000**	**17,000**	**18,000**	**20,000**	**13,000**
School bus driver	1,000	2,000	2,000	1,000	2,000	1,000
School bus passenger	7,000	10,000	6,000	8,000	8,000	6,000
Pedestrian	(a)	(a)	(a)	(a)	1,000	(a)
Pedalcyclist	(a)	(a)	(a)	(a)	(a)	(a)
Occupant of other vehicle	6,000	7,000	9,000	8,000	9,000	5,000
Other or Unknown	(a)	(a)	(a)	(a)	(a)	(a)

Source: National Highway Traffic Safety Administration. Traffic Safety Facts, *1996–2001 editions. Washington, DC: Author.*
ª Less than 500.

PEDESTRIAN DEATHS IN SCHOOL BUS–RELATED CRASHES, UNITED STATES, 1996–2001

	Age Group				
Year	All Ages	Under 5	5–9	10–15	16 and older
1996	23	1	11	3	8
Struck by bus	*16*	*0*	*7*	*1*	*8*
1997	18	0	8	3	7
Struck by bus	*16*	*0*	*6*	*3*	*7*
1998	23	3	9	1	10
Struck by bus	*20*	*3*	*6*	*1*	*10*
1999	25	0	13	4	8
Struck by bus	*19*	*0*	*10*	*2*	*7*
2000	25	5	10	2	8
Struck by bus	*16*	*2*	*8*	*0*	*6*
2001	22	3	6	4	9
Struck by bus	*18*	*3*	*5*	*1*	*9*

Source: National Highway Traffic Safety Administration. Traffic Safety Facts, *1996–2001 editions. Washington, DC: Author.*

AGE OF DRIVER

The table below shows the total number of licensed drivers and drivers involved in accidents by selected ages and age groups. The figures in the last two columns indicate the frequency of accident involvement on the basis of the number of drivers in each age group. The fatal accident involvement rates per 100,000 drivers in each age group ranged from a low of 18 for drivers 65 to 74 years of age to a high of 94 for drivers aged 16. The all accident involvement rates per 100 drivers in each age group ranged from 9 for drivers in the 65-to-74 and 75-and-over age groups to 54 for drivers aged 16.

On the basis of miles driven by each age group, however, involvement rates (not shown in the table) are highest for young and old drivers. For drivers aged 16 to 19, the fatal involvement rate per 100 million vehicle miles traveled was 9.2 in 1990, about three times the overall rate for all drivers in passenger vehicles, 3.0. The rate for drivers aged 75 and over was 11.5, the highest of all age groups. The same basic *U*-shaped curve is found for injury accident involvement rates.[a]

[a] Massie, D., Campbell, K., & Williams, A. (1995). Traffic accident involvement rates by driver age and gender. Accident Analysis and Prevention, 27 (1), 73–87.

AGE OF DRIVER — TOTAL NUMBER AND NUMBER IN ACCIDENTS, 2002

| Age Group | Licensed Drivers | | Drivers in Accidents | | | | | |
| | | | Fatal | | All | | Per No. of Drivers | |
	Number	Percent	Number	Percent	Number	Percent	Fatal[a]	All[b]
Total	193,300,000	100.0%	52,700	100.0%	30,700,000	100.0%	27	16
Under 16	48,000	(c)	400	0.8	120,000	0.4	(d)	(d)
16	1,382,000	0.7	1,300	2.5	740,000	2.4	94	54
17	2,228,000	1.2	1,300	2.5	910,000	3.0	58	41
18	2,674,000	1.4	1,600	3.0	940,000	3.1	60	35
19	3,176,000	1.6	1,500	2.8	910,000	3.0	47	29
19 and under	9,508,000	4.9	6,100	11.6	3,620,000	11.8	64	38
20	3,305,000	1.7	1,700	3.2	840,000	2.7	51	25
21	3,421,000	1.8	1,000	1.9	580,000	1.9	29	17
22	3,401,000	1.8	1,100	2.1	540,000	1.8	32	16
23	3,284,000	1.7	1,000	1.9	490,000	1.6	30	15
24	3,357,000	1.7	1,100	2.1	440,000	1.4	33	13
20–24	16,768,000	8.7	5,900	11.2	2,890,000	9.4	35	17
25–34	33,734,000	17.5	10,300	19.5	7,020,000	22.9	31	21
35–44	41,040,000	21.2	10,300	19.5	6,670,000	21.7	25	16
45–54	38,711,000	20.0	8,300	15.7	5,130,000	16.7	21	13
55–64	25,609,000	13.2	5,300	10.1	2,760,000	9.0	21	11
65–74	15,812,000	8.2	2,800	5.3	1,490,000	4.9	18	9
75 and over	12,118,000	6.3	3,700	7.0	1,120,000	3.6	31	9

Source: National Safety Council estimates. Drivers in accidents based on reports from 10 state traffic authorities. Total licensed drivers from the Federal Highway Administration; age distribution by National Safety Council.
Note: Percents may not add to total due to rounding.
[a] Drivers in fatal accidents per 100,000 licensed drivers in each age group.
[b] Drivers in all accidents per 100 licensed drivers in each age group.
[c] Less than 0.05.
[d] Rates for drivers under age 16 are substantially overstated due to the high proportion of unlicensed drivers involved.

SEX OF DRIVER

Of the estimated 193,300,000 licensed drivers in 2002, about 96,800,000 (50.1%) were males and 96,500,000 (49.9%) were females. Males account for about 62% of the miles driven each year, according to the latest estimates, and females for 38%. At least part of the difference in involvement rates, cited below, may be due to differences in the time, place, and circumstances of driving.

For fatal accidents, males have higher involvement rates than females. About 38,900 male drivers and 13,800 female drivers were involved in fatal accidents in 2002. The involvement rate per one billion miles driven was 22 for males and 13 for females. For all accidents, females have higher involvement rates than males. About 18,600,000 male drivers and 12,100,000 female drivers were involved in all accidents in 2002. Their involvement rates per 10 million miles driven were 106 and 113, respectively.

IMPROPER DRIVING

In most motor-vehicle accidents, factors are present relating to the driver, the vehicle, and the road, and it is the interaction of these factors that often sets up the series of events that results in an accident. The table below relates only to the driver, and shows the principal kinds of improper driving in accidents in 2002 as reported by police.

Exceeding the posted speed limit or driving at an unsafe speed was the most common error in fatal accidents. Right-of-way violations predominated in the injury and all accidents categories.

While some drivers were under the influence of alcohol or other drugs, this represents the driver's physical condition — not a driving error. See page 94 for a discussion of alcohol involvement in traffic accidents.

Correcting the improper practices listed below could reduce the number of accidents. This does not mean, however, that road and vehicle conditions can be disregarded.

IMPROPER DRIVING REPORTED IN ACCIDENTS, 2002

Kind of Improper Driving	Fatal Accidents	Injury Accidents	All Accidents
Total	100.0%	100.0%	100.0%
Improper driving	**59.5**	**54.7**	**50.3**
Speed too fast or unsafe	21.9	12.6	10.1
Right of way	17.4	18.9	16.4
Failed to yield	*10.1*	*14.3*	*11.4*
Disregarded signal	*4.0*	*3.3*	*3.4*
Passed stop sign	*3.3*	*1.3*	*1.6*
Drove left of center	5.7	0.9	0.7
Made improper turn	0.5	1.2	1.7
Improper overtaking	1.0	0.5	0.8
Followed too closely	0.4	2.8	3.8
Other improper driving	12.5	17.9	16.8
No improper driving stated	**40.5**	**45.3**	**49.7**

Source: Based on reports from 8 state traffic authorities. Percents may not add to totals due to rounding.

PEDESTRIANS

In 2002, there were an estimated 5,700 pedestrian deaths and 65,000 injuries in motor-vehicle accidents. About 45% of these deaths and injuries occur when pedestrians cross or enter streets. Walking in the roadway accounted for about 10% of pedestrian deaths and injuries, with more cases occurring while walking with traffic than against traffic.

The distribution of pedestrian deaths and injuries by action varies for persons of different ages. While crossing or entering at or between intersections was the leading type for each age group, this type varied from a low of 41.6% of the total for those aged 20 to 24 years, to a high of 53.6% for those aged 65 and over.

DEATHS AND INJURIES OF PEDESTRIANS BY AGE AND ACTION, 2002

Actions		Age of Persons Killed or Injured							
	Total[a]	0–4	5–9	10–14	15–19	20–24	25–44	45–64	65 & Over
All Actions	*100.0%*	*3.2%*	*6.8%*	*9.8%*	*11.1%*	*9.3%*	*27.3%*	*18.8%*	*9.4%*
Totals	**100.0%**	**100.0%**	**100.0%**	**100.0%**	**100.0%**	**100.0%**	**100.0%**	**100.0%**	**100.0%**
Crossing or entering at or between intersections	44.8%	47.7%	41.8%	48.0%	43.3%	41.6%	42.5%	49.8%	53.6%
Walking in the roadway	9.8%	6.5%	5.8%	11.0%	11.2%	11.1%	11.0%	10.4%	7.5%
with traffic	5.8%	5.2%	3.0%	4.9%	8.6%	6.0%	6.7%	6.2%	3.1%
against traffic	3.8%	1.3%	2.7%	5.9%	2.6%	4.7%	4.0%	4.0%	4.4%
Standing (or playing) in roadway	6.8%	9.8%	3.7%	3.4%	7.3%	9.4%	9.4%	7.1%	2.9%
Pushing/working on a vehicle in the roadway	0.3%	0.0%	0.0%	0.4%	0.0%	0.9%	0.3%	0.6%	0.2%
Other working in the roadway	1.2%	0.0%	0.0%	0.0%	0.4%	2.2%	2.4%	1.5%	0.4%
Not in the roadway	1.0%	0.0%	0.9%	0.2%	1.3%	1.3%	1.1%	1.1%	0.7%
Other	26.5%	27.5%	40.9%	29.3%	28.9%	25.8%	26.6%	22.3%	25.3%
Not stated	9.5%	8.5%	7.0%	7.6%	7.6%	7.6%	6.8%	7.2%	9.5%

Source: Based on reports from 13 state traffic authorities.
[a]Total includes "Age Unknown."

PEDESTRIAN DEATHS AND DEATH RATES BY SEX AND AGE GROUP, UNITED STATES, 2000

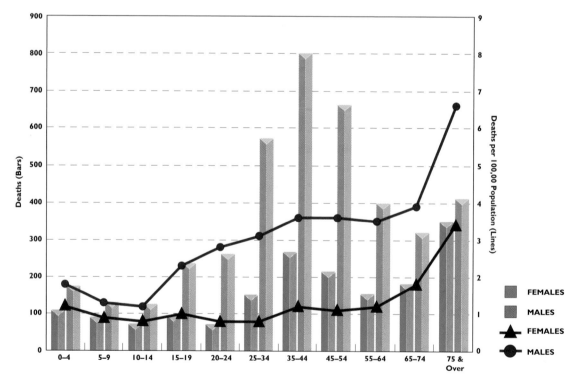

Source: National Safety Council based on National Center for Health Statistics data.

PEDALCYCLISTS

The estimated number of deaths from pedalcycle–motor-vehicle collisions increased from about 750 in 1940 to 1,200 in 1980, then declined to about 700 in 2002. Nonfatal disabling injuries were estimated to number 50,000 in 2002.

In 2000, 589 pedalcyclists died in motor-vehicle crashes and 151 in other accidents according to National Center for Health Statistics mortality data. Males accounted for more than 88% of all pedalcycle deaths, seven times the female fatalities.

Emergency-room–treated injuries associated with bicycles and bicycle accessories were estimated to total

546,236 in 2001, according to the U.S. Consumer Product Safety Commission (see also page 126). The CPSC reported that bike helmet use was 50% in 1998. About 38% of adults and 69% of children under 16 reported wearing bike helmets regularly. The Bicycle Helmet Safety Institute estimates that helmets reduce the risk of all head injuries by up to 85% and reduce the risk of brain injuries by as much as 88%. In 2003, 19 states, the District of Columbia, and at least 125 localities had bicycle helmet laws, according to the Bicycle Helmet Safety Institute.

Source: National Safety Council estimates and tabulations of National Center for Health Statistics mortality data. Rodgers, G.B., & Tinsworth, D. (1999). Bike Helmets. Consumer Product Safety Review, (4), 2–4. Data from Bicycle Helmet Safety Institute retrieved 6/30/03 from www.bhsi.org.

PEDALCYCLE FATALITIES BY SEX AND AGE GROUP, UNITED STATES, 2000

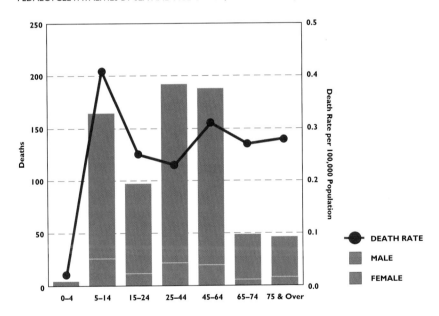

PEDALCYCLE FATALITIES BY MONTH, UNITED STATES, 2000

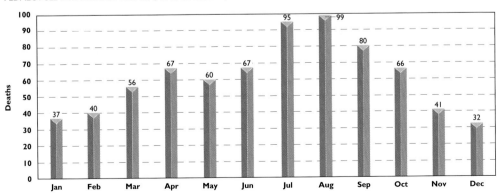

WORK ZONE DEATHS AND INJURIES

In 2001 there were 1,079 people killed and 46,174 people injured in work zone crashes (see table below). Compared to 2000, work zone fatalities and injuries decreased 1% and 8%, respectively. Of the 1,079 people killed in work zones, 886 were in construction zones, 106 were in maintenance zones, 8 were in utility zones, and 79 were in an unknown type of work zone.

Over the 10 years from 1992 through 2001, work zone deaths have ranged from 638 to 1,093 and averaged 821 per year.

Based on a National Safety Council survey in April 2003, 27 states reported having work zone speed laws and 49 states had special penalties for traffic violations in work zones, such as increased or doubled fines. Hawaii and District of Columbia were the only jurisdictions with neither.

PERSONS KILLED AND INJURED IN WORK ZONES, UNITED STATES, 2001

	Total	Vehicle Occupants	Pedestrians	Pedalcyclists	Other Nonmotorists
Killed	1,079	922	139	13	5
Injured	46,174	44,382	1,353	362	77

Source: National Safety Council tabulations of data from National Highway Traffic Safety Administration — 2001 Fatality Analysis Reporting System (FARS) and 2001 General Estimates Systems (GES).

EMERGENCY VEHICLES

CRASHES INVOLVING EMERGENCY VEHICLES, UNITED STATES, 2001

	Ambulance		Fire Truck/Car		Police Car	
	Total	Emergency Use[a]	Total	Emergency Use[a]	Total	Emergency Use[a]
Emergency vehicles in fatal crashes	25	13	18	10	117	38
Emergency vehicles in injury crashes	1,140	826	794	602	12,091	4,566
Emergency vehicles in all crashes	3,878	2,809	2,610	1,680	35,613	14,046
Emergency vehicle drivers killed	1	1	2	2	28	7
Emergency vehicle passengers killed	9	6	2	2	7	4
Other vehicle occupants killed	15	8	14	6	78	23
Nonmotorists killed	2	1	3	1	18	5
Total killed in crashes	27	16	21	11	131	39
Total injured in crashes	2,275	1,918	1,320	1,072	16,805	6,484

Source: National Safety Council tabulations of data from National Highway Traffic Safety Administration — 2001 Fatality Analysis Reporting System (FARS) and 2001 General Estimates Systems (GES).
[a]Emergency lights and/or sirens in use.

CELL PHONES

A recent study assessed the relationship between the use of cellular telephones while driving and collision risk by comparing passenger car drivers observed using cell phones to drivers observed at similar times and locations but not using cell phones at the time of observation. An observational study recorded a total of 3,869 cases that were matched with either a principal driver or registered owner. The data file was then merged with official records of the drivers' violations, police-reported collisions, and insurance claims.

Not-at-fault claims were used as a measure of exposure, while at-fault claims were used as a dependent variable of collision risk. The 84 different violation types identified were first reduced via factor analysis to three scales labeled "Alcohol," "Aggression," and "Inattention." The potential confounding variables of age, gender, number of not-at-fault claims, and the alcohol and aggression scales were controlled for in a logistic regression model, with the independent variable being the use of a cell phone while driving. The expected effects of age and gender were found, along with significant effects for not-at-fault claims, for drivers with a score of at least one on the alcohol violations scale, and for those scoring one or more on the aggression violations scale. Drivers observed using a cell phone had a risk of an at-fault crash 1.16 times greater than did drivers not using cell phones, adjusted for all other effects ($p<.04$).

The table below shows the results of the logistic regression analysis for the total sample of drivers on the dependent variable of being judged at fault for at least one crash. The column labeled "n" provides the number of observations for each predictor variable, the column labeled "RR ratio" provides the risk ratio for each of the predictor variables relative to the reference level of the variable (the level without a RR ratio), the 95% CI column gives the 95% confidence interval for the relative risk ratio, and the Chi-square and p-Value columns test the significance of the observed relative risk ratios. Note that for the regression analysis, the independent variables were reduced to categories, rather than counts.

An examination of collision configuration for cell phone users and nonusers showed that cell phone users appear to be overinvolved in rear-end collisions. The distribution of involvement in rear-end collisions versus all other types aggregated was significantly different for cell phone users and nonusers ($p<.04$).

The results of the study show that drivers who use cell phones in their vehicles have a higher risk of collision than drivers who either do not use cell phones or have lower usage while driving. In addition, driving records revealed that cell phone users had higher counts of violations over the previous four years, including speeding, alcohol, failure to use seat belts, nonmoving offenses, and aggressive violations. This finding led the authors to suggest that the type of people who make frequent use of cell phones while driving appear to be higher risk takers and that controlling for these types of fundamental differences poses the greatest challenge to estimating the direct risk of using a cell phone.

Source: Wilson, J., Fang, M., Wiggins, S., & Cooper, P. (2003). "Collision and violation involvement of drivers who use cellular telephones." Traffic Injury Prevention, 4(1), 45–52.

PROBABILITY ESTIMATION OF HAVING AT LEAST ONE AT-FAULT CRASH CLAIM, 1997–2000

Predictor variable	n	RR[a] ratio	95% CI	Chi-square	p-Value
Age					
16–24	211	1.74	(1.28–2.39)	12.11	.0002
25–34	1,044	1.53	(1.28–1.83)	21.31	.0001
35–44	1,266	1.15	(0.96–1.36)	2.34	.13
45+	1,348				
Gender					
Male	2,840	1.27	(1.08–1.50)	8.29	.0040
Female	1,029				
Not-at-fault claims					
More than 1	578	2.03	(1.70–2.47)	52.21	.0001
1	1,057	1.36	(1.16–1.60)	14.31	.0002
0	2,234				
Alcohol violations					
Yes	203	1.66	(1.23–2.22)	11.18	.0008
No	3,666				
Aggressive violations					
Yes	199	1.84	(1.37–2.48)	16.15	.0001
No	3,670				
Use of cell phone					
Yes	1,876	1.16	(1.00–1.33)	4.13	.04
No	1,993				

[a] *Relative Risk.*

MOTOR-VEHICLE DEATHS AND RATES

MOTOR-VEHICLE DEATHS AND RATES, UNITED STATES, 1913–2002

Year	No. of Deaths	Estimated No. of Vehicles (Millions)	Estimated Vehicle Miles (Billions)	Estimated No. of Drivers (Millions)	Death Rates		
					Per 10,000 Motor Vehicles	Per 100,000,000 Vehicle Miles	Per 100,000 Population
1913	4,200	1.3	(a)	2.0	33.38	(a)	4.4
1914	4,700	1.8	(a)	3.0	26.65	(a)	4.8
1915	6,600	2.5	(a)	3.0	26.49	(a)	6.6
1916	8,200	3.6	(a)	5.0	22.66	(a)	8.1
1917	10,200	5.1	(a)	7.0	19.93	(a)	10.0
1918	10,700	6.2	(a)	9.0	17.37	(a)	10.3
1919	11,200	7.6	(a)	12.0	14.78	(a)	10.7
1920	12,500	9.2	(a)	14.0	13.53	(a)	11.7
1921	13,900	10.5	(a)	16.0	13.25	(a)	12.9
1922	15,300	12.3	(a)	19.0	12.47	(a)	13.9
1923	18,400	15.1	85	22.0	12.18	21.65	16.5
1924	19,400	17.6	104	26.0	11.02	18.65	17.1
1925	21,900	20.1	122	30.0	10.89	17.95	19.1
1926	23,400	22.2	141	33.0	10.54	16.59	20.1
1927	25,800	23.3	158	34.0	11.07	16.33	21.8
1928	28,000	24.7	173	37.0	11.34	16.18	23.4
1929	31,200	26.7	197	40.0	11.69	15.84	25.7
1930	32,900	26.7	206	40.0	12.32	15.97	26.7
1931	33,700	26.1	216	39.0	12.91	15.60	27.2
1932	29,500	24.4	200	36.0	12.09	14.75	23.6
1933	31,363	24.2	201	35.0	12.96	15.60	25.0
1934	36,101	25.3	216	37.0	14.27	16.71	28.6
1935	36,369	26.5	229	39.0	13.72	15.88	28.6
1936	38,089	28.5	252	42.0	13.36	15.11	29.7
1937	39,643	30.1	270	44.0	13.19	14.68	30.8
1938	32,582	29.8	271	44.0	10.93	12.02	25.1
1939	32,386	31.0	285	46.0	10.44	11.35	24.7
1940	34,501	32.5	302	48.0	10.63	11.42	26.1
1941	39,969	34.9	334	52.0	11.45	11.98	30.0
1942	28,309	33.0	268	49.0	8.58	10.55	21.1
1943	23,823	30.9	208	46.0	7.71	11.44	17.8
1944	24,282	30.5	213	45.0	7.97	11.42	18.3
1945	28,076	31.0	250	46.0	9.05	11.22	21.2
1946	33,411	34.4	341	50.0	9.72	9.80	23.9
1947	32,697	37.8	371	53.0	8.64	8.82	22.8
1948	32,259	41.1	398	55.0	7.85	8.11	22.1
1949	31,701	44.7	424	59.3	7.09	7.47	21.3
1950	34,763	49.2	458	62.2	7.07	7.59	23.0
1951	36,996	51.9	491	64.4	7.13	7.53	24.1
1952	37,794	53.3	514	66.8	7.10	7.36	24.3
1953	37,956	56.3	544	69.9	6.74	6.97	24.0
1954	35,586	58.6	562	72.2	6.07	6.33	22.1
1955	38,426	62.8	606	74.7	6.12	6.34	23.4
1956	39,628	65.2	631	77.9	6.07	6.28	23.7
1957	38,702	67.6	647	79.6	5.73	5.98	22.7
1958	36,981	68.8	665	81.5	5.37	5.56	21.3
1959	37,910	72.1	700	84.5	5.26	5.41	21.5
1960	38,137	74.5	719	87.4	5.12	5.31	21.2
1961	38,091	76.4	738	88.9	4.98	5.16	20.8
1962	40,804	79.7	767	92.0	5.12	5.32	22.0
1963	43,564	83.5	805	93.7	5.22	5.41	23.1
1964	47,700	87.3	847	95.6	5.46	5.63	25.0
1965	49,163	91.8	888	99.0	5.36	5.54	25.4
1966	53,041	95.9	930	101.0	5.53	5.70	27.1
1967	52,924	98.9	962	103.2	5.35	5.50	26.8
1968	54,862	103.1	1,016	105.4	5.32	5.40	27.5
1969	55,791	107.4	1,071	108.3	5.19	5.21	27.7
1970	54,633	111.2	1,120	111.5	4.92	4.88	26.8
1971	54,381	116.3	1,186	114.4	4.68	4.57	26.3
1972	56,278	122.3	1,268	118.4	4.60	4.43	26.9
1973	55,511	129.8	1,309	121.6	4.28	4.24	26.3
1974	46,402	134.9	1,290	125.6	3.44	3.59	21.8
1975	45,853	137.9	1,330	129.8	3.33	3.45	21.3
1976	47,038	143.5	1,412	133.9	3.28	3.33	21.6

See source and footnotes on page 111.

MOTOR-VEHICLE DEATHS AND RATES
(CONT.)

MOTOR-VEHICLE DEATHS AND RATES, UNITED STATES, 1913–2002, Cont.

Year	No. of Deaths	Estimated No. of Vehicles (Millions)	Estimated Vehicle Miles (Billions)	Estimated No. of Drivers (Millions)	Death Rates		
					Per 10,000 Motor Vehicles	Per 100,000,000 Vehicle Miles	Per 100,000 Population
1977	49,510	148.8	1,477	138.1	3.33	3.35	22.5
1978	52,411	153.6	1,548	140.8	3.41	3.39	23.6
1979	53,524	159.6	1,529	143.3	3.35	3.50	23.8
1980	53,172	161.6	1,521	145.3	3.29	3.50	23.4
1981	51,385	164.1	1,556	147.1	3.13	3.30	22.4
1982	45,779	165.2	1,592	150.3	2.77	2.88	19.8
1983	44,452	169.4	1,657	154.2	2.62	2.68	19.0
1984	46,263	171.8	1,718	155.4	2.69	2.69	19.6
1985	45,901	177.1	1,774	156.9	2.59	2.59	19.3
1986	47,865	181.4	1,835	159.5	2.63	2.60	19.9
1987	48,290	183.9	1,924	161.8	2.63	2.51	19.9
1988	49,078	189.0	2,026	162.9	2.60	2.42	20.1
1989	47,575	191.7	2,107	165.6	2.48	2.26	19.3
1990	46,814	192.9	2,148	167.0	2.43	2.18	18.8
1991	43,536	192.5	2,172	169.0	2.26	2.00	17.3
1992	40,982	194.4	2,240	173.1	2.11	1.83	16.1
1993	41,893	198.0	2,297	173.1	2.12	1.82	16.3
1994	42,524	201.8	2,360	175.4	2.11	1.80	16.3
1995	43,363	205.3	2,423	176.6	2.11	1.79	16.5
1996	43,649	210.4	2,486	179.5	2.07	1.76	16.5
1997	43,458	211.5	2,562	182.7	2.05	1.70	16.2
1998	43,501	215.0	2,632	185.2	2.02	1.65	16.1
1999	42,401	220.5	2,691	187.2	1.92	1.58	15.5
2000[b]	43,354	225.8	2,747	190.6	1.92	1.58	15.8
2001[b]	43,700	235.3	2,782	191.3	1.86	1.57	15.7
2002[c]	44,000	242.5	2,829	193.3	1.81	1.56	15.7
Changes							
1992 to 2002	+7%	+25%	+26%	+12%	−14%	−15%	−2%
2001 to 2002	+1%	+3%	+2%	+1%	−3%	−1%	0%

Source: Deaths from National Center for Health Statistics except 1964, 2001, and 2002, which are National Safety Council estimates based on data from state traffic authorities. See Technical Appendix for comparability. Motor-vehicle registrations, mileage, and drivers estimated by Federal Highway Administration, except 2002 registrations and drivers, which are National Safety Council estimates.
[a] Mileage data inadequate prior to 1923.
[b] Revised.
[c] Preliminary.

MOTOR-VEHICLE DEATHS BY TYPE OF ACCIDENT

MOTOR-VEHICLE DEATHS BY TYPE OF ACCIDENT, UNITED STATES, 1913–2002

Year	Total Deaths	Deaths from Collision with —							Deaths from Noncollision Accidents	Nontraffic Deaths[a]
		Pedestrians	Other Motor Vehicles	Railroad Trains	Streetcars	Pedal-cycles	Animal-Drawn Vehicle or Animal	Fixed Objects		
1913	4,200	(b)	(b)	(b)	(b)	(b)	(b)	(b)	(b)	(c)
1914	4,700	(b)	(b)	(b)	(b)	(b)	(b)	(b)	(b)	(c)
1915	6,600	(b)	(b)	(b)	(b)	(b)	(b)	(b)	(b)	(c)
1916	8,200	(b)	(b)	(b)	(b)	(b)	(b)	(b)	(b)	(c)
1917	10,200	(b)	(b)	(b)	(b)	(b)	(b)	(b)	(b)	(c)
1918	10,700	(b)	(b)	(b)	(b)	(b)	(b)	(b)	(b)	(c)
1919	11,200	(b)	(b)	(b)	(b)	(b)	(b)	(b)	(b)	(c)
1920	12,500	(b)	(b)	(b)	(b)	(b)	(b)	(b)	(b)	(c)
1921	13,900	(b)	(b)	(b)	(b)	(b)	(b)	(b)	(b)	(c)
1922	15,300	(b)	(b)	(b)	(b)	(b)	(b)	(b)	(b)	(c)
1923	18,400	(b)	(b)	(b)	(b)	(b)	(b)	(b)	(b)	(c)
1924	19,400	(b)	(b)	1,130	410	(b)	(b)	(b)	(b)	(c)
1925	21,900	(b)	(b)	1,410	560	(b)	(b)	(b)	(b)	(c)
1926	23,400	(b)	(b)	1,730	520	(b)	(b)	(b)	(b)	(c)
1927	25,800	10,820	3,430	1,830	520	(b)	(b)	(b)	(b)	(c)
1928	28,000	11,420	4,310	2,140	570	(b)	(b)	540	8,070	(c)
1929	31,200	12,250	5,400	2,050	530	(b)	(b)	620	9,380	(c)
1930	32,900	12,900	5,880	1,830	480	(b)	(b)	720	9,970	(c)
1931	33,700	13,370	6,820	1,710	440	(b)	(b)	870	9,570	(c)
1932	29,500	11,490	6,070	1,520	320	350	400	800	8,500	(c)
1933	31,363	12,840	6,470	1,437	318	400	310	900	8,680	(c)
1934	36,101	14,480	8,110	1,457	332	500	360	1,040	9,820	(c)
1935	36,369	14,350	8,750	1,587	253	450	250	1,010	9,720	(c)
1936	38,089	15,250	9,500	1,697	269	650	250	1,060	9,410	(c)
1937	39,643	15,500	10,320	1,810	264	700	200	1,160	9,690	(c)
1938	32,582	12,850	8,900	1,490	165	720	170	940	7,350	(c)
1939	32,386	12,400	8,700	1,330	150	710	200	1,000	7,900	(c)
1940	34,501	12,700	10,100	1,707	132	750	210	1,100	7,800	(c)
1941	39,969	13,550	12,500	1,840	118	910	250	1,350	9,450	(c)
1942	28,309	10,650	7,300	1,754	124	650	240	850	6,740	(c)
1943	23,823	9,900	5,300	1,448	171	450	160	700	5,690	(c)
1944	24,282	9,900	5,700	1,663	175	400	140	700	5,600	(c)
1945	28,076	11,000	7,150	1,703	163	500	130	800	6,600	(c)
1946	33,411	11,600	9,400	1,703	174	450	130	950	8,900	(c)
1947	32,697	10,450	9,900	1,736	102	550	150	1,000	8,800	(c)
1948	32,259	9,950	10,200	1,474	83	500	100	1,000	8,950	(c)
1949	31,701	8,800	10,500	1,452	56	550	140	1,100	9,100	838
1950	34,763	9,000	11,650	1,541	89	440	120	1,300	10,600	900
1951	36,996	9,150	13,100	1,573	46	390	100	1,400	11,200	966
1952	37,794	8,900	13,500	1,429	32	430	130	1,450	11,900	970
1953	37,956	8,750	13,400	1,506	26	420	120	1,500	12,200	1,026
1954	35,586	8,000	12,800	1,289	28	380	90	1,500	11,500	1,004
1955	38,426	8,200	14,500	1,490	15	410	90	1,600	12,100	989
1956	39,628	7,900	15,200	1,377	11	440	100	1,600	13,000	888
1957	38,702	7,850	15,400	1,376	13	460	80	1,700	11,800	1,016
1958	36,981	7,650	14,200	1,316	9	450	80	1,650	11,600	929
1959	37,910	7,850	14,900	1,202	6	480	70	1,600	11,800	948
1960	38,137	7,850	14,800	1,368	5	460	80	1,700	11,900	995
1961	38,091	7,650	14,700	1,267	5	490	80	1,700	12,200	1,065
1962	40,804	7,900	16,400	1,245	3	500	90	1,750	12,900	1,029
1963	43,564	8,200	17,600	1,385	10	580	80	1,900	13,800	990
1964	47,700	9,000	19,600	1,580	5	710	100	2,100	14,600	1,123
1965	49,163	8,900	20,800	1,556	5	680	120	2,200	14,900	1,113
1966	53,041	9,400	22,200	1,800	2	740	100	2,500	16,300	1,108
1967	52,924	9,400	22,000	1,620	3	750	100	2,350	16,700	1,165
1968	54,862	9,900	22,400	1,570	4	790	100	2,700	17,400	1,061
1969	55,791	10,100	23,700	1,495	2	800	100	3,900d	15,700d	1,155
1970	54,633	9,900	23,200	1,459	3	780	100	3,800	15,400	1,140
1971	54,381	9,900	23,100	1,378	2	800	100	3,800	15,300	1,015
1972	56,278	10,300	23,900	1,260	2	1,000	100	3,900	15,800	1,064
1973	55,511	10,200	23,600	1,194	2	1,000	100	3,800	15,600	1,164
1974	46,402	8,500	19,700	1,209	1	1,000	100	3,100	12,800	1,088
1975	45,853	8,400	19,550	979	1	1,000	100	3,130	12,700	1,033
1976	47,038	8,600	20,100	1,033	2	1,000	100	3,200	13,000	1,026

See source and footnotes on page 113.

MOTOR-VEHICLE DEATHS BY TYPE OF ACCIDENT, UNITED STATES, 1913–2002, Cont.

Year	Total Deaths	Deaths from Collision with —							Deaths from Noncollision Accidents	Nontraffic Deaths[a]
		Pedestrians	Other Motor Vehicles	Railroad Trains	Streetcars	Pedal-cycles	Animal-Drawn Vehicle or Animal	Fixed Objects		
1977	49,510	9,100	21,200	902	3	1,100	100	3,400	13,700	1,053
1978	52,411	9,600	22,400	986	1	1,200	100	3,600	14,500	1,074
1979	53,524	9,800	23,100	826	1	1,200	100	3,700	14,800	1,271
1980	53,172	9,700	23,000	739	1	1,200	100	3,700	14,700	1,242
1981	51,385	9,400	22,200	668	1	1,200	100	3,600	14,200	1,189
1982	45,779	8,400	19,800	554	1	1,100	100	3,200	12,600	1,066
1983	44,452	8,200	19,200	520	1	1,100	100	3,100	12,200	1,024
1984	46,263	8,500	20,000	630	0	1,100	100	3,200	12,700	1,055
1985	45,901	8,500	19,900	538	2	1,100	100	3,200	12,600	1,079
1986	47,865	8,900	20,800	574	2	1,100	100	3,300	13,100	998
1987	48,290	7,500[e]	20,700	554	1	1,000[e]	100	13,200[e]	5,200[e]	993
1988	49,078	7,700	20,900	638	2	1,000	100	13,400	5,300	1,054
1989	47,575	7,800	20,300	720	2	900	100	12,900	4,900	989
1990	46,814	7,300	19,900	623	2	900	100	13,100	4,900	987
1991	43,536	6,600	18,200	541	1	800	100	12,600	4,700	915
1992	40,982	6,300	17,600	521	2	700	100	11,700	4,100	997
1993	41,893	6,400	18,300	553	3	800	100	11,500	4,200	994
1994	42,524	6,300	18,900	549	1	800	100	11,500	4,400	1,017
1995	43,363	6,400	19,000	514	(c)	800	100	12,100	4,400	1,032
1996	43,649	6,100	19,600	373	(c)	800	100	12,100	4,600	1,127
1997	43,458	5,900	19,900	371	(c)	800	100	12,000	4,400	1,118
1998	43,501	5,900	19,700	309	(c)	700	100	12,200	4,600	1,310
1999	42,401	6,100	18,600	314	1	800	100	11,800	4,700	1,436
2000[f]	43,354	5,900	19,100	321	(c)	800	100	12,300	4,800	1,360
2001[f]	43,700	6,100	18,400	300	(c)	800	100	12,800	5,200	1,400
2002[g]	44,000	5,700	18,200	300	(c)	700	100	13,500	5,500	1,400

Changes in Deaths										
1992 to 2002	+7%	−10%	+3%	−42%	—	0%	0%	+15%	+34%	+40%
2001 to 2002	+1%	−7%	−1%	0%	—	−13%	0%	+5%	+6%	0%

Source: Total deaths from National Center for Health Statistics except 1964, 2001, and 2002, which are National Safety Council estimates based on data from state traffic authorities. Most totals by type are estimated and may not add to the total deaths. See Technical Appendix for comparability.
[a] *See definition, page 175. Nontraffic deaths are included in appropriate accident type totals in table; in 2000, 34% of the nontraffic deaths were pedestrians.*
[b] *Insufficient data for approximations.*
[c] *Data not available.*
[d] *1969 through 1986 totals are not comparable to previous years.*
[e] *Procedures and benchmarks for estimating deaths for certain types of accidents were changed for the 1990 edition. Estimates for 1987 and later years are not comparable to earlier years.*
[f] *Revised.*
[g] *Preliminary.*

MOTOR-VEHICLE DEATHS BY AGE

MOTOR-VEHICLE DEATHS BY AGE, UNITED STATES, 1913–2002

Year	All Ages	Under 5 Years	5–14 Years	15–24 Years	25–44 Years	45–64 Years	65–74 Years	75 & Over[a]
1913	4,200	300	1,100	600	1,100	800	300	
1914	4,700	300	1,200	700	1,200	900	400	
1915	6,600	400	1,500	1,000	1,700	1,400	600	
1916	8,200	600	1,800	1,300	2,100	1,700	700	
1917	10,200	700	2,400	1,400	2,700	2,100	900	
1918	10,700	800	2,700	1,400	2,500	2,300	1,000	
1919	11,200	900	3,000	1,400	2,500	2,100	1,300	
1920	12,500	1,000	3,300	1,700	2,800	2,300	1,400	
1921	13,900	1,100	3,400	1,800	3,300	2,700	1,600	
1922	15,300	1,100	3,500	2,100	3,700	3,100	1,800	
1923	18,400	1,200	3,700	2,800	4,600	3,900	2,200	
1924	19,400	1,400	3,800	2,900	4,700	4,100	2,500	
1925	21,900	1,400	3,900	3,600	5,400	4,800	2,800	
1926	23,400	1,400	3,900	3,900	5,900	5,200	3,100	
1927	25,800	1,600	4,000	4,300	6,600	5,800	3,500	
1928	28,000	1,600	3,800	4,900	7,200	6,600	3,900	
1929	31,200	1,600	3,900	5,700	8,000	7,500	4,500	
1930	32,900	1,500	3,600	6,200	8,700	8,000	4,900	
1931	33,700	1,500	3,600	6,300	9,100	8,200	5,000	
1932	29,500	1,200	2,900	5,100	8,100	7,400	4,800	
1933	31,363	1,274	3,121	5,649	8,730	7,947	4,642	
1934	36,101	1,210	3,182	6,561	10,232	9,530	5,386	
1935	36,369	1,253	2,951	6,755	10,474	9,562	5,374	
1936	38,089	1,324	3,026	7,184	10,807	10,089	5,659	
1937	39,643	1,303	2,991	7,800	10,877	10,475	6,197	
1938	32,582	1,122	2,511	6,016	8,772	8,711	5,450	
1939	32,386	1,192	2,339	6,318	8,917	8,292	5,328	
1940	34,501	1,176	2,584	6,846	9,362	8,882	5,651	
1941	39,969	1,378	2,838	8,414	11,069	9,829	6,441	
1942	28,309	1,069	1,991	5,932	7,747	7,254	4,316	
1943	23,823	1,132	1,959	4,522	6,454	5,996	3,760	
1944	24,282	1,203	2,093	4,561	6,514	5,982	3,929	
1945	28,076	1,290	2,386	5,358	7,578	6,794	4,670	
1946	33,411	1,568	2,508	7,445	8,955	7,532	5,403	
1947	32,697	1,502	2,275	7,251	8,775	7,468	5,426	
1948	32,259	1,635	2,337	7,218	8,702	7,190	3,173	2,004
1949	31,701	1,667	2,158	6,772	8,892	7,073	3,116	2,023
1950	34,763	1,767	2,152	7,600	10,214	7,728	3,264	2,038
1951	36,996	1,875	2,300	7,713	11,253	8,276	3,444	2,135
1952	37,794	1,951	2,295	8,115	11,380	8,463	3,472	2,118
1953	37,956	2,019	2,368	8,169	11,302	8,318	3,508	2,271
1954	35,586	1,864	2,332	7,571	10,521	7,848	3,247	2,203
1955	38,426	1,875	2,406	8,656	11,448	8,372	3,455	2,214
1956	39,628	1,770	2,640	9,169	11,551	8,573	3,657	2,268
1957	38,702	1,785	2,604	8,667	11,230	8,545	3,560	2,311
1958	36,981	1,791	2,710	8,388	10,414	7,922	3,535	2,221
1959	37,910	1,842	2,719	8,969	10,358	8,263	3,487	2,272
1960	38,137	1,953	2,814	9,117	10,189	8,294	3,457	2,313
1961	38,091	1,891	2,802	9,088	10,212	8,267	3,467	2,364
1962	40,804	1,903	3,028	10,157	10,701	8,812	3,696	2,507
1963	43,564	1,991	3,063	11,123	11,356	9,506	3,786	2,739
1964	47,700	2,120	3,430	12,400	12,500	10,200	4,150	2,900
1965	49,163	2,059	3,526	13,395	12,595	10,509	4,077	3,002
1966	53,041	2,182	3,869	15,298	13,282	11,051	4,217	3,142
1967	52,924	2,067	3,845	15,646	12,987	10,902	4,285	3,192
1968	54,862	1,987	4,105	16,543	13,602	11,031	4,261	3,333
1969	55,791	2,077	4,045	17,443	13,868	11,012	4,210	3,136
1970	54,633	1,915	4,159	16,720	13,446	11,099	4,084	3,210
1971	54,381	1,885	4,256	17,103	13,307	10,471	4,108	3,251
1972	56,278	1,896	4,258	17,942	13,758	10,836	4,138	3,450
1973	55,511	1,998	4,124	18,032	14,013	10,216	3,892	3,236
1974	46,402	1,546	3,332	15,905	11,834	8,159	3,071	2,555
1975	45,853	1,576	3,286	15,672	11,969	7,663	3,047	2,640
1976	47,038	1,532	3,175	16,650	12,112	7,770	3,082	2,717

See source and footnotes on page 115.

MOTOR-VEHICLE DEATHS BY AGE, UNITED STATES, 1913–2002, Cont.

Year	All Ages	Under 5 Years	5–14 Years	15–24 Years	25–44 Years	45–64 Years	65–74 Years	75 & Over[a]
1977	49,510	1,472	3,142	18,092	13,031	8,000	3,060	2,713
1978	52,411	1,551	3,130	19,164	14,574	8,048	3,217	2,727
1979	53,524	1,461	2,952	19,369	15,658	8,162	3,171	2,751
1980	53,172	1,426	2,747	19,040	16,133	8,022	2,991	2,813
1981	51,385	1,256	2,575	17,363	16,447	7,818	3,090	2,836
1982	45,779	1,300	2,301	15,324	14,469	6,879	2,825	2,681
1983	44,452	1,233	2,241	14,289	14,323	6,690	2,827	2,849
1984	46,263	1,138	2,263	14,738	15,036	6,954	3,020	3,114
1985	45,901	1,195	2,319	14,277	15,034	6,885	3,014	3,177
1986	47,865	1,188	2,350	15,227	15,844	6,799	3,096	3,361
1987	48,290	1,190	2,397	14,447	16,405	7,021	3,277	3,553
1988	49,078	1,220	2,423	14,406	16,580	7,245	3,429	3,775
1989	47,575	1,221	2,266	12,941	16,571	7,287	3,465	3,824
1990	46,814	1,123	2,059	12,607	16,488	7,282	3,350	3,905
1991	43,536	1,076	2,011	11,664	15,082	6,616	3,193	3,894
1992	40,982	1,020	1,904	10,305	14,071	6,597	3,247	3,838
1993	41,893	1,081	1,963	10,500	14,283	6,711	3,116	4,239
1994	42,524	1,139	2,026	10,660	13,966	7,097	3,385	4,251
1995	43,363	1,004	2,055	10,600	14,618	7,428	3,300	4,358
1996	43,649	1,035	1,980	10,576	14,482	7,749	3,419	4,408
1997	43,458	933	1,967	10,208	14,167	8,134	3,370	4,679
1998	43,501	921	1,868	10,026	14,095	8,416	3,410	4,765
1999	42,401	834	1,771	10,128	13,516	8,342	3,276	4,534
2000[b]	43,354	819	1,772	10,560	13,811	8,867	3,038	4,487
2001[b]	43,700	800	1,600	10,800	13,900	9,000	3,000	4,600
2002[c]	44,000	900	1,400	11,700	13,700	9,700	2,300	4,300
Changes in Deaths								
1992 to 2002	+7%	−12%	−26%	+14%	−3%	+47%	−29%	+12%
2001 to 2002	+1%	+13%	−13%	+8%	+1%	+8%	−23%	−6%

Source: 1913 to 1932 calculated from National Center for Health Statistics data for registration states; 1933 to 1963, 1965 to 2000 are NCHS totals. All other figures are National Safety Council estimates. See Technical Appendix for comparability.
[a] Includes "age unknown." In 2000 these deaths numbered 26.
[b] Revised.
[c] Preliminary.

MOTOR-VEHICLE DEATH RATES[a] BY AGE, UNITED STATES, 1913–2002

Year	All Ages	Under 5 Years	5–14 Years	15–24 Years	25–44 Years	45–64 Years	65–74 Years	75 & Over
1913	4.4	2.3	5.5	3.1	3.8	5.3	8.5	
1914	4.8	2.5	5.7	3.5	4.1	6.2	9.3	
1915	6.6	3.5	7.3	5.0	5.6	8.8	13.5	
1916	8.1	4.7	8.6	6.0	7.0	10.7	15.8	
1917	10.0	5.6	10.6	7.4	8.6	12.6	18.6	
1918	10.3	6.9	12.3	7.7	8.3	13.7	21.2	
1919	10.7	7.5	13.9	7.5	8.1	12.4	24.1	
1920	11.7	8.6	14.6	8.7	8.8	13.5	27.0	
1921	12.9	9.0	14.5	9.2	10.2	15.4	31.0	
1922	13.9	9.2	15.0	10.8	11.1	17.2	34.9	
1923	16.5	9.7	15.6	13.4	13.6	21.0	40.5	
1924	17.1	11.1	16.1	14.3	13.7	21.8	43.7	
1925	19.1	11.0	15.6	17.2	15.8	25.0	48.9	
1926	20.1	11.0	15.9	18.6	17.1	26.3	51.4	
1927	21.8	12.8	16.0	20.0	18.8	28.9	56.9	
1928	23.4	12.7	15.5	21.9	20.2	32.4	62.2	
1929	25.7	13.4	15.6	25.6	22.3	35.6	68.6	
1930	26.7	13.0	14.7	27.4	23.9	37.0	72.5	
1931	27.2	13.3	14.5	27.9	24.8	37.4	70.6	
1932	23.6	11.3	12.0	22.6	22.0	32.9	63.6	
1933	25.0	12.0	12.7	24.8	23.4	34.7	63.1	
1934	28.6	11.7	13.0	28.6	27.2	40.7	71.0	
1935	28.6	12.3	12.2	29.2	27.6	39.9	68.9	
1936	29.7	13.2	12.6	30.8	28.2	41.3	70.5	
1937	30.8	13.0	12.7	33.2	28.2	42.0	75.1	
1938	25.1	11.0	10.8	25.4	22.5	34.3	64.1	
1939	24.7	11.2	10.4	26.5	22.6	32.2	60.2	
1940	26.1	11.1	11.5	28.7	23.5	33.9	62.1	
1941	30.0	12.7	12.6	35.7	27.5	37.0	68.6	
1942	21.1	9.5	8.8	25.8	19.2	26.9	44.5	
1943	17.8	9.4	8.6	20.6	16.1	21.9	37.6	
1944	18.3	9.6	9.1	22.5	16.6	21.6	38.2	
1945	21.2	10.0	10.3	27.8	19.7	24.2	44.1	
1946	23.9	11.9	10.8	34.4	21.1	26.4	49.6	
1947	22.8	10.5	9.7	32.8	20.3	25.7	48.2	
1948	22.1	11.0	9.8	32.5	19.8	24.3	39.6	55.4
1949	21.3	10.7	9.0	30.7	19.9	23.4	37.8	53.9
1950	23.0	10.8	8.8	34.5	22.5	25.1	38.8	52.4
1951	24.1	10.9	9.2	36.0	24.7	26.5	39.5	53.0
1952	24.3	11.3	8.7	38.6	24.7	26.7	38.5	50.8
1953	24.0	11.5	8.5	39.1	24.5	25.8	37.7	52.6
1954	22.1	10.4	8.1	36.2	22.6	24.0	33.9	49.0
1955	23.4	10.2	8.0	40.9	24.5	25.2	35.1	47.1
1956	23.7	9.4	8.4	42.9	24.6	25.3	36.2	46.4
1957	22.7	9.2	8.0	39.7	23.9	24.8	34.4	45.5
1958	21.3	9.1	8.1	37.0	22.3	22.6	33.5	42.3
1959	21.5	9.1	7.9	38.2	22.2	23.2	32.3	41.8
1960	21.2	9.6	7.9	37.7	21.7	22.9	31.3	41.1
1961	20.8	9.2	7.6	36.5	21.8	22.5	30.7	40.5
1962	22.0	9.3	8.1	38.4	22.9	23.7	32.2	41.7
1963	23.1	9.8	8.0	40.0	24.3	25.2	32.6	44.3
1964	25.0	10.5	8.8	42.6	26.8	26.6	35.5	45.2
1965	25.4	10.4	8.9	44.2	27.0	27.0	34.6	45.4
1966	27.1	11.4	9.7	48.7	28.5	27.9	35.4	46.2
1967	26.8	11.2	9.5	48.4	27.8	27.1	35.6	45.4
1968	27.5	11.1	10.1	49.8	28.8	27.0	35.1	46.0
1969	27.7	12.0	9.9	50.7	29.1	26.6	34.3	42.0
1970	26.8	11.2	10.2	46.7	27.9	26.4	32.7	42.2
1971	26.3	10.9	10.5	45.7	27.4	24.7	32.4	41.3
1972	26.9	11.1	10.7	47.1	27.4	25.3	32.0	42.6
1973	26.3	11.9	10.5	46.3	27.2	23.6	29.4	39.1
1974	21.8	9.4	8.6	40.0	22.4	18.8	22.6	30.1
1975	21.3	9.8	8.6	38.7	22.1	17.5	21.9	30.1
1976	21.6	9.8	8.4	40.3	21.8	17.6	21.6	30.1

See source and footnotes on page 117.

MOTOR-VEHICLE DEATH RATES[a] BY AGE, UNITED STATES, 1913–2002, Cont.

Year	All Ages	Under 5 Years	5–14 Years	15–24 Years	25–44 Years	45–64 Years	65–74 Years	75 & Over
1977	22.5	9.5	8.5	43.3	22.7	18.1	20.9	29.3
1978	23.6	9.9	8.6	45.4	24.6	18.2	21.5	28.7
1979	23.8	9.1	8.3	45.6	25.6	18.4	20.7	28.1
1980	23.4	8.7	7.9	44.8	25.5	18.0	19.1	28.0
1981	22.4	7.4	7.5	41.1	25.2	17.6	19.4	27.5
1982	19.8	7.5	6.7	36.8	21.5	15.5	17.5	25.2
1983	19.0	7.0	6.6	34.8	20.6	15.0	17.2	26.0
1984	19.6	6.4	6.7	36.4	21.0	15.6	18.2	27.7
1985	19.3	6.7	6.9	35.7	20.5	15.4	17.9	27.5
1986	19.9	6.6	7.0	38.5	21.0	15.2	18.1	28.3
1987	19.9	6.6	7.1	37.1	21.3	15.7	18.8	29.1
1988	20.1	6.7	7.1	37.8	21.2	15.9	19.5	30.2
1989	19.3	6.6	6.5	34.6	20.8	15.9	19.4	29.8
1990	18.8	6.0	5.8	34.2	20.4	15.7	18.5	29.7
1991	17.3	5.6	5.6	32.1	18.3	14.2	17.5	28.9
1992	16.1	5.2	5.2	28.5	17.1	13.6	17.6	27.8
1993	16.3	5.5	5.3	29.1	17.3	13.5	16.7	30.0
1994	16.3	5.8	5.4	29.5	16.8	13.9	18.1	29.4
1995	16.5	5.1	5.4	29.3	17.5	14.2	17.6	29.4
1996	16.5	5.4	5.2	29.2	17.3	14.4	18.3	29.0
1997	16.2	4.9	5.1	27.9	17.0	14.7	18.2	29.9
1998	16.1	4.9	4.8	26.9	16.9	14.7	18.5	29.8
1999	15.5	4.4	4.5	26.8	16.3	14.1	18.0	27.8
2000[b]	15.7	4.3	4.5	27.5	16.8	14.5	16.7	27.0
2001[b]	15.7	4.2	4.0	27.6	17.0	14.2	16.5	27.2
2002[c]	15.7	4.8	3.5	29.0	17.0	14.2	14.3	26.2
Changes in Rates								
1992 to 2002	–2%	–8%	–33%	+2%	–1%	+4%	–19%	–6%
2001 to 2002	0%	+14%	–13%	+5%	0%	0%	–13%	–4%

Source: 1913 to 1932 calculated from National Center for Health Statistics data for registration states; 1933 to 1963, 1965 to 2000 are NCHS totals. All other figures are National Safety Council estimates. See Technical Appendix for comparability.
[a] *Death rates are deaths per 100,000 population in each age group.*
[b] *Revised.*
[c] *Preliminary.*

INJURY FACTS®

NATIONAL SAFETY COUNCIL

The Home and Community venue is the combination of the Home class and the Public class. Home and Community together with the Occupational and Transportation venues make up the totality of unintentional injuries. Home and Community includes all unintentional injuries that are not work related and do not involve motor vehicles on streets and highways.

In 2002, an estimated 52,900 unintentional-injury deaths occurred in the Home and Community venue, or 53% of all unintentional-injury deaths that year. The number of deaths increased by 3% from the revised 2001 total of 51,600. Another 14,500,000 people suffered nonfatal disabling injuries. The death rate per 100,000 population was 18.9, an increase of 2% from the revised 2001 rate of 18.6.

About 1 out of 19 people experience an unintentional injury in the Home and Community venue each year and about 1 out of 5,300 people die from such an injury. About 41% of the deaths and disabling injuries involve workers while they are away from work (off the job).

The graph on the next page shows the five leading causes of unintentional-injury deaths in the Home and Community venue and the broad age groups (children, youths and adults, and the elderly) affected by them. This is one way to prioritize issues in this venue. Also shown on the next page is a graph of the trend in deaths and death rates from 1992 to the present. Similar graphs for the Public and Home classes are on pages 122 and 134.

The Council adopted the Bureau of Labor Statistics' Census of Fatal Occupational Injuries count for work-related unintentional injuries retroactive to 1992 data. Because of the lower Work class total resulting from this change, several thousand unintentional-injury deaths that had been classified by the Council as work-related had to be reassigned to the Home and Public classes. Long-term historical comparisons for these three classes should be made with caution. Also, beginning with 1999 data, deaths are now classified according to the 10th revision of the *International Classification of Diseases*. Caution should be used in comparing data classified under the two systems. See the Technical Appendix for more information about both changes.

Deaths	52,900
Disabling injuries	14,500,000
Death rate per 100,000 population	18.9
Costs	$215.0 billion

LEADING CAUSES OF UNINTENTIONAL-INJURY DEATHS IN HOME AND COMMUNITY, UNITED STATES, 2002

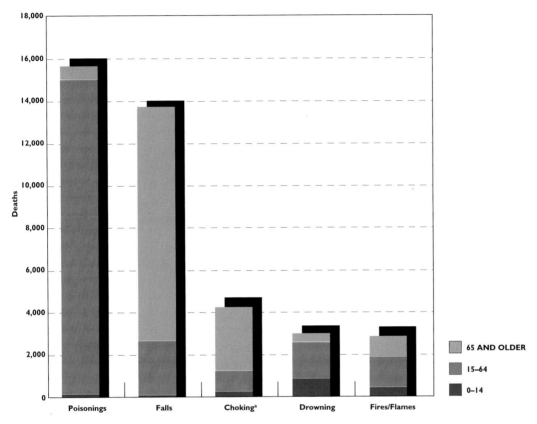

65 AND OLDER

15–64

0–14

ᵃInhalation and ingestion of food or other object that obstructs breathing.

HOME AND COMMUNITY DEATHS AND DEATH RATES, UNITED STATES, 1992–2002

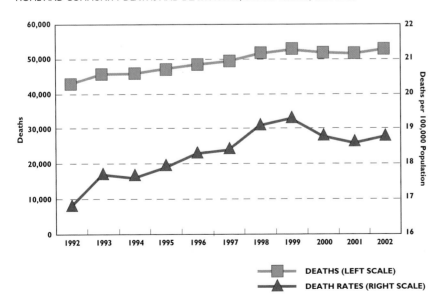

DEATHS (LEFT SCALE)

DEATH RATES (RIGHT SCALE)

PUBLIC, 2002

Between 1912 and 2002, public unintentional-injury deaths per 100,000 population were reduced 77% from 30 to 7. In 1912, an estimated 28,000 to 30,000 persons died from public nonmotor-vehicle injuries. In 2002, with a population tripled, and travel and recreational activity greatly increased, only 19,600 persons died of public unintentional injuries and 6,500,000 suffered disabling injuries. The public class excludes deaths involving motor vehicles and persons at work or at home.

The number of public unintentional-injury deaths decreased by 400, or 2%, from the revised 2001 figure of 20,000. The death rate per 100,000 population decreased from 7.2 to 7.0, or 3%.

With an estimated 6,500,000 disabling unintentional injuries occurring in public places and a population of more than 280 million people, on average about one person in 43 experienced such an injury.

The Council adopted the Bureau of Labor Statistics' Census of Fatal Occupational Injuries count for work-related unintentional injuries retroactive to 1992 data. Because of the lower Work class total resulting from this change, several thousand unintentional-injury deaths that had been classified by the Council as work-related had to be reassigned to the Home and Public classes. For this reason, long-term historical comparisons for these three classes should be made with caution. See the Technical Appendix for an explanation of the methodological changes.

Beginning with 1999 data, which became available in September 2001, deaths are now classified according to the 10th revision of the *International Classification of Diseases*. Overall, about 3% more deaths are classified as due to "unintentional injuries" under the new classification system than under the 9th revision. The difference varies across causes of death. See the Technical Appendix for more information on comparability. Caution should be used in comparing data classified under the two systems.

Deaths **19,600**
Disabling Injuries **6,500,000**
Death Rate per 100,000 Population **7.0**
Costs . . . . **$88.3 billion**

PUBLIC DEATHS AND DEATH RATES, UNITED STATES, 1992–2002

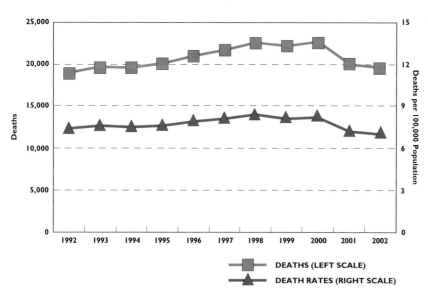

PRINCIPAL TYPES OF PUBLIC UNINTENTIONAL-INJURY DEATHS, UNITED STATES, 1982–2002

Year	Total Public[a]	Falls	Drowning	Poisoning	Suffocation by Ingestion	Fires/ Burns	Firearms	Mechnical Suffocation	Air Transport	Water Transport	Rail Transport[b]
1982	19,500	4,100	4,000	(c)	(c)	500	700	(c)	1,200	1,100	400
1983	19,400	4,100	4,000	(c)	(c)	500	700	(c)	1,000	1,100	400
1984	18,300	4,100	3,300	(c)	(c)	500	700	(c)	900	900	400
1985	18,800	4,100	3,300	(c)	(c)	500	600	(c)	1,000	900	400
1986	18,700	3,900	3,600	(c)	(c)	500	600	(c)	800	900	400
1987	18,400	4,000	3,200	(c)	(c)	500	600	(c)	900	800	400
1988	18,400	4,100	3,100	(c)	(c)	500	600	(c)	700	800	400
1989	18,200	4,200	3,000	(c)	(c)	500	600	(c)	800	700	400
1990	17,400	4,300	2,800	(c)	(c)	400	500	(c)	700	800	400
1991	17,600	4,500	2,800	(c)	(c)	400	600	(c)	700	700	500
1992	19,000	4,400	2,500	(c)	(c)	200	400	(c)	700	700	600
1993	19,700	4,600	2,800	(c)	(c)	200	400	(c)	600	700	600
1994	19,600	4,700	2,400	(c)	(c)	200	400	(c)	600	600	600
1995	20,100	5,000	2,800	(c)	(c)	200	300	(c)	600	700	500
1996	21,000	5,300	2,500	(c)	(c)	200	300	(c)	700	600	500
1997	21,700	5,600	2,600	(c)	(c)	200	300	(c)	500	600	400
1998	22,600	6,000	2,900	(c)	(c)	200	300	(c)	500	600	500
1999[d]	22,200	4,800	2,600	2,800	2,000	200	300	500	500	600	400
2000[e]	22,700	5,500	2,400	2,900	2,200	(c)	(c)	300	500	500	400
2001[e]	20,000	5,400	2,300	2,900	1,900	(c)	(c)	200	700	500	500
2002[f]	19,600	5,700	2,000	3,100	1,900	(c)	(c)	200	600	600	600

Source: National Safety Council estimates based on data from the National Center for Health Statistics and state vital statistics departments. The Council adopted the Bureau of Labor Statistics' Census of Fatal Occupational Injuries count for work-related unintentional injuries retroactive to 1992 data. Because of the lower Work class total resulting from this change, several thousand unintentional-injury deaths that had been classified by the Council as work-related, had to be reassigned to the Home and Public classes. For this reason long-term historical comparisons for these three classes should be made with caution. See the Technical Appendix for an explanation of the methodological changes.
[a] Includes some deaths not shown separately.
[b] Includes subways and elevateds.
[c] Estimates not available.
[d] In 1999, a revision was made in the International Classification of Diseases. See the Technical Appendix for comparability with earlier years.
[e] Revised.
[f] Preliminary.

PRINCIPAL TYPES OF PUBLIC UNINTENTIONAL-INJURY DEATHS, UNITED STATES, 2002

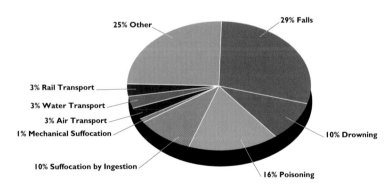

25% Other
29% Falls
3% Rail Transport
3% Water Transport
3% Air Transport
1% Mechanical Suffocation
10% Suffocation by Ingestion
16% Poisoning
10% Drowning

DEATHS DUE TO UNINTENTIONAL PUBLIC INJURIES, 2002

TYPE OF EVENT AND AGE OF VICTIM

All Public

Includes deaths in public places or places used in a public way and not involving motor vehicles. Most sports, recreation, and transportation deaths are included. Excludes deaths in the course of employment.

	Total	Change from 2001	Death Rate[a]
Deaths	19,600	–2%	7.0

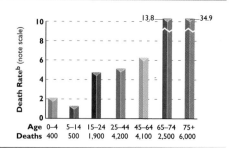

Falls

Includes deaths from falls from one level to another or on the same level in public places. Excludes deaths from falls in moving vehicles.

	Total	Change from 2001	Death Rate[a]
Deaths	5,700	+6%	2.0

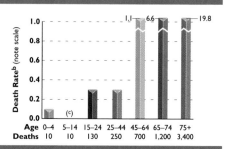

Poisoning

Includes deaths from drugs, medicines, other solid and liquid substances, and gases and vapors. Excludes poisonings from spoiled foods, salmonella, etc., which are classified as disease deaths.

	Total	Change from 2001	Death Rate[a]
Deaths	3,100	+7%	1.1

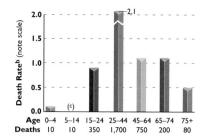

Drowning

Includes drownings of person swimming or playing in water, or falling into water, except on home premises or at work. Excludes drownings involving boats, which are in water transportation.

	Total	Change from 2001	Death Rate[a]
Deaths	2,000	–13%	0.7

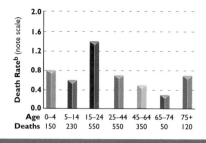

Suffocation by Ingestion

Includes deaths from unintentional ingestion or inhalation of food or other objects resulting in the obstruction of respiratory passages.

	Total	Change from 2001	Death Rate[a]
Deaths	1,900	0%	0.7

See footnotes on page 125.

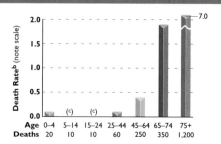

TYPE OF EVENT AND AGE OF VICTIM

Air Transport

Includes deaths in private flying, passengers in commercial aviation, and deaths of military personnel in the U.S. Excludes crews and persons traveling in the course of employment.

	Total	Change from 2001	Death Rate^a
Deaths	600	−14%	0.2

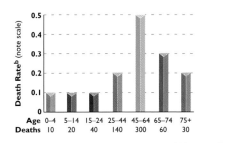

Age	0–4	5–14	15–24	25–44	45–64	65–74	75+
Deaths	10	20	40	140	300	60	30

Railroad

Includes deaths arising from railroad vehicles in motion (except involving motor vehicles), subway and elevated trains, and persons boarding or alighting from standing trains. Excludes crews and persons traveling in the course of employment.

	Total	Change from 2001	Death Rate^a
Deaths	600	+20%	0.2

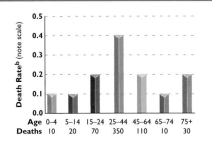

Age	0–4	5–14	15–24	25–44	45–64	65–74	75+
Deaths	10	20	70	350	110	10	30

Water Transport

Includes deaths in water transport accidents from falls, burns, etc., as well as drownings. Excludes crews and persons traveling in the course of employment.

	Total	Change from 2001	Death Rate^a
Deaths	600	+20%	0.2

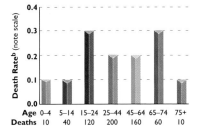

Age	0–4	5–14	15–24	25–44	45–64	65–74	75+
Deaths	10	40	120	200	160	60	10

Mechanical Suffocation

Includes deaths from hanging and strangulation, and suffocation in enclosed or confined spaces, cave-ins, or by bed clothes, plastic bags, or similar materials.

	Total	Change from 2001	Death Rate^a
Deaths	200	0%	0.1

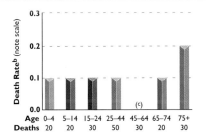

Age	0–4	5–14	15–24	25–44	45–64	65–74	75+
Deaths	20	20	30	50	30	20	30

All Other Public

Most important types included are: excessive natural heat or cold, firearms, fires and flames, and machinery.

	Total	Change from 2001	Death Rate^a
Deaths	4,900	−13%	1.7

^{a}Deaths per 100,000 population.
^{b}Deaths per 100,000 population in each age group.
^{c}Deaths rates less than 0.05.

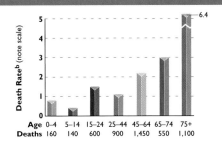

Age	0–4	5–14	15–24	25–44	45–64	65–74	75+
Deaths	160	140	600	900	1,450	550	1,100

SPORTS AND RECREATION INJURIES

Basketball accounted for more than 650,000 emergency department visits in 2001.

The table below shows estimates of injuries treated in hospital emergency departments and participants associated with various sports and recreational activities. Differences between the two sources in methods, coverage, classification systems, and definitions can affect comparisons among sports. Because this list of sports is not complete, because the frequency and duration of participation is not known, and because the number of participants varies greatly, no inference should be made concerning the relative hazard of these sports or rank with respect to risk of injury. In particular, it is *not* appropriate to calculate injury rates from these data.

SPORTS PARTICIPATION AND INJURIES, UNITED STATES, 2001

Sport or Activity	Participants	Injuries	Percent of Injuries by Age				
			0–4	5–14	15–24	25–64	65 & Over
Archery	4,700,000	4,042	2.4	17.1	15.8	57.8	6.9
Baseball	14,900,000	173,945	3.5	48.7	25.5	21.8	0.4
Basketball	28,100,000	653,661	0.3	31.4	46.9	21.1	0.2
Bicycle riding[a]	39,000,000	546,236	6.5	50.7	16.1	24.6	2.1
Billiards, pool	32,700,000	5,610	4.5	17.5	35.3	41.2	1.5
Bowling	40,300,000	22,933	6.7	18.8	20.3	44.6	9.6
Boxing	1,700,000	11,506	1.5	15.1	48.5	34.9	0.0
Exercise	(b)	202,186[c]	3.0	16.4	22.2	50.1	8.2
Fishing	44,400,000	79,369	3.4	22.7	12.7	52.7	8.5
Football[d]	17,500,000	414,607	0.3	46.8	42.8	10.1	0.1
Golf	26,600,000	46,089[e]	7.7	21.8	8.3	44.8	17.4
Gymnastics	(b)	33,700[f]	2.7	72.5	21.0	3.9	0.0
Hockey: street, roller, & field	(b)	7,144[g,h]	0.0	39.3	46.4	14.2	0.0
Horseback riding	9,500,000[i]	79,745	1.7	17.8	16.9	60.6	3.0
Horseshoe pitching	9,100,000	2,516	8.7	20.4	14.4	52.0	4.5
Ice hockey	2,200,000	16,854[h]	0.2	32.6	41.4	25.4	0.0
Ice skating	5,300,000	23,620[i]	1.7	47.0	19.6	30.8	0.9
Martial arts	5,100,000	23,555	0.1	22.1	25.3	52.5	0.0
Mountain climbing	3,400,000[i]	4,433	0.1	14.0	42.6	43.2	0.0
Racquetball, squash, & paddleball	3,400,000	8,726	0.9	4.6	33.6	59.0	1.9
Roller skating	26,900,000	118,647[j,k]	1.0	60.5	16.0	22.1	0.4
Rugby	(b)	12,486	0.7	2.7	67.8	28.8	0.0
Skateboarding	9,600,000	104,449	1.0	53.9	36.9	8.0	0.1
Snowmobiling	4,600,000	15,333	1.1	8.0	25.9	63.8	1.1
Soccer	13,900,000	175,470	0.4	45.2	37.0	17.3	0.2
Softball	13,200,000	127,171	0.3	20.0	29.3	49.6	0.7
Swimming	54,800,000	174,812[l]	9.3	44.4	18.8	25.2	2.4
Tennis	10,900,000	24,885	1.6	16.4	21.3	44.5	16.2
Track & field	(b)	17,103	0.0	49.5	46.0	4.6	0.0
Volleyball	12,000,000	57,929	0.0	27.7	38.3	33.3	0.7
Water skiing	5,500,000	10,978	0.0	7.2	33.1	59.1	0.6
Weight lifting	21,200,000	74,656	4.0	10.8	37.2	46.8	1.2
Wrestling	3,500,000	53,791	0.9	33.5	52.0	13.3	0.3

Source: Participants — National Sporting Goods Association; figures include those seven years of age or older who participated more than once per year except for bicycle riding and swimming, which include those who participated six or more times per year. Injuries — Consumer Product Safety Commission; figures include only injuries treated in hospital emergency departments.
[a] Excludes mountain biking.
[b] Data not available.
[c] Includes exercise equipment (34,990 injuries) and exercise activity (167,196 injuries).
[d] Includes touch and tackle football.
[e] Excludes golf carts (10,634 injuries).
[f] Excludes trampolines (91,870 injuries).
[g] There were 4,094 injuries in field hockey, 3,050 in roller hockey, and no estimate for street hockey.
[h] Excludes 37,068 injuries in hockey, unspecified.
[i] Estimates for 2000.
[j] Excludes 19,846 injuries in skating, unspecified.
[k] Includes 2x2 (48,933 injuries) and in-line (69,714 injuries).
[l] Includes injuries associated with swimming, swimming pools, pool slides, diving or diving boards, and swimming pool equipment.

Football

There were five fatalities directly related to football during the 2002 season compared to eight in 2001. Three were associated with high school football, one with professional, and one with youth football. All five of the direct fatalities resulted from an injury to the brain. In 2002, there were 10 indirect fatalities caused by systemic failure as a result of exertion while participating in football activities or by a complication compared to 15 in 2001. In 2002, five were associated with high school, four with college, and one with youth football. Four of the high school indirect deaths were heart related, and one was asthma related. Three of the college indirect deaths were heart related, and one was listed as an undetermined death. The youth league indirect death was also heart related.

Source: Mueller, F.O., & Diehl, J.L. (2003). Annual Survey of Football Injury, Research, 1931–2002. Indianapolis, IN: National Collegiate Athletic Association.

Other Sports

In 2002, the U.S. Parachute Association reported 33 fatalities. The Divers Alert Network reported 75 recreational underwater diving fatalities in 2001. The International Hunter Education Association recorded 75 fatal and 716 nonfatal hunting injuries in 2001 in the United States. The U.S. Hang Gliding Association (USHGA) reported no paragliding fatalities in 2001, following one fatality in each of the two previous years, continuing the downward trend from four fatalities in each of the years from 1996–1998. The USHGA also reported three hang gliding fatalities in 2000, the most recent year for which data were available.

Recreational Boating

The United States Coast Guard reported 681 recreational boating fatalities in the United States and its territories in 2001, a 3% decline from 2000. Florida and California experienced the greatest number of deaths with 52 and 48, respectively, followed by Louisiana with 43 and Texas with 41. Alcohol was reported to be involved in 232 (34%) of the deaths in 2001, an increase of 3 percentage points from 2000 and 8 percentage points from 1999. Coast Guard estimates found that persons with a blood alcohol concentration (BAC) of 0.10% are more than 10 times as likely to be killed in a boating accident than boaters with a BAC of zero.

The number of injuries declined by about 2%, from 4,355 in 2000 to 4,274 in 2001. These injuries occurred in an estimated total of 6,419 reported boating accidents, although both the injury and accident figures are probably under reported. There were 498 drowning deaths in 2001. About 8 out of every 10 victims in fatal boating accidents were not wearing life jackets. The Coast Guard estimates that life jackets could have saved about 420 of the boaters who drowned in 2001. The property damage due to recreational boating accidents is estimated at more than $31.3 million in 2001. There were a total of 12,876,346 numbered recreational vessels in the United States and its territories in 2001, with the number varying significantly by state.

RECREATIONAL BOATING ACCIDENTS, FATALITIES, AND FATALITIES DUE TO DROWNING, BY ACCIDENT TYPE, UNITED STATES AND TERRITORIES, 2001

Accident Type	Reported Accidents	Drowning Deaths	Total Fatalities
Total U.S.	6,419	498	681
Collision with Vessel	2,062	19	68
Collision with Fixed Object	644	17	49
Falls Overboard	514	156	176
Capsizing	466	193	210
Skier Mishap	439	1	9
Grounding	412	4	10
Flooding/Swamping	339	34	47
Falls Within Boat	284	4	7
Struck by Boat	166	1	6

Accident Type	Reported Accidents	Drowning Deaths	Total Fatalities
Fire/Explosion (Fuel)	153	2	2
Sinking	150	15	15
Struck Submerged Object	128	4	10
Fire/Explosion (Other than Fuel)	112	0	1
Collision with Floating Object	109	1	2
Struck by Motor/Propeller	100	0	5
Ejected from Vessel	18	11	17
Departed Vessel	16	14	15
Carbon Monoxide Poisoning	14	0	4
Electrocution	4	2	4
Other casualty; Unknown	289	20	24

TYPES OF RECREATIONAL BOATS IN ACCIDENTS, 2001

Type of Boat	Reported Boats in Accidents	Reported Fatalities	Reported Injuries
Total U.S.	8,974	681	4,274
Open Motorboat	3,606	352	1,970
Personal Watercraft	2,562	50	1,424
Cabin Motorboat	1,296	41	401
Auxiliary Sail	293	12	33
Pontoon	191	7	73
Canoe/Kayak	168	101	98

Type of Boat	Reported Boats in Accidents	Reported Fatalities	Reported Injuries
Sail (only)	103	18	34
Houseboat	103	8	30
Rowboat	75	49	34
Inflatable	33	16	18
Airboat	13	1	7
Jet Boat	13	0	3
Other/Unknown	518	26	149

Source: United States Coast Guard, www.uscgboating.org/statistics/Boating_statistics_2001.pdf.

WEATHER

High temperatures caused 35% of weather-related deaths in 2002.

A variety of weather events resulted in 482 deaths in the 50 United States and District of Columbia in 2002, according to data compiled by the National Climatic Data Center, which is part of the National Oceanic and Atmospheric Administration. Thirty seven percent of those deaths were due to hot or cold weather — 167 and 11 deaths, respectively. For the past five years excessive heat has been the leading cause of weather-related deaths.

Tornadoes, lightning, floods, thunderstorms and high winds, and ocean or lake surf each resulted in from 9% to 11% of the deaths, and together accounted for half of the total.

July and August had the most weather-related deaths because of the high number of heat-related deaths. November had the third highest total because of the tornado-related deaths that month. May was fourth highest due to flood-related deaths.

WEATHER-RELATED FATALITIES BY MONTH, UNITED STATES, 2002

Event	Total	Jan	Feb	Mar	Apr	May	Jun	Jul	Aug	Sep	Oct	Nov	Dec
Total	482	15	14	30	23	43	40	135	68	24	22	47	21
Temperature extreme	178	3	2	3	1	2	25	99	39	1		1	2
Tornado	55				7	4					3	37	4
Lightning	51		1			3	9	17	19	2			
Flood	49	2		4	3	16		12	2	1	4	2	3
Thunderstorm and high wind	45	2	2	10	4	6	1	3	2	7		2	6
Ocean/lake surf	44	1		2	3	7	5	3	5	10	3	5	
Snow and ice	33	6	5	11	4	3							4
Fog	19	1	4								12		2
Hurricane and tropical storm	3									3			
Dust storm	2					2							
Hail	1							1					
Wild/forest fire	1								1				
Precipitation (without flood)	1				1								
Drought	0												

Source: National Safety Council tabulations of National Climatic Data Center data.

WEATHER-RELATED FATALITIES BY MONTH, UNITED STATES, 2002

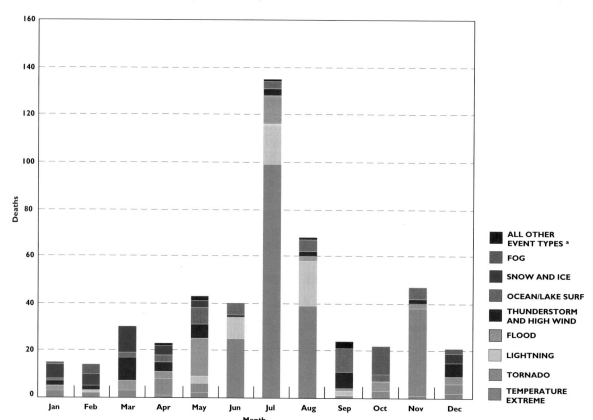

ᵃIncludes hurricane and tropical storm, dust storm, hail, wild/forest fire, and precipitation (without flood).

FIREARMS

Unintentional firearms-related deaths down 49% from 1993 high.

Firearm-related deaths from unintentional, intentional, and undetermined causes totaled 28,663 in 2000, a decrease of 0.7% from 1999. Suicides accounted for 58% of firearms deaths, about 38% were homicides, and almost 3% were unintentional deaths. Males dominate all categories of firearms deaths and accounted for more than 85% of the total.

The numbers of homicide, suicide, and unintentional deaths by firearms have decreased each of the last seven years. Compared to 1993, homicides were down

41%, suicides were down 12%, and unintentional decreased 49%.

Hospital emergency department surveillance data indicate an estimated 17,696 nonfatal unintentional firearm-related injuries in 2001. For assault there were an estimated 41,044 nonfatal injuries and 3,267 intentionally self-inflicted nonfatal injuries.

Source: Miniño, A.M., Arias, E., Kochanek, K.D., Murphy, S.L., & Smith, B.L. (2002). Deaths: Final data for 2000. National Vital Statistics Report, 50(15), 69–70; and Centers for Disease Control and Prevention, National Center for Injury Prevention and Control, WISQARS™ (http://www.cdc.gov/ncipc/wisqars/).

DEATHS INVOLVING FIREARMS, BY AGE AND SEX, UNITED STATES, 2000

Type & Sex	All Ages	Under 5 Years	5–14 Years	15–19 Years	20–24 Years	25–44 Years	45–64 Years	65–74 Years	75 & Over
Total Firearms Deaths	**28,663**	**59**	**377**	**2,606**	**3,969**	**11,147**	**6,223**	**1,941**	**2,341**
Male	24,582	37	302	2,323	3,583	9,366	5,154	1,684	2,133
Female	4,081	22	75	283	386	1,781	1,069	257	208
Unintentional	**776**	**19**	**67**	**107**	**95**	**284**	**128**	**41**	**35**
Male	671	11	62	97	86	234	113	34	34
Female	105	8	5	10	9	50	15	7	1
Suicide	**16,586**	**—**	**110**	**897**	**1,370**	**5,644**	**4,691**	**1,700**	**2,174**
Male	14,454	—	90	793	1,250	4,780	3,977	1,528	2,036
Female	2,132	—	20	104	120	864	714	172	138
Homicide	**10,801**	**40**	**187**	**1,549**	**2,414**	**4,980**	**1,326**	**184**	**121**
Male	9,006	26	138	1,381	2,167	4,137	996	108	53
Female	1,795	14	49	168	247	843	330	76	68
Legal Intervention	**270**	**0**	**3**	**27**	**45**	**148**	**40**	**5**	**2**
Male	261	0	3	27	43	142	39	5	2
Female	9	0	0	0	2	6	1	0	0
Undetermined[a]	**230**	**0**	**10**	**26**	**45**	**91**	**38**	**11**	**9**
Male	190	0	9	25	37	73	29	9	8
Female	40	0	1	1	8	18	9	2	1

[a]Undetermined means the intentionality of the deaths (unintentional, homicide, suicide) was not determined.

FIREARMS DEATHS BY INTENTIONALITY AND YEAR, UNITED STATES, 1991–2000

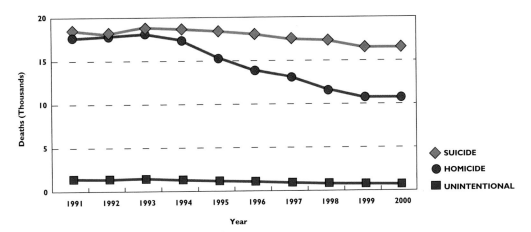

TRANSPORTATION ACCIDENT COMPARISONS

Passenger transportation incidents account for over one-fifth of all unintentional-injury deaths. But the risk of death to the passenger, expressed on a per mile basis, varies greatly by transportation mode. Highway travel by personal vehicle presents the greatest risk; air, rail, and bus travel have much lower death rates. The tables below show the latest information on passenger transportation deaths and death rates.

The automobile statistics shown in the tables below represent all passenger car usage, both intercity and local. A new category has been added this year that includes vans, sport utility vehicles, pickups, and other light trucks. The bus data also include intercity and local (transit) bus travel. Railroad includes both intercity (Amtrak) and local commuting travel. Scheduled airlines includes both large airlines and commuter airlines but excludes on-demand air taxis and charter operations. In comparing the four modes, drivers of automobiles (except taxis), vans, SUVs, and pickup trucks are considered passengers. Bus drivers and airline or railroad crews are not considered passengers.

Other comparisons are possible based on passenger-trips, vehicle-miles, or vehicle-trips, but passenger-miles is the most commonly used basis for comparing the safety of various modes of travel.

TRANSPORTATION ACCIDENT DEATH RATES, 1999–2001

Mode of Transportation	2001			1999–2001 Average Death Rate
	Passenger Deaths	Passenger Miles (Billions)	Deaths per 100,000,000 Passenger Miles	
Passenger automobiles[a]	20,221	2,574.9	0.79	0.81
Vans, SUVs, pickup trucks[b]	11,690	1,537.5	0.76	0.75
Buses[c]	11[d]	63.7	0.02	0.03
Transit buses	2	22.2	0.01	0.01
Intercity buses	2	41.5	0.005	0.03
Railroad passenger trains[e]	3	15.3	0.02	0.05
Scheduled airlines[f]	279	487.9	0.06	0.03

Source: Highway passenger deaths — Fatality Analysis Reporting System data. Railroad passenger deaths — Federal Railroad Administration. Airline passenger deaths — National Transportation Safety Board. Passenger miles for intercity buses, railroad, and airlines — National Safety Council estimates based on historical data from Wilson, R. A. (2001). Transportation in America, 18th edition. Washington, DC: Eno Transportation Foundation, Inc. Passenger miles for transit buses — American Public Transit Association. All other figures — National Safety Council estimates.

[a] Includes taxi passengers. Drivers of passenger automobiles are considered passengers.
[b] Includes 2-axle, 4-tire vehicles under 10,000 lbs GVWR other than automobiles.
[c] Figures exclude school buses.
[d] Deaths include "other" and "unknown" bus types.
[e] Includes commutation.
[f] Includes large airlines and scheduled commuter airlines; excludes cargo service and suicide/sabotage (265 in 2001).

PASSENGER DEATHS AND DEATH RATES, UNITED STATES, 1992–2001

Year	Passenger Automobiles		Vans, SUVs, Pickup Trucks		Buses		Railroad Passenger Trains		Scheduled Airlines	
	Deaths	Rate[a]	Deaths	Rate[a]	Deaths	Rate[a]	Deaths	Rate[a]	Deaths	Rate[a]
1992	21,257	0.83	—	—	17	0.04	3	0.02	38	0.01
1993	21,414	0.86	—	—	9	0.02	58	0.45	19	0.01
1994	21,813	0.91	—	—	13	0.03	5	0.04	245	0.06
1995	22,288	0.97	—	—	16	0.03	0	0.00	159	0.04
1996	22,359	0.96	—	—	10	0.02	12	0.09	329	0.08
1997	21,920	0.92	—	—	4	0.01	6	0.05	42	0.01
1998	21,099	0.86	—	—	26	0.05	4	0.03	0	0.00
1999	20,763	0.83	10,666	0.72	39	0.07	14	0.10	17	0.003
2000	20,444	0.80	11,435	0.76	3	0.01	4	0.03	87	0.02
2001	20,221	0.79	11,690	0.76	11	0.02	3	0.02	279	0.06
10-year average	21,358	0.87	—	—	15	0.03	11	0.08	122	0.03

Source: See table above. Note: Dashes (—) indicate data not available.
[a] Deaths per 100,000,000 passenger miles.

PASSENGER DEATH RATES, UNITED STATES, 1999–2001

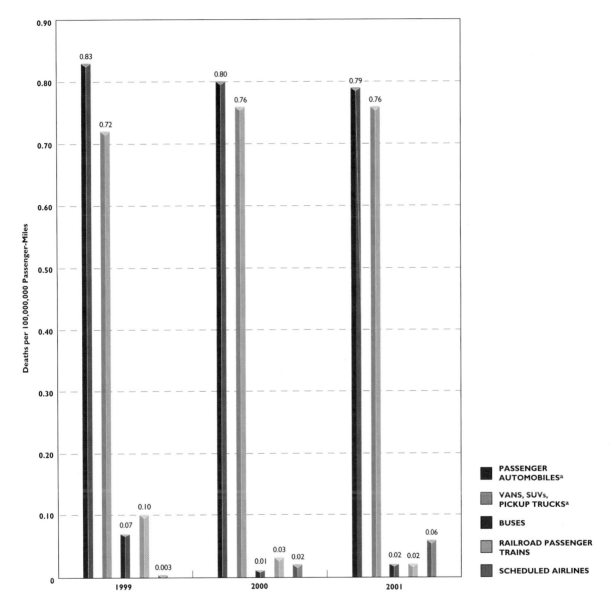

PASSENGER
AUTOMOBILES[a]

VANS, SUVs,
PICKUP TRUCKS[a]

BUSES

RAILROAD PASSENGER
TRAINS

SCHEDULED AIRLINES

[a]Drivers of passenger automobiles are considered passengers.

AVIATION

Worldwide passenger deaths in scheduled air service totaled 791 in 2002, according to preliminary data compiled by the International Civil Aviation Organization, a specialized United Nations agency with 188 member states. The death rate per 100 million passenger kilometers in 2002 was 0.025, up from 0.02 in 2001. Aircraft accidents involving a passenger fatality totaled 14. Passenger deaths per year averaged 834 for the last 10 years.

WORLDWIDE SCHEDULED AIR SERVICE ACCIDENTS, DEATHS, AND DEATH RATES, 1987–2002

Year	Fatal Accidents[a]	Passenger Deaths	Death Rate[b]	Year	Fatal Accidents[a]	Passenger Deaths	Death Rate[b]
1987	25	900	0.06	1995	25	711	0.03
1988	29	742	0.04	1996	24	1,146	0.05
1989	29	879	0.05	1997	25	921	0.04
1990	27	544	0.03	1998	20	904	0.03
1991	29	638	0.03	1999	21	499	0.02
1992	28	1,070	0.06	2000	18	757	0.03
1993	33	864	0.04	2001	13	577	0.02
1994	27	1,170	0.05	2002[c]	14	791	0.025

Source: International Civil Aviation Organization. Figures include the USSR up to 1992 and the Commonwealth of Independent States thereafter.
[a] Involving a passenger fatality and an aircraft with maximum take-off mass >2250 kg.
[b] Passenger deaths per 100 million passenger kilometers.
[c] Preliminary.

U.S. CIVIL AVIATION ACCIDENTS, DEATHS, AND DEATH RATES, 1998–2002

| | | | | Accident Rates | | | |
| | Accidents | | | Per 100,000 Flight-Hours | | Per Million Aircraft-Miles | |
Year	Total	Fatal	Total Deaths[a]	Total	Fatal	Total	Fatal
Large Airlines[b]							
1998	43	1	1	0.270	0.006	0.0068	0.0002
1999	46	2	12	0.276	0.012	0.0069	0.0003
2000	50	3	92	0.286	0.017	0.0070	0.0004
2001[c]	41	6	531	0.216	0.012	0.0053	0.0003
2002	34	0	0	0.195	0	0.0048	0
Commuter Airlines[b]							
1998	8	0	0	2.262	0	0.1576	0
1999	13	5	12	3.793	1.459	0.2481	0.0954
2000	12	1	5	3.247	0.271	0.2670	0.0222
2001	7	2	13	2.330	0.666	0.1624	0.0464
2002	8	0	0	2.595	0	0.1939	0
On-Demand Air Taxis[b]							
1998	77	17	45	2.03	0.45	—	—
1999	73	12	38	2.21	0.36	—	—
2000	80	22	71	2.25	0.62	—	—
2001	72	18	60	2.27	0.57	—	—
2002	58	17	33	1.90	0.56	—	—
General Aviation[b]							
1998[c]	1,904	364	624	7.44	1.41	—	—
1999[c]	1,906	340	619	6.40	1.14	—	—
2000[c]	1,837	344	595	6.30	1.16	—	—
2001[c]	1,726	325	562	6.28	1.18	—	—
2002[c]	1,714	343	576	6.56	1.30	—	—

Source: National Transportation Safety Board: 2002 preliminary, 1998-2001 revised; exposure data for rates from Federal Aviation Administration.
Note: Dash (—) indicates data not available.
[a] Includes passengers, crew members, and others such as persons on the ground.
[b] Civil aviation accident statistics collected by the National Transportation Safety Board are classified according to the Federal air regulations under which the flights were made. The classifications are (1) large airlines operating scheduled service under Title 14, Code of Federal Regulations, part 121 (14 CFR 121); (2) commuter carriers operating scheduled service under 14 CFR 135; (3) unscheduled, "on-demand" air taxis under 14 CFR 135; and (4) "general aviation," which includes accidents involving aircraft flown under rules other than 14 CFR 121 and 14 CFR 135. Not shown in the table is nonscheduled air carrier operations under 14 CFR 121, which experienced seven accidents and no fatalities in 2002. Since 1997, Large Airlines includes aircraft with 10 or more seats, formerly operated as commuter carriers under 14 CFR 135.
[c] Suicide/sabotage and stolen/unauthorized cases are included in "accident" and fatality totals but excluded from rates — Large Airlines, 2001 (4 crashes/265 deaths), General Aviation, 1998 (6/4), 1999 (3/1), 2000 (6/6), 2001 (2/0), 2002 (3/3).

Highway-rail grade-crossing incidents and trespassing accounted for approximately 94% of all rail-related deaths over the 1993–2002 period. Injuries to on-duty railroad employees accounted for approximately 73% of all nonfatal conditions. About 43% of deaths not associated with highway-rail incidents or trespassing were to employees on duty. Passengers on trains and persons lawfully on railroad property accounted for the remainder.

DEATHS AND NONFATAL CASES IN RAILROAD ACCIDENTS AND INCIDENTS, UNITED STATES, 1993–2002

Year	Total	Highway-Rail Crossing Incident?		Occuring in Other Than Highway-Rail Crossing Incident		Employees On Duty At Highway-Rail Crossing?		Passengers on Trains[a] At Highway-Rail Crossing?	
		Yes	No	Trespassers	Others	Yes	No	Yes	No
Deaths									
1993	1,279	626	653	523	130	3	44	0	58
1994	1,226	615	611	529	82	1	30	0	5
1995	1,146	579	567	494	73	2	32	0	0
1996	1,039	488	551	471	80	1	32	0	12
1997	1,063	461	602	533	69	0	37	0	6
1998	1,008	431	577	536	41	4	23	2	2
1999	932	402	530	479	51	2	29	11	3
2000	937	425	512	463	49	2	22	0	4
2001	971	421	550	511	39	1	21	0	3
2002	952	355	597	544	53	1	19	0	7
Nonfatal conditions									
1993	19,121	1,837	17,284	509	16,775	143	15,220	44	515
1994	16,812	1,961	14,851	452	14,399	125	12,955	84	413
1995	14,440	1,894	12,546	461	12,085	123	10,654	30	543
1996	12,558	1,610	10,948	474	10,474	79	9,120	24	489
1997	11,767	1,540	10,227	516	9,711	111	8,184	43	558
1998	11,459	1,303	10,156	513	9,643	122	8,276	19	516
1999	11,700	1,396	10,304	445	9,859	140	8,482	43	438
2000	11,643	1,219	10,424	414	10,010	100	8,323	10	648
2001	10,985	1,157	9,828	404	9,424	97	7,718	20	726
2002	10,921	993	9,928	392	9,536	109	6,426	24	816

Source: Federal Railroad Administration.
[a] Passengers on trains are persons on, boarding, or alighting, other than railroad employees.

HIGHWAY-RAIL GRADE-CROSSING CASUALTIES, UNITED STATES, 1993–2002

Year	Deaths				Nonfatal Conditions			
	Total	Motor-Vehicles	Pedestrians	Others	Total	Motor-Vehicles	Pedestrians	Others
1993	626	554	48	24	1,837	1,760	28	49
1994	615	542	50	23	1,961	1,885	30	46
1995	579	508	47	24	1,894	1,825	28	41
1996	488	415	60	13	1,610	1,545	31	34
1997	461	419	38	4	1,540	1,494	33	13
1998	431	369	50	12	1,303	1,257	33	13
1999	402	345	45	12	1,396	1,338	35	23
2000	425	361	51	13	1,219	1,169	34	16
2001	421	345	67	9	1,157	1,110	31	16
2002	355	308	35	12	993	933	29	31

Source: Federal Railroad Administration. Includes both public and private grade crossings.

Between 1912 and 2002, unintentional-home-injury deaths per 100,000 population were reduced 57% from 28 to 12. In 1912, when there were 21 million households, an estimated 26,000 to 28,000 persons were killed by unintentional home injuries. In 2002, with more than 105 million households and the population tripled, home deaths numbered 33,300.

The injury total of 8,000,000 means that 1 person in 35 in the United States was disabled one full day or more by unintentional injuries received in the home in 2002. Disabling injuries are more numerous in the home than in the workplace and in motor-vehicle crashes combined.

The National Health Interview Survey indicates that about 13,177,000 episodes of home injuries occurred in 1998 (the latest year available). This means that about 1 person in 21 incurred a home injury requiring medical attention. About 41% of all medically attended injuries occurred at home. See page 23 for definitions and numerical differences between National Health Interview Survey and National Safety Council figures.

The Council adopted the Bureau of Labor Statistics' Census of Fatal Occupational Injuries count for work-related unintentional injuries retroactive to 1992 data. Because of the lower Work class total resulting from this change, several thousand unintentional-injury deaths that had been classified by the Council as work-related had to be reassigned to the Home and Public classes. For this reason long-term historical comparisons for these three classes should be made with caution. See the Technical Appendix for an explanation of the methodological changes.

Beginning with 1999 data, which became available in September 2001, deaths are now classified according to the 10th revision of the *International Classification of Diseases.* Overall, about 3% more deaths are classified as due to "unintentional injuries" under the new classification system than under the 9th revision. The difference varies across causes of death. See the Technical Appendix for more information on comparability. Caution should be used in comparing data classified under the two systems.

Deaths **33,300**
Disabling Injuries **8,000,000**
Death Rate per 100,000 Population **11.9**
Costs . . . . **$126.7 billion**

HOME DEATHS AND DEATH RATES, UNITED STATES, 1992–2002

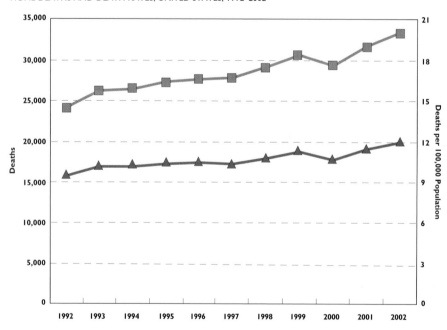

PRINCIPAL TYPES OF HOME UNINTENTIONAL-INJURY DEATHS, UNITED STATES, 1982–2002

Year	Total Home	Falls	Fires/ Burns[a]	Suffocation, Ing. Obj.	Suffocation, Mechanical	Drowning	Poisoning	Natural Heat/Cold	Firearms	Other
1982	21,200	6,500	4,300	2,100	600	(b)	3,500	(b)	1,000	3,200
1983	21,200	6,500	4,100	2,200	600	(b)	3,500	(b)	900	3,400
1984	21,200	6,400	4,100	2,300	600	(b)	3,700	(b)	900	3,200
1985	21,600	6,500	4,000	2,400	600	(b)	3,900	(b)	900	3,300
1986	21,700	6,100	4,000	2,500	600	(b)	4,300	(b)	800	3,400
1987	21,400	6,300	3,900	2,500	600	(b)	4,100	(b)	800	3,200
1988	22,700	6,600	4,100	2,600	600	(b)	4,800	(b)	800	3,200
1989	22,500	6,600	3,900	2,500	600	(b)	5,000	(b)	800	3,100
1990	21,500	6,700	3,400	2,300	600	(b)	4,500	(b)	800	3,200
1991	22,100	6,900	3,400	2,200	700	(b)	5,000	(b)	800	3,100
1992	24,000	7,700	3,700	1,500	700	900	5,200	(b)	1,000	3,300
1993	26,100	7,900	3,700	1,700	700	900	6,500	(b)	1,100	3,600
1994	26,300	8,100	3,700	1,600	800	900	6,800	(b)	900	3,500
1995	27,200	8,400	3,500	1,500	800	900	7,000	(b)	900	4,200
1996	27,500	9,000	3,500	1,500	800	900	7,300	(b)	800	3,700
1997	27,700	9,100	3,200	1,500	800	900	7,800	(b)	700	3,500
1998	29,000	9,500	2,900	1,800	800	1,000	8,400	(b)	600	4,000
1999[c]	30,500	7,600	3,000	1,900	1,100	900	9,300	700	600	5,400
2000[d]	29,200	7,100	2,700	2,100	1,000	1,000	9,800	400	500	4,600
2001[d]	31,600	8,100	2,700	2,100	1,000	900	11,000	500	600	4,700
2002[e]	33,300	8,000	2,200	2,300	1,100	900	12,500	400	500	5,400

Source: National Safety Council estimates based on data from National Center for Health Statistics and state vital statistics departments. The Council adopted the Bureau of Labor Statistics' Census of Fatal Occupational Injuries count for work-related unintentional injuries retroactive to 1992 data. Because of the lower Work class total resulting from this change, several thousand unintentional-injury deaths that had been classified by the Council as work-related, had to be reassigned to the Home and Public classes. For this reason long-term historical comparisons for these three classes should be made with caution. See the Technical Appendix for an explanation of the methodological changes.
[a] Includes deaths resulting from conflagration, regardless of nature of injury.
[b] Included in Other.
[c] In 1999, a revision was made in the International Classification of Diseases. See the Technical Appendix for comparability with earlier years.
[d] Revised.
[e] Preliminary.

PRINCIPAL TYPES OF HOME UNINTENTIONAL-INJURY DEATHS, UNITED STATES, 2002

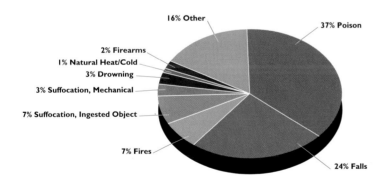

16% Other
2% Firearms
1% Natural Heat/Cold
3% Drowning
3% Suffocation, Mechanical
7% Suffocation, Ingested Object
7% Fires
24% Falls
37% Poison

DEATHS DUE TO UNINTENTIONAL HOME INJURIES, 2002

All Home

Includes deaths in the home and on home premises to occupants, guests, and trespassers. Also includes hired household workers but excludes other persons working on home premises.

	Total	Change from 2001	Death Rate[a]
Deaths	33,300	+5%	11.9

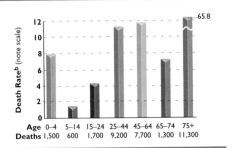

Poisoning

Includes deaths from drugs, medicines, other solid and liquid substances, and gases and vapors. Excludes poisonings from spoiled foods, salmonella, etc., which are classified as disease deaths.

	Total	Change from 2001	Death Rate[a]
Deaths	12,500	+14%	4.5

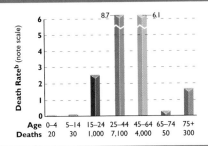

Falls

Includes deaths from falls from one level to another or on the same level in the home or on home premises.

	Total	Change from 2001	Death Rate[a]
Deaths	8,000	−1%	2.9

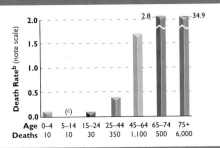

Suffocation by Ingested Object

Includes deaths from unintentional ingestion or inhalation of objects or food resulting in the obstruction of respiratory passages.

	Total	Change from 2001	Death Rate[a]
Deaths	2,300	+10%	0.8

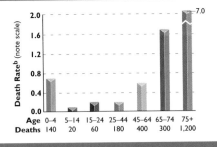

Fires, Flames, and Smoke Associated with Fires

Includes deaths from fires, smoke, and injuries in conflagrations in the home — such as asphyxiation, falls, and struck by falling objects. Excludes burns from hot objects or liquids.

	Total	Change from 2001	Death Rate[a]
Deaths	2,200	−19%	0.8

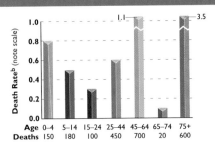

See footnotes on page 137.

TYPE OF EVENT AND AGE OF VICTIM

Mechanical Suffocation

Includes deaths from smothering by bed clothes, thin plastic materials, etc.; suffocation by cave-ins or confinement in closed spaces; and mechanical strangulation and hanging.

	Total	Change from 2001	Death Rate[a]
Deaths	1,100	+10%	0.4

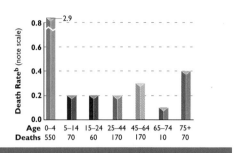

Age	0–4	5–14	15–24	25–44	45–64	65–74	75+
Deaths	550	70	60	170	170	10	70

Drowning

Includes drownings of persons in or on home premises — such as in swimming pools and bathtubs. Excludes drowning in floods and other cataclysms.

	Total	Change from 2001	Death Rate[a]
Deaths	900	0%	0.3

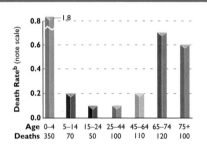

Age	0–4	5–14	15–24	25–44	45–64	65–74	75+
Deaths	350	70	50	100	110	120	100

Firearms

Includes firearms injuries in or on home premises — such as while cleaning or playing with guns. Excludes deaths from explosive materials.

	Total	Change from 2001	Death Rate[a]
Deaths	500	–17%	0.2

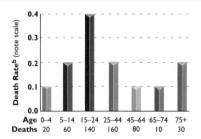

Age	0–4	5–14	15–24	25–44	45–64	65–74	75+
Deaths	20	60	140	160	80	10	30

Natural Heat or Cold

Includes deaths resulting from exposure to excessive natural heat and cold (e.g., extreme weather conditions).

	Total	Change from 2001	Death Rate[a]
Deaths	400	–20%	0.1

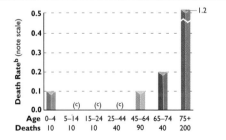

Age	0–4	5–14	15–24	25–44	45–64	65–74	75+
Deaths	10	10	10	40	90	40	200

All Other Home

Most important types included are: struck by or against objects, machinery, and electric current.

	Total	Change from 2001	Death Rate[a]
Deaths	5,400	+15%	1.9

[a] Deaths per 100,000 population.
[b] Deaths per 100,000 population in each age group.
[c] Death rate less than 0.05.

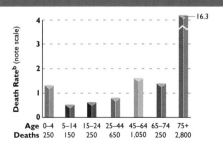

Age	0–4	5–14	15–24	25–44	45–64	65–74	75+
Deaths	250	150	250	650	1,050	250	2,800

UNINTENTIONAL POISONINGS

Approximately 2.3 million human poisoning exposure cases were reported in 2001.

Deaths from unintentional poisoning numbered 12,757 in 2000, the latest year for which detailed tabulations are available. The death rate per 100,000 population was 4.6–6.8 for males and 2.6 for females.

Total poisoning deaths increased approximately 5% from 12,186 in 1999 to 12,757 in 2000 and have nearly doubled since 1991.

Almost half of the poisoning deaths (48%) were classified in the "narcotics and psychodysleptics (hallucinogens), not elsewhere classified," category, which includes many illegal drugs such as cocaine, heroin, cannabinol, and LSD.

Carbon monoxide poisoning is included in the category of "other gases and vapors." Deaths due to alcohol poisoning numbered 302 in 2000, but alcohol may also be present in combination with other drugs.

In 2000, 2.2 million human poisoning exposure cases, both fatal and nonfatal, were reported to 63 poison control centers, which covered 96.2% of the U.S. population. That is equivalent to about 8.0 reported exposures per 1,000 population, according to the American Association of Poison Control Centers. In 2001, 2.3 million cases were reported to 64 centers covering 98.8% of the population for a rate of 8.1 exposures per 1,000 population.

UNINTENTIONAL POISONING DEATHS BY TYPE, AGE, AND SEX, UNITED STATES, 2000

Type of Poison	All Ages	0–4 Years	5–14 Years	15–19 Years	20–24 Years	25–44 Years	45–64 Years	65 Years & Over
Both Sexes								
Total Poisoning Deaths	**12,757**	**46**	**45**	**351**	**809**	**7,043**	**3,749**	**714**
Deaths per 100,000 population	*4.6*	*0.2*	*0.1*	*1.8*	*4.4*	*8.6*	*6.1*	*2.0*
Nonopioid analgesics, antipyretics, and antirheumatics (X40)[a]	176	3	1	2	6	80	56	28
Antiepileptic, sedative-hypnotic, antiparkinsonism, and psychotropic drugs, n.e.c. (X41)	704	1	3	26	50	364	221	39
Narcotics and psychodysleptics (hallucinogens), n.e.c. (X42)	6,139	8	6	136	404	3,642	1,866	77
Other drugs acting on the autonomic nervous system (X43)	21	0	1	1	2	10	1	6
Other and unspecified drugs, medicaments, and biological substances (X44)	4,672	7	6	126	292	2,588	1,274	379
Alcohol (X45)	302	1	1	14	13	145	119	9
Organic solvents and halogenated hydrocarbons and their vapors (X46)	38	3	0	4	2	13	11	5
Other gases and vapors (X47)	593	18	23	37	32	182	165	136
Pesticides (X48)	8	1	0	0	1	1	3	2
Other and unspecified chemical and noxious substances (X49)	104	4	4	5	7	18	33	33
Males								
Total Poisoning Deaths	**9,138**	**32**	**27**	**273**	**647**	**5,204**	**2,624**	**331**
Deaths per 100,000 population	*6.8*	*0.3*	*0.1*	*2.7*	*6.9*	*12.7*	*8.9*	*2.3*
Nonopioid analgesics, antipyretics, and antirheumatics (X40)	74	1	0	1	4	33	23	12
Antiepileptic, sedative-hypnotic, antiparkinsonism, and psychotropic drugs, n.e.c. (X41)	436	1	1	17	34	249	120	14
Narcotics and psychodysleptics (hallucinogens), n.e.c. (X42)	4,841	7	4	111	338	2,852	1,480	49
Other drugs acting on the autonomic nervous system (X43)	12	0	0	1	0	7	1	3
Other and unspecified drugs, medicaments, and biological substances (X44)	3,005	5	4	93	225	1,761	763	154
Alcohol (X45)	232	1	1	11	10	118	89	2
Organic solvents and halogenated hydrocarbons and their vapors (X46)	36	3	0	4	2	13	10	4
Other gases and vapors (X47)	435	11	15	31	28	155	119	76
Pesticides (X48)	6	1	0	0	0	1	2	2
Other and unspecified chemical and noxious substances (X49)	61	2	2	4	6	15	17	15
Females								
Total Poisoning Deaths	**3,619**	**14**	**18**	**78**	**162**	**1,839**	**1,125**	**383**
Deaths per 100,000 population	*2.6*	*0.2*	*0.1*	*0.8*	*1.8*	*4.4*	*3.6*	*1.9*
Nonopioid analgesics, antipyretics, and antirheumatics (X40)	102	2	1	1	2	47	33	16
Antiepileptic, sedative-hypnotic, antiparkinsonism, and psychotropic drugs, n.e.c. (X41)	268	0	2	9	16	115	101	25
Narcotics and psychodysleptics (hallucinogens), n.e.c. (X42)	1,298	1	2	25	66	790	386	28
Other drugs acting on the autonomic nervous system (X43)	9	0	1	0	2	3	0	3
Other and unspecified drugs, medicaments, and biological substances (X44)	1,667	2	2	33	67	827	511	225
Alcohol (X45)	70	0	0	3	3	27	30	7
Organic solvents and halogenated hydrocarbons and their vapors (X46)	2	0	0	0	0	0	1	1
Other gases and vapors (X47)	158	7	8	6	4	27	46	60
Pesticides (X48)	2	0	0	0	1	0	1	0
Other and unspecified chemical and noxious substances (X49)	43	2	2	1	1	3	16	18

Source: National Safety Council tabulations of National Center for Health Statistics mortality data.
Note: n.e.c. = not elsewhere classified.
[a] Numbers following titles refer to external cause of injury and poisoning classifications in ICD-10.

UNINTENTIONAL POISONING DEATHS, UNITED STATES, 1991–2000

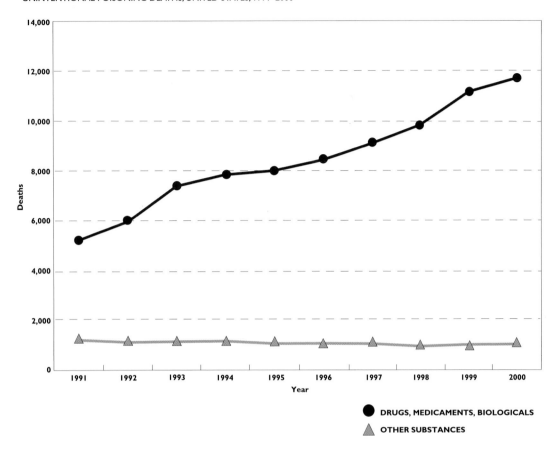

DRUGS, MEDICAMENTS, BIOLOGICALS

OTHER SUBSTANCES

Note: Classification system changed in 1999 (see the Technical Appendix).

INJURIES ASSOCIATED WITH CONSUMER PRODUCTS

Stairs and steps were associated with more than 1,000,000 emergency department visits in 2001.

The following list of items found in and around the home was selected from the U.S. Consumer Product Safety Commission's National Electronic Injury Surveillance System (NEISS) for 2001. The NEISS estimates are calculated from a statistically representative sample of hospitals in the United States. Injury totals represent estimates of the number of hospital emergency department-treated cases nationwide associated with various products. However, product involvement may or may not be the cause of the injury.

ESTIMATED HOSPITAL EMERGENCY DEPARTMENT VISITS RELATED TO SELECTED CONSUMER PRODUCTS, UNITED STATES, 2001
(excluding most sports or sports equipment; see also page 126)

Description	Injuries[a]
Home Workshop Equipment	
Saws (hand or power)	93,872
Hammers	43,055
Household Packaging & Containers	
Household containers & packaging	220,118
Bottles and jars	83,753
Bags	37,411
Paper products	24,001
Housewares	
Knives	460,580
Tableware and flatware (excl. knives)	116,125
Drinking glasses	91,979
Scissors	35,138
Cookware, bowls, and canisters	31,685
Waste containers, trash baskets, etc.	30,388
Home Furnishing, Fixtures, and Accessories	
Beds	519,001
Chairs	314,953
Tables, n.e.c.[b]	310,121
Bathtubs and showers	211,250
Ladders	175,179
Sofas, couches, davenports, divans, etc.	137,860
Rugs and carpets	112,779
Other furniture[c]	107,426
Toilets	60,882
Stools	48,162
Misc. decorating items	47,094
Benches	29,130
Sinks	23,848
Electric lighting equipment	23,802
Mirrors or mirror glass	23,655
Home Structures and Construction Materials	
Stairs or steps	1,087,546
Floors or flooring materials	957,367
Other doors[d]	349,679
Ceilings and walls	319,011
Household cabinets, racks, & shelves	262,407
Nails, screws, tacks, or bolts	179,757
Porches, balconies, open-side floors	142,872
House repair and construction materials	140,899
Windows	139,113
Fences or fence posts	117,826
Poles	49,175
Door sills or frames	45,085
Handrails, railings, or banisters	43,194

Description	Injuries[a]
Home Structures and Construction Materials (CONT.)	
Counters or countertops	39,549
Glass doors	36,120
General Household Appliances	
Refrigerators	31,240
Ranges	25,840
Heating, Cooling, and Ventilating Equipment	
Pipes (excluding smoking pipes)	34,073
Home Communication and Entertainment Equipment	
Televisions	47,210
Personal Use Items	
Footwear	118,501
Wheelchairs	93,873
Jewelry	76,327
Crutches, canes, walkers	72,355
First aid equipment	56,058
Desk supplies	40,750
Daywear	40,186
Razors and shavers	38,531
Coins	31,214
Other clothing[e]	29,789
Hair grooming equipment & accessories	25,358
Yard and Garden Equipment	
Lawn mowers	87,506
Pruning, trimming, & edging equipment	44,712
Chainsaws	30,150
Other unpowered garden tools[f]	26,947
Recreation Equipment	
All-terrain vehicles	111,700
Scooters (unpowered)	99,812
Trampolines	91,870
Monkey bars or other playground climbing	87,444
Toys, n.e.c.	83,413
Swimming pools	83,168
Swings or swing sets	71,804
Minibikes or trailbikes	59,556
Slides or sliding boards	50,249
Dancing	45,498
Other playground equipment[g]	33,031
Aquariums and other pet supplies	32,889
Sleds	23,186
Miscellaneous Products	
Carts	48,000
Hot water	44,062

Source: U.S. Consumer Product Safety Commission, National Electronic Injury Surveillance System, Product Summary Report, All Products, CY2001. Products are listed above if the estimate was greater than 23,000 cases.
[a] *Estimated number of product-related injuries in the United States and territories that were treated in hospital emergency departments.*
[b] *Excludes baby changing and television tables or stands.*
[c] *Excludes cabinets, racks, shelves, desks, bureaus, chests, buffets, etc.*

[d] *Excludes glass doors and garage doors.*
[e] *Excludes costumes, masks, daywear, footwear, nightwear, and outerwear.*
[f] *Includes cultivators, hoes, pitchforks, rakes, shovels, spades, and trowels.*
[g] *Excludes monkey bars, seesaws, slides, and swings.*
n.e.c. = not elsewhere classified.

Civilian deaths in residential fires numbered 3,140 in 2001 according to the National Fire Protection Association, a decrease of 8.9% from 2000. Of these deaths, 460 occurred in apartment fires, a decrease of 8.0%. Another 2,650 civilians died in one- and two-family dwellings, a decrease of 9.2% or 270 fewer deaths than for the previous year. In addition to the fatalities, there were an estimated 15,575 civilian injuries in residential fires in 2001, a significant 10.5% decrease from 2000.

Fires in the home (one- and two-family dwellings and apartments) resulted in 3,110 civilian deaths in 2001, a decrease of 9.1% from 2000 and down over 48% from their peak of 6,015 in 1978. The historical pattern of home fire deaths shows a steady decline to 4,820 from the 1978 high during the period 1979–1982 except for

1981, followed by a fairly level period between 4,655 to 4,955 from 1982–1988, except for 1984 when only 4,075 fire deaths occurred (see figure). From 1989 to 2001, home fire deaths decreased substantially below the 1982–1988 plateau and remained between 3,110 and 3,720 from 1991 to 2001, except for 1996 when 4,035 deaths occurred, and 1999 when 2,895 deaths occurred. The 2001 figure is the second lowest ever recorded, with 1999 having the lowest.

Communities of one million or higher population had the highest average number of fires, civilian deaths, civilian injuries, and property loss due to residential fires in 2001 (see table). The average for each of these quantities declines as community population decreases.

Source: Karter, M. J., Jr. (2002, November). Fire loss in the United States During 2001. Quincy, MA: National Fire Protection Association.

CIVILIAN FIRE DEATHS IN THE HOME, UNITED STATES, 1977–2001

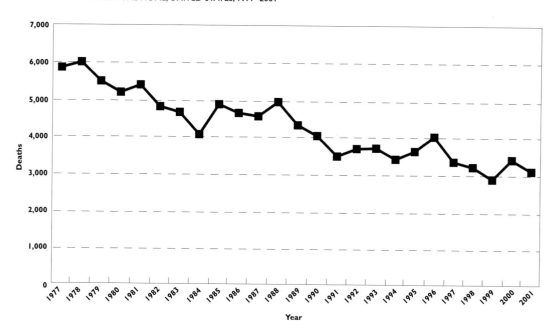

AVERAGE[a] RESIDENTIAL FIRE EXPERIENCE BY COMMUNITY SIZE, UNITED STATES, 2001

Population of Community	Number of Fires	Civilian Deaths	Civilian Injuries	Property Loss ($)
1,000,000 or more	4,867	29.25	116.20	27,790,000
500,000 to 999,999	929	6.12	37.00	14,447,500
250,000 to 499,999	404	3.60	27.07	6,369,200
100,000 to 249,999	196	1.55	11.42	2,565,800
50,000 to 99,999	79	0.53	4.84	992,800
25,000 to 49,999	38	0.35	2.20	570,000
10,000 to 24,999	20	0.17	0.75	251,000
5,000 to 9,999	12	0.08	0.28	204,800
2,500 to 4,999	5	0.06	0.11	127,300
Under 2,500	2	0.02	0.05	46,300

[a] Average over all communities in each size group.

CHOKING AND CHILDREN

Choking on food and nonfood objects is the fifth leading cause of unintentional-injury deaths among children under 15 years of age. In 2000, 160 children died from inhalation or ingestion of foreign objects that obstructed the respiratory tract. About 40% of the deaths involved food and 60% involved nonfood objects.

The Centers for Disease Control and Prevention estimated, through its National Electronic Injury Surveillance System-All Injury Program, that 17,537 children under 15 years old were treated in hospital emergency departments in 2001 for choking-related episodes, or about 29.9 episodes per 100,000 population. The table shows the number, percent, and rate of episodes for various characteristics of nonfatal choking episodes.

Candy and gum accounted for about one fifth of all nonfatal choking episodes treated in hospital emergency departments and nearly two thirds of these cases were associated with hard candy. Candy and gum were associated with about one fourth of cases in the 1–4 and 5–14 age groups.

Coins were associated with about one out of eight choking episodes overall and about 18% in the 1–4 age group.

Source: Centers for Disease Control and Prevention. (2002). Nonfatal choking-related episodes among children — United States, 2001. Morbidity and Mortality Weekly Report, 51(42), 945-948.

NONFATAL CHOKING EPISODES AMONG CHILDREN 0–14 YEARS OLD BY SELECTED CHARACTERISTICS, UNITED STATES, 2001

Characteristic	Number[a]	Percent	Rate[b]
Total	**17,537**	**100.0%**	**29.9**
Age			
Under 1	5,341	30.5	140.4
1	3,942	22.5	104.9
2	2,124	12.1	56.5
3	2,104	12.0	55.9
4	915	5.2	23.9
5–9	2,179	12.4	11.1
10–14	931	5.3	4.6
Sex			
Male	9,656	55.1	32.1
Female	7,831	44.7	27.3
Unknown	50	0.3	—
Substance			
Food	*10,438*	*59.5*	*17.8*
Candy and gum	3,325	19.0	5.7
Other solid food[c]	5,192	29.6	8.8
Liquid	1,328	7.6	2.3
Unspecified	594	3.4	1.0
Nonfood	*5,513*	*31.4*	*9.4*
Coins	2,229	12.7	3.8
Other[d]	3,284	18.7	5.6
Unknown	*1,586*	*9.0*	*2.7*

Source: Centers for Disease Control and Prevention, National Electronic Injury Surveillance System-All Injury Program.
[a] *Numbers might not add to total due to rounding.*
[b] *Per 100,000 population.*
[c] *Includes cookies, chips/crackers, popcorn, nuts/seeds, bones, bread/sandwich, meat/fish/poultry, fruit, pasta/rice/cereal, vegetables, and other specified food.*
[d] *Includes toys, marbles, balloons, puzzle pieces, paper, pen caps, tape, screws and other hardware, keys, plastic, cellophane, plants, rocks, jewelry, hair accessories, soda can tabs, and other specified nonfood items.*

NONFATAL CHOKING EPISODES BY SUBSTANCE INVOLVED, CHILDREN 0–14 YEARS OLD, UNITED STATES, 2001

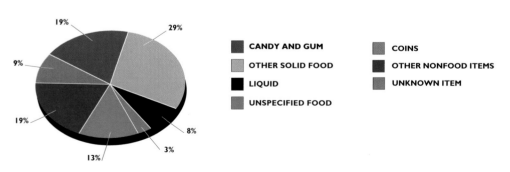

CHILDREN'S PRODUCTS

Toys

The Consumer Product Safety Commission (CPSC) estimated that, in 2000, there were 191,000 people treated in hospital emergency departments for toy-related injuries. Of these injuries, 79% involved children under 15 years old and 37% were under 5 years old. The CPSC also identified 17 deaths of children associated with toys in 2000.

Nursery products

The CPSC estimated that there were 69,100 injuries associated with nursery products in 2000. Estimates by type of product are shown in the table. Over the three years from 1996 to 1998, CPSC identified 231 deaths associated with nursery products, or about 77 each year, among children under five years old.

Source: McDonald, J. (2002). Children's products. Consumer Product Safety Review, 6(3), 1–2.

NURSERY PRODUCT-RELATED INJURIES AND DEATHS, CHILDREN <5 YEARS OLD, UNITED STATES

Product	Estimated Injuries, 2000	Deaths, 1996–1998
Total[a]	69,100	231
Infant carriers and car seats[b]	14,530	19
Strollers and carriages	12,520	6
Cribs	11,640	97
Baby walkers and jumpers	8,310	7
High chairs	7,770	7
Changing tables	3,170	1
Baby gates and barriers	1,130	1
Playpens and play yards	1,600	36
Baby bath seats	—	24
Other	8,810	33

Source: Consumer Product Safety Commission.
[a] Due to rounding, injury estimates do not add to the total.
[b] Excludes injuries occurring in motor-vehicle crashes.

BB/PELLET GUN INJURIES

Eighty percent of BB/pellet guns sold in the U.S. have muzzle velocities greater than 350 feet per second, which, at close range, can cause injuries similar to those caused by bullets from small caliber handguns. In 2001, the Consumer Product Safety Commission (CPSC) estimated that there were 10,241 BB/pellet-associated injuries treated in hospital emergency departments. More than half (53%) of them involved children 5–14 years old, and another 30% involved children and youths 15–24 years old.

A recent study of data for 1993–1999 by the National Center for Injury Prevention and Control found that 53.3% of the injuries were to an extremity, 15.4% were to the face, 12.1% to the trunk, 11.7% to the head or neck, and 5.9% to the eye. The graph shows the intentionality of the BB/pellet gun injury episodes.

Source: Consumer Product Safety Commission and Nguyen, M. H., Annest, J. L., Mercey, J. A., Ryan, G. W., & Fingerhut, L.A. (2002). Trends in BB/pellet gun injuries in children and teenagers in the United States, 1985-99. Injury Prevention, 8(3), 185–191.

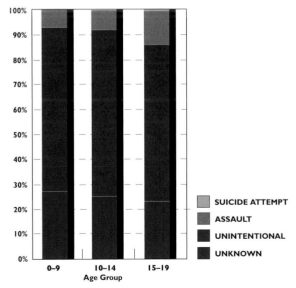

BB/PELLET GUN INJURIES BY AGE GROUP AND INTENTIONALITY, UNITED STATES, 1993–1999

AIR QUALITY

Over the 10 years from 1992 through 2001, progress has been made in reducing emissions of most important air pollutants known as criteria pollutants. According to estimates made by the Environmental Protection Agency, emissions of the six criteria pollutants decreased 15%. Emissions of carbon monoxide, nitrogen oxides, volatile organic compounds, sulfur dioxide, and 10-micrometer particulate matter were all lower in 2001 than in 1992. Only emissions of 2.5-micrometer particulate matter had risen. At the same time, the U.S. population grew 11%, the economy grew 36%, energy consumption increased 13%, and vehicle-miles traveled were up 24%.

Source: U.S. EPA. (2003). Average Annual Emissions, All Criteria Pollutants, Years Including 1980, 1985, 1989–2001. At www.epa.gov/ttn/chief/trends/trends01/trends2001.pdf accessed March 7, 2003.

AVERAGE ANNUAL EMISSIONS OF CRITERIA POLLUTANTS, UNITED STATES, 1992–2001

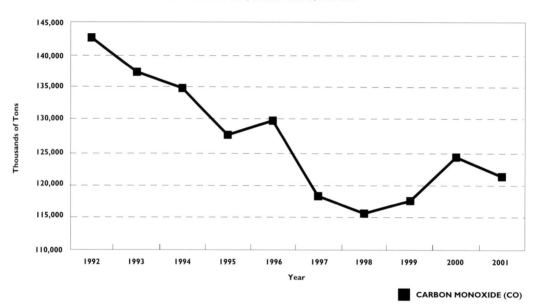

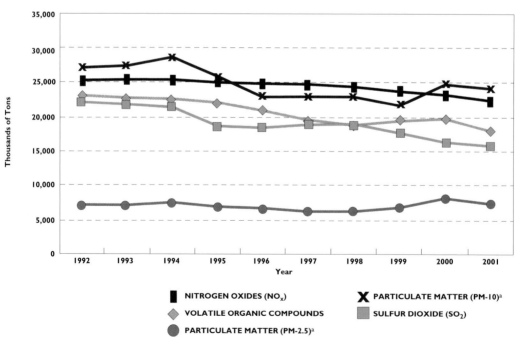

[a]Particulate matter 2.5 μm or 10 μm in diameter or less.

WATERBORNE DISEASE

Estimating the total number of cases of waterborne disease in the United States is difficult. Not everyone who gets sick goes to a doctor or clinic. Not every case of gastroenteritis is diagnosed as being caused by a specific germ, and even then the source of the exposure may remain unknown. The Centers for Disease Control and Prevention (CDC), the Environmental Protection Agency (EPA), and state epidemiologists maintain a surveillance system for waterborne disease. The CDC points out, however, that not all waterborne disease outbreaks (WBDOs) are recognized, investigated, and reported to CDC or EPA, and the extent to which WBDOs are unrecognized and underreported is unknown.

In 1999–2000, there were 39 reported outbreaks associated with drinking water. These outbreaks occurred in 25 states, including one outbreak that spanned ten states. An estimated 2,068 persons were ill and two died. Twenty seven (69%) of the 39 outbreaks involved well water, 7 (18%) involved surface water such as rivers, streams, and creeks, 3 (8%) involved irrigation systems, and 2 (5%) involved springs.

During the same period, there were 59 outbreaks associated with recreational water. These occurred in 23 states and affected 2,093 persons. Twenty-five (42%) of these outbreaks occurred in pools, 17 (29%) in lakes or ponds, 11 (19%) in hot tubs or whirlpools, and the remainder in other or unspecified locations.

Source: Centers for Disease Control and Prevention. (2002). Surveillance for Waterborne-Disease Outbreaks, United States, 1999–2000. Morbidity and Mortality Weekly Report, 51, SS–8.

WATERBORNE-DISEASE OUTBREAKS, UNITED STATES, 1999–2000

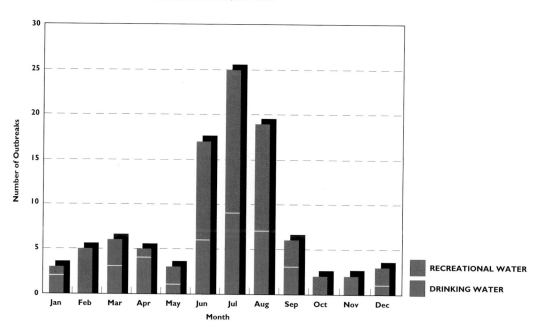

WATERBORNE-DISEASE OUTBREAKS BY EXPOSURE, UNITED STATES, 1999–2000

ASTHMA

Asthma is a chronic, episodic, inflammatory condition of the lungs. Asthma attacks can be triggered by infections, exercise, weather, and environmental pollutants such as sulfur dioxide, dust mites, cockroaches, animal dander, tobacco smoke, and mold. For this reason, asthma is considered to be an environmental health problem.

The lifetime prevalence of asthma was measured in the National Health Interview Survey (NHIS) by asking if the respondent had ever been told by a health professional that they had asthma. In 2001, 3.1 million people, or 114 per 1,000 population, had been diagnosed with asthma.

The current prevalence of asthma was estimated to be 20.3 million people, or 73 per 1,000 population, based on the NHIS. This includes people who had been diagnosed with asthma by a health professional and still had asthma.

The attack prevalence is also available from the NHIS. This is the number of people who had at least one asthma attack in the previous year. In 2001, 12 million people, or 43 per 1,000 population, had experienced at least one attack in the past year.

Health care for asthma patients may take place in number of settings from office visits to hospitalizations. Estimates of health care utilization for asthma in 2000 are:

- 10.4 million visits to physician's offices and hospital clinics
- 1.8 million visits to hospital emergency departments
- 465,000 hospitalizations with an average length of stay of 3.2 days

Deaths from asthma totaled 4,487 people in 2000, or 1.6 per 1,000 population.

Source: National Center for Health Statistics. (2003). Asthma prevalence, health care use and mortality, 2000–2001. At www.cdc.gov.nchs/products/pubs/pubd/hestats/asthma/asthma.htm accessed March 6, 2003.

CURRENT ASTHMA PREVALENCE, UNITED STATES, 2001

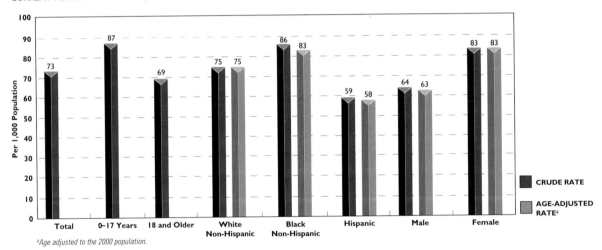

ᵃAge adjusted to the 2000 population.

ASTHMA DEATH RATES, UNITED STATES, 2000

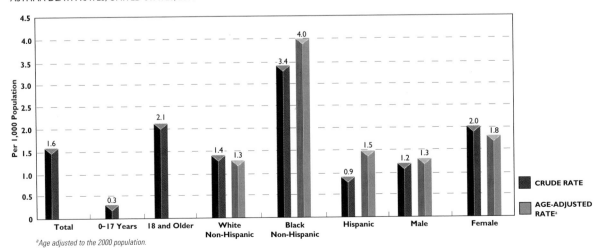

ᵃAge adjusted to the 2000 population.

Environmental tobacco smoke (ETS), or secondhand smoke, consists of the smoke given off by burning tobacco and the smoke exhaled by smokers. It contains more than 4,000 substances of which more than 40 are known carcinogens and many are strong irritants. These substances can cause serious health problems.

Environmental tobacco smoke (ETS) is responsible for at least 3,000 lung cancer deaths each year, according to Environmental Protection Agency (EPS) estimates, as well as 35,000 cardiovascular deaths, and exacerbation of hundreds of thousands of cases of asthma and lower respiratory tract infections.

ETS is particularly serious for children. The EPA estimates the ETS casuses 150,000 to 300,000 lower respiratory tract infection in infants and children under 18 months old each year of which 7,500 to 15,000 are hospitalized. The EPA also estimates that from 200,000 to 1,000,000 children with asthma have their conditions made worse by ETS and that ETS is a risk factor for the development of thousands of cases of asthma in children annually.

There has been success in reducing exposure to ETS in the United States. Median continine levels among nonsmokers aged 3 and older have dropped more than 75% from the late 1980s through 1999. Cotinine is a metabolite of nicotine.

In the workplace, 79% of worksites with 50 or more employees have formal policies that prohibit smoking or limit smoking to separately ventilated areas. In total, 69% of people aged 15 and older are protected from ETS at their worksites. In homes, more than 60% of people aged 15 and older were protected from ETS by a ban on tobacco smoke there.

The table below shows the extent to which people in each state are protected from ETS by smoking policies at work and at home.

Source: Centers for Disease Control. (2002) Tobacco control state highlights 2002. At www.cdc.gov/tobacco/statehi/statehi_2002.htm accessed March 6, 2003. Environmental Protection Agency. Appendix F — Secondhand Smoke (SHS), or Environmental Tobacco Smoke (ETS). In IAQ Tools for Schools Kit — IAQ Coordinator's Guide. At www.epa.gov/iap/schools/tfs/guidef.html accessed March 7, 2003.

PERCENT OF PEOPLE PROTECTED FROM ENVIRONMENTAL TOBACCO SMOKE BY SMOKING POLICIES, UNITED STATES, 1998–1999

State	Worksite	Home	State	Worksite	Home
Total U.S.	**69.0%**	**61.1%**	Missouri	65.9	54.9
Alabama	63.9	58.1	Montana	69.1	61.4
Alaska	73.6	61.5	Nebraska	67.6	59.6
Arizona	68.7	71.5	Nevada	48.9	64.5
Arkansas	63.5	53.2	New Hampshire	74.3	61.0
California	77.6	74.3	New Jersey	72.9	62.4
Colorado	72.8	67.0	New Mexico	68.3	63.0
Connecticut	73.8	61.0	New York	72.6	58.8
Delaware	70.8	55.4	North Carolina	60.9	52.1
District of Columbia	74.6	57.1	North Dakota	65.8	58.2
Florida	69.0	66.8	Ohio	63.2	51.0
Georgia	66.6	62.2	Oklahoma	67.3	54.2
Hawaii	72.2	64.7	Oregon	66.3	71.1
Idaho	71.4	71.8	Pennsylvania	68.9	57.1
Illinois	67.5	54.6	Rhode Island	72.3	61.8
Indiana	58.3	50.1	South Carolina	64.4	60.6
Iowa	69.9	54.5	South Dakota	60.0	57.0
Kansas	73.4	59.6	Tennessee	63.4	52.9
Kentucky	57.1	39.7	Texas	66.4	65.9
Louisiana	64.2	56.7	Utah	84.4	81.7
Maine	75.3	55.4	Vermont	77.1	61.3
Maryland	81.7	64.9	Virginia	70.5	58.4
Massachusetts	77.3	62.0	Washington	73.9	68.8
Michigan	61.0	53.5	West Virginia	63.5	42.5
Minnesota	74.3	63.4	Wisconsin	64.4	55.4
Mississippi	61.5	54.4	Wyoming	66.1	59.9

Source: Centers for Disease Control. (2002). Tobacco control state highlights 2002. At www.cdc.gov/tobacco/statehi/statehi_2002.htm accessed March 6, 2003.

INJURY FACTS®

NATIONAL SAFETY COUNCIL

STATE DATA

Motor-vehicle crashes are the leading cause of U-I deaths in every state.

This section on state-level data includes data for occupational and motor-vehicle injuries as well as general injury mortality.

Death rates for unintentional injuries (U-I) can vary greatly from one type of injury to the next and from state to state. The graph on the next page shows for each state the death rates (per 100,000 population) for total unintentional-injury deaths and the four leading types of unintentional-injury deaths nationally — motor-vehicle crashes, falls, poisonings, and choking (inhalation or ingestion of food or other object that obstructs breathing).

The map on page 152 shows graphically the overall unintentional-injury death rates by state.

The charts on pages 153 through 155 show (a) total unintentional-injury deaths and where U-I rank as a cause of death in each state and (b) the five leading causes of U-I deaths in each state.

Unintentional injuries as a whole are the fifth leading cause of death in the United States and in 32 states. U-I are the third leading cause of death in Alaska, the District of Columbia, New Mexico, and Wyoming, and the fourth leading cause in eight states. U-I rank sixth in four states (Maine, New Jersey, New York, and Ohio), seventh in Maryland and Rhode Island, and eighth in Massachusetts.

Motor-vehicle crashes were the leading cause of U-I deaths in every state except Rhode Island where it was tied with falls. Poisoning was the leading cause in the District of Columbia. The second leading cause of U-I deaths was falls in 31 states and falls tied with poisoning for second place in Wyoming. Poisoning was second in 17 states and motor-vehicle crashes was second in the District of Columbia. The most common third leading causes of U-I deaths were poisoning in

23 states, falls in 14 states and the District of Columbia, choking in five states, fires in four states, and drowning in two states. Drowning was tied with air transport for third place in Alaska. Choking was the fourth leading cause of U-I deaths in 25 states, while the fourth ranking cause was drowning in 13 states, fires and flames in six states and the District of Columbia, poisoning in three states, and falls and machinery in one state each.

The table on pages 156 and 157 shows the number of U-I deaths by state for the 15 most common types of injury events. State populations are also shown to facilitate computation of detailed death rates.

The table on page 158 consists of a 4-year state-by-state comparison of unintentional-injury deaths and death rates for 1997 through 2000. Because of the change in mortality classification schemes from ICD-9 to ICD-10 in 1999, caution must be exercised in making comparisons of 1999 and later data with earlier years. A comparability study conducted by the National Center for Health Statistics indicates that if the 1998 mortality data had been coded according to ICD-10, then the U-I death total would have been about 3% greater. See the Technical Appendix for more information.

Page 159 shows fatal occupational injuries by state and counts of deaths for some of the principal types of events — transportation accidents, assaults and violent acts, contacts with objects and equipment, falls, exposure to harmful substances or environments, and fires and explosions.

Nonfatal occupational injury and illness incidence rates for most states are shown in the table on page 160 and graphically in the map on page 161.

Pages 162 and 163 show motor-vehicle–related deaths and death rates by state both in tables and maps.

UNINTENTIONAL-INJURY DEATH RATES BY STATE, UNITED STATES, 2000

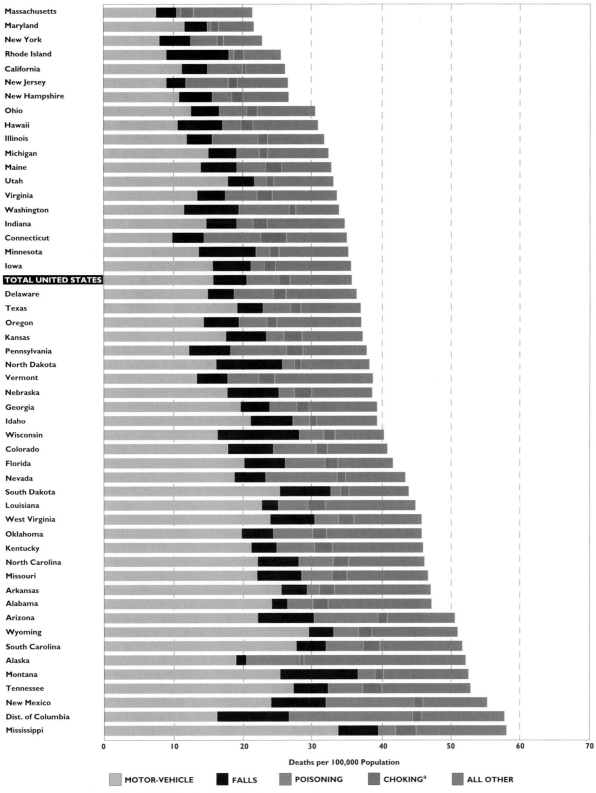

Deaths per 100,000 Population

MOTOR-VEHICLE FALLS POISONING CHOKING[a] ALL OTHER

[a] Suffocation by inhalation or ingestion of food or other objects.

UNINTENTIONAL-INJURY DEATH RATES BY STATE

UNINTENTIONAL-INJURY DEATHS PER 100,000 POPULATION BY STATE, 2000

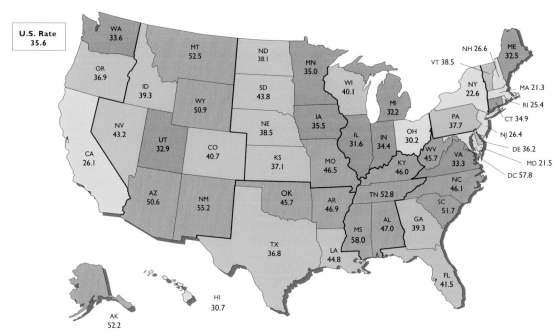

U.S. Rate
35.6

WA 33.6
MT 52.5
ND 38.1
MN 35.0
NH 26.6
ME 32.5
VT 38.5
OR 36.9
ID 39.3
WY 50.9
SD 43.8
WI 40.1
NY 22.6
MA 21.3
RI 25.4
CT 34.9
NV 43.2
UT 32.9
CO 40.7
NE 38.5
IA 35.5
MI 32.2
PA 37.7
NJ 26.4
DE 36.2
MD 21.5
DC 57.8
CA 26.1
AZ 50.6
NM 55.2
KS 37.1
IL 31.6
IN 34.4
OH 30.2
WV 45.7
VA 33.3
KY 46.0
NC 46.1
MO 46.5
OK 45.7
AR 46.9
TN 52.8
SC 51.7
TX 36.8
MS 58.0
AL 47.0
GA 39.3
LA 44.8
FL 41.5
AK 52.2
HI 30.7

REGIONAL RATES

New England (CT, ME, MA, NH, RI, VT)	27.2
Middle Atlantic (NJ, NY, PA)	28.2
East N. Central (IL, IN, MI, OH, WI)	32.8
West N. Central (IA, KS, MN, MO, NE, ND, SD)	39.5
South Atlantic (DE, DC, FL, GA, MD, NC, SC, VA, WV)	39.6
East S. Central (AL, KY, MS, TN)	50.5
West S. Central (AR, LA, OK, TX)	39.8
Mountain (AZ, CO, ID, MT, NV, NM, UT, WY)	45.0
Pacific (AK, CA, HI, OR, WA)	28.5

BELOW 31.6: 9 STATES

31.6 TO 35.6: 10 STATES

35.7 TO 44.8: 16 STATES

ABOVE 44.8: 15 STATES AND
DISTRICT OF COLUMBIA

Source: National Center for Health Statistics, and U.S. Census Bureau.

The following series of charts is a state-by-state ranking of the five leading causes of deaths due to unintentional injuries (U-I) based on 2000 data. The first line of each section gives the rank of unintentional-injury deaths among all causes of death, the total number of U-I deaths, and the rate of U-I deaths per 100,000 population. The following lines list the five leading types of unintentional-injury deaths along with the number and rate for each type.

TOTAL UNITED STATES

Rank	Cause	Deaths	Rate
5	All U-I	97,900	35.6
1	Motor-vehicle	43,354	15.7
2	Falls	13,322	4.8
3	Poisoning[a]	12,757	4.6
4	Choking[c]	4,313	1.6
5	Drowning[b]	3,482	1.3

ALABAMA

Rank	Cause	Deaths	Rate
4	All U-I	2,099	47.0
1	Motor-vehicle	1,072	24.0
2	Poisoning[a]	159	3.6
3	Fires, flames, smoke	116	2.6
4	Falls	101	2.3
5	Choking[c]	96	2.2

ALASKA

Rank	Cause	Deaths	Rate
3	All U-I	342	52.2
1	Motor-vehicle	124	18.9
2	Poisoning[a]	50	7.6
3	Drowning[b]	29	4.4
3	Air transport	29	4.4
5	Water transport	20	3.1

ARIZONA

Rank	Cause	Deaths	Rate
5	All U-I	2,432	50.6
1	Motor-vehicle	1,058	22.0
2	Poisoning[a]	443	9.2
3	Falls	390	8.1
4	Drowning[b]	107	2.2
5	Choking[c]	69	1.4

ARKANSAS

Rank	Cause	Deaths	Rate
5	All U-I	1,237	46.9
1	Motor-vehicle	669	25.4
2	Falls	97	3.7
3	Fires, flames, smoke	66	2.5
4	Choking[c]	55	2.1
5	Drowning[b]	54	2.0

CALIFORNIA

Rank	Cause	Deaths	Rate
5	All U-I	8,510	26.1
1	Motor-vehicle	3,652	11.2
2	Poisoning[a]	1,637	5.0
3	Falls	1,208	3.7
4	Drowning[b]	368	1.1
5	Fires, flames, smoke	191	0.6

COLORADO

Rank	Cause	Deaths	Rate
5	All U-I	1,702	40.7
1	Motor-vehicle	743	17.8
2	Falls	273	6.5
3	Poisoning[a]	254	6.1
4	Choking[c]	68	1.6
5	Drowning[b]	34	0.8

CONNECTICUT

Rank	Cause	Deaths	Rate
5	All U-I	1,150	34.9
1	Motor-vehicle	324	9.8
2	Poisoning[a]	267	8.1
3	Falls	153	4.6
4	Choking[c]	122	3.7
5	Drowning[b]	25	0.8

DELAWARE

Rank	Cause	Deaths	Rate
5	All U-I	279	36.2
1	Motor-vehicle	115	14.9
2	Poisoning[a]	43	5.6
3	Falls	29	3.8
4	Choking[c]	14	1.8
5	Drowning[b]	8	1.0

DISTRICT OF COLUMBIA

Rank	Cause	Deaths	Rate
3	All U-I	303	57.8
1	Poisoning[a]	94	17.9
2	Motor-vehicle	85	16.2
3	Falls	54	10.3
4	Fires, flames, smoke	19	3.6
5	Natural heat/cold	9	1.7

FLORIDA

Rank	Cause	Deaths	Rate
5	All U-I	6,337	41.5
1	Motor-vehicle	3,075	20.1
2	Falls	906	5.9
3	Poisoning[a]	873	5.7
4	Drowning[b]	357	2.3
5	Choking[c]	269	1.8

GEORGIA

Rank	Cause	Deaths	Rate
4	All U-I	3,099	39.3
1	Motor-vehicle	1,549	19.6
2	Falls	334	4.2
3	Poisoning[a]	298	3.8
4	Choking[c]	144	1.8
5	Fires, flames, smoke	132	1.7

HAWAII

Rank	Cause	Deaths	Rate
4	All U-I	387	30.7
1	Motor-vehicle	134	10.6
2	Falls	82	6.5
3	Drowning[b]	48	3.8
4	Poisoning[a]	33	2.6
5	Choking[c]	21	1.7

IDAHO

Rank	Cause	Deaths	Rate
5	All U-I	531	39.3
1	Motor-vehicle	284	21.0
2	Falls	83	6.1
3	Poisoning[a]	32	2.4
4	Drowning[b]	20	1.5
5	Air transportation	15	1.1

ILLINOIS

Rank	Cause	Deaths	Rate
5	All U-I	3,815	31.6
1	Motor-vehicle	1,435	11.9
2	Poisoning[a]	784	6.5
3	Falls	453	3.8
4	Choking[c]	164	1.4
5	Fires, flames, smoke	154	1.3

INDIANA

Rank	Cause	Deaths	Rate
5	All U-I	2,086	34.4
1	Motor-vehicle	892	14.7
2	Falls	264	4.4
3	Poisoning[a]	139	2.3
4	Choking[c]	121	2.0
5	Drowning[b]	79	1.3

IOWA

Rank	Cause	Deaths	Rate
5	All U-I	1,031	35.5
1	Motor-vehicle	454	15.6
2	Falls	160	5.5
3	Poisoning[a]	56	1.9
4	Choking[c]	46	1.6
5	Fires, flames, smoke	44	1.5

KANSAS

Rank	Cause	Deaths	Rate
5	All U-I	993	37.1
1	Motor-vehicle	467	17.5
2	Falls	155	5.8
3	Choking[c]	69	2.6
4	Poisoning[a]	68	2.5
5	Fires, flames, smoke	41	1.5

See footnotes on page 155.

KENTUCKY

Rank	Cause	Deaths	Rate
5	All U-I	1,841	46.0
1	Motor-vehicle	845	21.1
2	Poisoning[a]	216	5.4
3	Falls	150	3.7
4	Choking[c]	101	2.5
5	Fires and flames	85	2.1

MARYLAND

Rank	Cause	Deaths	Rate
7	All U-I	1,135	21.5
1	Motor-vehicle	614	11.6
2	Falls	172	3.3
3	Choking[c]	59	1.1
4	Fires, flames, smoke	46	0.9
5	Drowning[b]	43	0.8

MINNESOTA

Rank	Cause	Deaths	Rate
5	All U-I	1,695	35.0
1	Motor-vehicle	659	13.6
2	Falls	395	8.2
3	Poisoning[a]	99	2.0
4	Drowning[b]	65	1.3
5	Choking[c]	61	1.3

MONTANA

Rank	Cause	Deaths	Rate
5	All U-I	500	52.5
1	Motor-vehicle	240	25.2
2	Falls	107	11.2
3	Poisoning[a]	24	2.5
4	Drowning[b]	17	1.8
5	Natural heat/cold	14	1.5

NEW HAMPSHIRE

Rank	Cause	Deaths	Rate
5	All U-I	326	26.6
1	Motor-vehicle	133	10.8
2	Falls	59	4.8
3	Poisoning[a]	34	2.8
4	Choking[c]	20	1.6
5	Fires, flames, smoke	11	0.9

NEW YORK

Rank	Cause	Deaths	Rate
6	All U-I	4,118	22.6
1	Motor-vehicle	1,449	8.0
2	Falls	812	4.5
3	Poisoning[a]	700	3.8
4	Fires, flames, smoke	194	1.1
5	Choking[c]	155	0.9

LOUISIANA

Rank	Cause	Deaths	Rate
4	All U-I	1,988	44.8
1	Motor-vehicle	1,003	22.6
2	Poisoning[a]	188	4.2
3	Choking[c]	111	2.5
4	Fires, flames, smoke	107	2.4
5	Falls	105	2.4

MASSACHUSETTS

Rank	Cause	Deaths	Rate
8	All U-I	1,322	21.3
1	Motor-vehicle	467	7.5
2	Falls	186	3.0
3	Choking[c]	111	1.8
4	Fires, flames, smoke	62	1.0
5	Drowning[b]	41	0.7

MISSISSIPPI

Rank	Cause	Deaths	Rate
4	All U-I	1,637	58.0
1	Motor-vehicle	945	33.5
2	Falls	166	5.9
3	Fires, flames, smoke	85	3.0
4	Choking[c]	84	3.0
5	Poisoning[a]	71	2.5

NEBRASKA

Rank	Cause	Deaths	Rate
5	All U-I	658	38.5
1	Motor-vehicle	303	17.7
2	Falls	126	7.4
3	Choking[c]	42	2.5
4	Poisoning[a]	38	2.2
5	Drowning[b]	16	0.9

NEW JERSEY

Rank	Cause	Deaths	Rate
6	All U-I	2,165	26.4
1	Motor-vehicle	739	9.0
2	Poisoning[a]	501	6.1
3	Falls	229	2.8
4	Choking[c]	109	1.3
5	Fires, flames, smoke	67	0.8

NORTH CAROLINA

Rank	Cause	Deaths	Rate
5	All U-I	3,596	46.1
1	Motor-vehicle	1,717	22.0
2	Falls	457	5.9
3	Poisoning[a]	382	4.9
4	Choking[c]	171	2.2
5	Drowning[b]	135	1.7

MAINE

Rank	Cause	Deaths	Rate
6	All U-I	410	32.5
1	Motor-vehicle	175	13.9
2	Falls	65	5.2
3	Poisoning[a]	52	4.1
4	Choking[c]	29	2.3
5	Fires, flames, smoke	16	1.3

MICHIGAN

Rank	Cause	Deaths	Rate
5	All U-I	3,127	32.2
1	Motor-vehicle	1,456	15.0
2	Falls	401	4.1
3	Poisoning[a]	309	3.2
4	Fires and flames	142	1.5
5	Choking[c]	119	1.2

MISSOURI

Rank	Cause	Deaths	Rate
5	All U-I	2,584	46.5
1	Motor-vehicle	1,215	21.9
2	Falls	355	6.4
3	Poisoning[a]	245	4.4
4	Choking[c]	115	2.1
5	Fires, flames, smoke	99	1.8

NEVADA

Rank	Cause	Deaths	Rate
5	All U-I	811	43.2
1	Motor-vehicle	350	18.7
2	Poisoning[a]	192	10.2
3	Falls	84	4.5
4	Drowning[b]	29	1.5
5	Choking[c]	22	1.2

NEW MEXICO

Rank	Cause	Deaths	Rate
3	All U-I	1,029	55.2
1	Motor-vehicle	445	23.9
2	Poisoning[a]	238	12.8
3	Falls	147	7.9
4	Choking[c]	25	1.3
5	Natural heat/cold	24	1.3

NORTH DAKOTA

Rank	Cause	Deaths	Rate
5	All U-I	253	38.1
1	Motor-vehicle	107	16.1
2	Falls	63	9.5
3	Poisoning[a]	11	1.7
4	Machinery	10	1.5
5	Drowning[b]	8	1.2

See footnotes on page 155.

OHIO

Rank	Cause	Deaths	Rate
6	All U-I	3,427	30.2
1	Motor-vehicle	1,413	12.5
2	Falls	463	4.1
3	Poisoning[a]	437	3.9
4	Choking[c]	173	1.5
5	Fires, flames, smoke	129	1.1

PENNSYLVANIA

Rank	Cause	Deaths	Rate
5	All U-I	4,615	37.7
1	Motor-vehicle	1,498	12.2
2	Poisoning[a]	973	8.0
3	Falls	737	6.0
4	Choking[c]	285	2.3
5	Fires, flames, smoke	179	1.5

SOUTH DAKOTA

Rank	Cause	Deaths	Rate
5	All U-I	341	43.8
1	Motor-vehicle	196	25.2
2	Falls	57	7.3
3	Drowning[b]	13	1.7
4	Poisoning[a]	11	1.4
5	Choking[c]	9	1.2

UTAH

Rank	Cause	Deaths	Rate
4	All U-I	727	32.9
1	Motor-vehicle	394	17.8
2	Falls	85	3.8
3	Poisoning[a]	37	1.7
4	Drowning[b]	35	1.6
5	Choking[c]	24	1.1

WASHINGTON

Rank	Cause	Deaths	Rate
5	All U-I	1,971	33.6
1	Motor-vehicle	673	11.5
2	Falls	461	7.9
3	Poisoning[a]	420	7.2
4	Drowning[b]	70	1.2
5	Fires, flames, smoke	61	1.0

WYOMING

Rank	Cause	Deaths	Rate
3	All U-I	268	51.0
1	Motor-vehicle	154	29.3
2	Falls	19	3.6
2	Poisoning[a]	19	3.6
4	Choking[c]	10	1.9
5	Drowning[b]	7	1.3

OKLAHOMA

Rank	Cause	Deaths	Rate
5	All U-I	1,546	45.7
1	Motor-vehicle	667	19.7
2	Poisoning[a]	188	5.6
3	Falls	155	4.6
4	Drowning[b]	70	2.1
5	Choking[c]	69	2.0

RHODE ISLAND

Rank	Cause	Deaths	Rate
7	All U-I	254	25.4
1	Motor-vehicle	90	9.0
1	Falls	90	9.0
3	Fires, flames, smoke	16	1.6
4	Choking[c]	14	1.4
5	Poisoning[a]	7	0.7

TENNESSEE

Rank	Cause	Deaths	Rate
5	All U-I	2,993	52.8
1	Motor-vehicle	1,535	27.1
2	Falls	285	5.0
3	Poisoning[a]	283	5.0
4	Choking[c]	159	2.8
5	Fires, flames, smoke	132	2.3

VERMONT

Rank	Cause	Deaths	Rate
5	All U-I	238	38.4
1	Motor-vehicle	82	13.2
2	Falls	28	4.5
3	Poisoning[a]	27	4.4
4	Fires, flames, smoke	17	2.7
5	Choking[c]	14	2.3

WEST VIRGINIA

Rank	Cause	Deaths	Rate
5	All U-I	843	45.7
1	Motor-vehicle	440	23.8
2	Falls	119	6.4
3	Poisoning[a]	62	3.4
4	Choking[c]	40	2.2
5	Fires, flames, smoke	32	1.7

OREGON

Rank	Cause	Deaths	Rate
5	All U-I	1,255	36.9
1	Motor-vehicle	486	14.3
2	Falls	174	5.1
3	Poisoning[a]	135	4.0
4	Drowning[b]	64	1.9
5	Choking[c]	49	1.4

SOUTH CAROLINA

Rank	Cause	Deaths	Rate
4	All U-I	1,998	51.7
1	Motor-vehicle	1,064	27.5
2	Poisoning[a]	207	5.4
3	Falls	168	4.3
4	Choking[c]	93	2.4
5	Fires, flames, smoke	91	2.4

TEXAS

Rank	Cause	Deaths	Rate
4	All U-I	7,418	36.8
1	Motor-vehicle	3,860	19.1
2	Poisoning[a]	809	4.0
3	Falls	742	3.7
4	Drowning[b]	322	1.6
5	Choking[c]	274	1.4

VIRGINIA

Rank	Cause	Deaths	Rate
5	All U-I	2,337	33.3
1	Motor-vehicle	939	13.4
2	Poisoning[a]	314	4.5
3	Falls	285	4.1
4	Choking[c]	151	2.2
5	Fires, flames, smoke	96	1.4

WISCONSIN

Rank	Cause	Deaths	Rate
5	All U-I	2,141	40.1
1	Motor-vehicle	869	16.3
2	Falls	623	11.7
3	Poisoning[a]	188	3.5
4	Choking[c]	84	1.6
5	Drowning[b]	64	1.2

Source: National Safety Council tabulations of National Center for Health Statistics mortality data for 2000.
[a] Solid, liquid, gas, and vapor poisoning.
[b] Excludes transport drownings.
[c] Inhalation or ingestion of food or other object.

UNINTENTIONAL-INJURY DEATHS BY STATE AND EVENT

UNINTENTIONAL-INJURY DEATHS BY STATE AND TYPE OF EVENT, UNITED STATES, 2000

State	Population (000)	Total[a]	Motor-vehicle[b]	Falls	Poisoning	Choking[c]	Drowning[d]	Fires, Flames, and Smoke	Mechanical Suffocation
Total U.S.	**275,306**	**97,900**	**43,354**	**13,322**	**12,757**	**4,313**	**3,482**	**3,377**	**1,335**
Alabama	4,462	2,099	1,072	101	159	96	85	116	22
Alaska	655	342	124	10	50	4	29	12	10
Arizona	4,810	2,432	1,058	390	443	69	107	43	19
Arkansas	2,637	1,237	669	97	47	55	54	66	11
California	32,600	8,510	3,652	1,208	1,637	176	368	191	92
Colorado	4,178	1,702	743	273	254	68	34	18	24
Connecticut	3,292	1,150	324	153	267	122	25	21	9
Delaware	770	279	115	29	43	14	8	7	5
Dist. of Columbia	524	303	85	54	94	7	3	19	0
Florida	15,270	6,337	3,075	906	873	269	357	139	80
Georgia	7,894	3,099	1,549	334	298	144	92	132	49
Hawaii	1,260	387	134	82	33	21	48	3	6
Idaho	1,350	531	284	83	32	14	20	8	6
Illinois	12,080	3,815	1,435	453	784	164	90	154	86
Indiana	6,060	2,086	892	264	139	121	79	79	58
Iowa	2,907	1,031	454	160	56	46	28	44	11
Kansas	2,675	993	467	155	68	69	26	41	22
Kentucky	4,005	1,841	845	150	216	101	59	85	32
Louisiana	4,436	1,988	1,003	105	188	111	97	107	25
Maine	1,262	410	175	65	52	29	14	16	2
Maryland	5,288	1,135	614	172	24	59	43	46	13
Massachusetts	6,214	1,322	467	186	39	111	41	62	14
Michigan	9,703	3,127	1,456	401	309	119	103	142	56
Minnesota	4,842	1,695	659	395	99	61	65	31	45
Mississippi	2,823	1,637	945	166	71	84	52	85	20
Missouri	5,554	2,584	1,215	355	245	115	78	99	31
Montana	952	500	240	107	24	11	17	7	6
Nebraska	1,709	658	303	126	38	42	16	14	12
Nevada	1,876	811	350	84	192	22	29	20	10
New Hampshire	1,227	326	133	59	34	20	9	11	4
New Jersey	8,198	2,165	739	229	501	109	57	67	27
New Mexico	1,865	1,029	445	147	238	25	19	15	8
New York	18,190	4,118	1,449	812	700	155	97	194	56
North Carolina	7,796	3,596	1,717	457	382	171	135	133	24
North Dakota	664	253	107	63	11	6	8	6	2
Ohio	11,347	3,427	1,413	463	437	173	98	129	53
Oklahoma	3,381	1,546	667	155	188	69	70	48	21
Oregon	3,405	1,255	486	174	135	49	64	33	17
Pennsylvania	12,232	4,615	1,498	737	973	285	93	179	84
Rhode Island	1,000	254	90	90	7	14	3	16	2
South Carolina	3,867	1,998	1,064	168	207	93	68	91	28
South Dakota	779	341	196	57	11	9	13	6	9
Tennessee	5,671	2,993	1,535	285	283	159	93	132	27
Texas	20,168	7,418	3,860	742	809	274	322	248	77
Utah	2,212	727	394	85	37	24	35	9	10
Vermont	619	238	82	28	27	14	5	17	9
Virginia	7,014	2,337	939	285	314	151	60	96	23
Washington	5,872	1,971	673	461	420	55	70	61	35
West Virginia	1,845	843	440	119	62	40	25	32	11
Wisconsin	5,339	2,141	869	623	188	84	64	43	31
Wyoming	526	268	154	19	19	10	7	4	1

See source and footnotes on page 157.

UNINTENTIONAL-INJURY DEATHS BY STATE AND TYPE OF EVENT, UNITED STATES, 2000, Cont.

State	Natural Heat or Cold	Struck By/Against Object	Firearms	Machinery	Electric Current	Water Transport	Air Transport	Rail Transport	All Other Accidents
Total U.S.	1,043	877	776	676	395	630	777	482	10,304
Alabama	22	13	36	11	9	9	6	10	332
Alaska	11	5	2	1	2	20	29	1	32
Arizona	44	13	14	5	7	13	42	13	152
Arkansas	23	19	16	7	7	14	6	4	142
California	57	62	68	47	30	51	158	67	646
Colorado	18	13	4	13	6	9	26	6	193
Connecticut	10	12	4	9	4	0	0	2	188
Delaware	1	3	2	0	0	3	0	1	48
Dist. of Columbia	9	1	5	0	1	0	0	1	24
Florida	25	43	12	29	22	72	50	37	348
Georgia	28	37	36	29	18	16	23	21	293
Hawaii	1	1	4	1	0	3	13	0	37
Idaho	8	8	5	9	0	11	15	1	27
Illinois	46	30	11	24	18	15	15	42	448
Indiana	24	19	24	18	13	3	10	9	334
Iowa	13	6	6	14	8	8	3	3	171
Kansas	6	13	9	5	3	1	10	5	93
Kentucky	24	26	27	20	8	8	14	5	221
Louisiana	29	19	28	9	13	39	8	2	205
Maine	6	4	2	7	1	14	3	1	19
Maryland	9	8	1	11	5	7	5	8	110
Massachusetts	28	7	3	2	1	3	9	5	344
Michigan	31	19	16	23	11	19	16	11	395
Minnesota	19	11	6	9	3	6	10	3	273
Mississippi	31	23	25	8	13	26	8	3	77
Missouri	33	22	30	22	9	5	10	13	302
Montana	14	6	4	6	0	4	8	3	43
Nebraska	12	8	6	4	2	2	3	3	67
Nevada	4	1	6	5	1	2	16	2	67
New Hampshire	2	3	2	4	0	3	0	0	42
New Jersey	22	14	11	11	5	13	13	13	334
New Mexico	24	13	10	5	2	0	17	2	59
New York	30	33	23	29	12	19	4	37	468
North Carolina	30	38	28	16	11	15	17	10	412
North Dakota	3	7	2	10	2	3	1	2	20
Ohio	28	34	35	35	10	13	11	12	483
Oklahoma	27	8	20	14	10	5	12	10	222
Oregon	9	16	5	14	3	15	9	5	221
Pennsylvania	56	30	41	15	12	3	32	16	561
Rhode Island	2	3	0	0	0	0	3	1	23
South Carolina	30	27	17	13	11	13	6	7	155
South Dakota	6	3	4	1	0	0	7	2	17
Tennessee	27	35	53	28	11	17	12	10	286
Texas	86	74	63	49	55	48	53	36	622
Utah	5	11	3	7	6	8	14	4	75
Vermont	5	5	2	1	2	4	0	1	36
Virginia	22	21	12	23	12	17	13	9	340
Washington	8	21	7	14	6	27	13	7	93
West Virginia	8	10	8	11	4	1	2	9	61
Wisconsin	23	15	14	26	4	21	18	5	113
Wyoming	4	4	4	2	2	2	4	2	30

Source: National Safety Council tabulations of National Center for Health Statistics mortality data.
[a] Deaths are by place of occurrence and exclude nonresident aliens. See also page 152.
[b] See page 162 for motor-vehicle deaths by place of residence.
[c] Suffocation by inhalation or ingestion of food or other object.
[d] Excludes water transport drownings.

UNINTENTIONAL-INJURY TRENDS BY STATE

Unintentional-injury (U-I) deaths decreased 14% from 1997 to 2000 in Maryland and New York, but increased 20% in Illinois and Alaska. Death rates, on the other hand, decreased 17% in Maryland and Idaho while increasing 17% in the District of Columbia and 20% in Illinois. Nationwide, U-I deaths increased 2% over the four years and the death rate decreased less than 0.5%.

The table below shows the trend in unintentional-injury deaths and death rates by state over the most recent four years for which data are available.

UNINTENTIONAL-INJURY DEATHS BY STATE, UNITED STATES, 1997–2000

State	Deaths[a]				Death Rate[c]			
	2000[b]	1999	1998	1997	2000[b]	1999	1998	1997
Total U.S.	97,900	97,860	97,835	95,644	35.6	35.9	35.9	35.7
Alabama	2,099	2,313	2,181	2,255	47.0	52.9	49.9	52.2
Alaska	342	294	267	286	52.2	47.5	43.1	47.0
Arizona	2,432	2,214	2,314	2,192	50.6	46.3	48.4	48.2
Arkansas	1,237	1,287	1,197	1,262	46.9	50.4	46.9	50.0
California	8,510	9,198	9,132	8,897	26.1	27.8	27.6	27.6
Colorado	1,702	1,519	1,542	1,476	40.7	37.4	38.0	37.9
Connecticut	1,150	1,034	1,063	980	34.9	31.5	32.4	30.0
Delaware	279	267	292	286	36.2	35.4	38.8	38.9
Dist. of Columbia	303	161	309	260	57.8	31.0	59.5	49.2
Florida	6,337	5,961	5,976	5,640	41.5	39.4	39.5	38.4
Georgia	3,099	3,078	3,140	3,091	39.3	39.5	40.3	41.3
Hawaii	387	293	319	365	30.7	24.7	26.9	30.7
Idaho	531	597	585	575	39.3	47.7	46.7	47.5
Illinois	3,815	4,125	3,668	3,176	31.6	34.0	30.2	26.4
Indiana	2,086	2,309	2,165	2,077	34.4	38.9	36.4	35.4
Iowa	1,031	1,123	1,068	1,060	35.5	39.1	37.2	37.1
Kansas	993	1,126	1,086	959	37.1	42.4	40.9	36.7
Kentucky	1,841	1,730	1,728	1,757	46.0	43.7	43.6	45.0
Louisiana	1,988	1,940	1,955	1,957	44.8	44.4	44.7	45.0
Maine	410	458	452	444	32.5	36.6	36.1	35.7
Maryland	1,135	1,296	1,334	1,326	21.5	25.1	25.8	26.0
Massachusetts	1,322	1,303	1,311	1,269	21.3	21.1	21.2	20.8
Michigan	3,127	3,188	3,059	3,081	32.2	32.3	31.0	31.5
Minnesota	1,695	1,772	1,747	1,681	35.0	37.1	36.6	35.9
Mississippi	1,637	1,642	1,697	1,570	58.0	59.3	61.3	57.5
Missouri	2,584	2,465	2,645	2,562	46.5	45.1	48.4	47.4
Montana	500	461	495	487	52.5	52.2	56.1	55.5
Nebraska	658	668	679	669	38.5	40.1	40.8	40.4
Nevada	811	710	777	722	43.2	39.2	42.9	43.1
New Hampshire	326	329	349	334	26.6	27.4	29.1	28.5
New Jersey	2,165	2,227	2,133	2,268	26.4	27.3	26.2	28.2
New Mexico	1,029	969	1,065	1,076	55.2	55.7	61.2	62.5
New York	4,118	4,797	4,520	4,803	22.6	26.4	24.8	26.5
North Carolina	3,596	3,290	3,332	3,128	46.1	43.0	43.6	42.1
North Dakota	253	267	303	274	38.1	42.1	47.8	42.8
Ohio	3,427	3,630	3,463	3,388	30.2	32.2	30.8	30.2
Oklahoma	1,546	1,609	1,565	1,600	45.7	47.9	46.6	48.3
Oregon	1,255	1,199	1,411	1,342	36.9	36.2	42.5	41.4
Pennsylvania	4,615	4,614	4,563	4,819	37.7	38.5	38.0	40.1
Rhode Island	254	243	252	227	25.4	24.5	25.4	23.0
South Carolina	1,998	1,901	1,841	1,708	51.7	48.9	47.4	45.1
South Dakota	341	351	369	311	43.8	47.9	50.3	42.6
Tennessee	2,993	2,677	2,914	2,847	52.8	48.8	53.1	52.9
Texas	7,418	7,227	7,426	7,148	36.8	36.1	37.0	36.9
Utah	727	650	720	734	32.9	30.5	33.8	35.5
Vermont	238	209	223	220	38.5	35.2	37.6	37.4
Virginia	2,337	2,214	2,295	2,279	33.3	32.2	33.4	33.9
Washington	1,971	1,914	1,893	1,865	33.6	33.3	32.9	33.3
West Virginia	843	798	842	797	45.7	44.2	46.6	43.9
Wisconsin	2,141	1,955	1,914	1,855	40.1	37.2	36.5	35.7
Wyoming	268	258	259	259	50.9	53.8	54.0	54.0

Source: National Safety Council estimates based on data from National Center for Health Statistics and U.S. Bureau of the Census. See Technical Appendix for comparability.
[a] Deaths for each state are by place of occurrence. All death totals exclude nonresident aliens.
[b] Latest official figures.
[c] Rates are deaths per 100,000 population.

FATAL OCCUPATIONAL INJURIES BY STATE

In general, the states with the largest number of persons employed have the largest number of work-related fatalities. The four largest states — California, Florida, New York, and Texas — accounted for more than one fourth of the total fatalities in the United States. Each state's industry mix, geographical features, age of population, and other characteristics of the workforce must be considered when evaluating state fatality profiles.

FATAL OCCUPATIONAL INJURIES BY STATE AND EVENT OR EXPOSURE, UNITED STATES, 2001

State	Deaths per 100,000 workers	Total[a]	Transportation[b]	Assaults & Violent Acts[c]	Contact with Objects & Equipment	Falls	Exposure to Harmful Substances or Environments	Fires & Explosions	All Other
Total	4.3	5,900	2,517	902	962	782	499	188	50
Alabama	6.9	138	65	13	22	12	12	13	—
Alaska	20.6	64	48	5	5	—	—	—	—
Arizona	3.6	87	37	21	11	9	8	—	—
Arkansas	5.8	68	36	—	13	6	5	—	—
California	3.2	511	212	96	59	90	45	—	6
Colorado	6.1	139	56	26	26	18	8	—	—
Connecticut	2.4	40	19	6	—	9	—	—	—
Delaware	2.4	10	5	—	—	—	—	—	—
Dist. of Columbia	3.6	11	—	6	—	—	—	—	—
Florida	4.9	368	151	68	34	59	47	—	5
Georgia	5.8	235	97	46	31	35	19	—	—
Hawaii	6.9	41	18	8	10	—	—	—	—
Idaho	7.0	45	21	5	13	—	—	—	—
Illinois	3.8	231	75	43	37	38	27	10	—
Indiana	5.1	152	65	24	28	13	12	10	—
Iowa	4.0	62	30	—	16	8	5	—	—
Kansas	7.0	93	49	6	14	13	8	—	—
Kentucky	5.6	105	41	11	29	9	7	5	—
Louisiana	6.1	117	57	9	25	13	12	—	—
Maine	3.7	24	11	—	—	5	—	—	—
Maryland	2.4	64	24	18	7	7	7	—	—
Massachusetts	1.6	53	11	13	11	11	—	—	—
Michigan	3.6	175	64	37	32	23	11	7	—
Minnesota	2.8	76	28	—	22	16	7	—	—
Mississippi	9.0	111	53	12	16	11	15	—	—
Missouri	5.0	143	58	17	30	20	14	—	—
Montana	13.2	58	27	13	10	—	—	—	—
Nebraska	6.2	57	33	—	11	5	—	—	—
Nevada	3.9	40	21	7	5	—	—	—	—
New Hampshire	1.4	9	—	—	—	—	—	—	—
New Jersey	3.2	129	43	25	18	22	12	9	—
New Mexico	7.2	59	28	8	13	6	—	—	—
New York	2.6	220	89	44	32	37	8	10	—
North Carolina	5.1	203	93	31	33	25	18	—	—
North Dakota	7.4	25	16	—	—	—	—	—	—
Ohio	3.8	209	84	43	24	24	19	14	—
Oklahoma	7.2	115	44	13	25	13	13	—	—
Oregon	2.6	44	20	—	10	8	—	—	—
Pennsylvania	3.9	225	95	38	38	24	18	8	—
Rhode Island	3.3	17	6	—	—	—	—	—	—
South Carolina	4.8	89	37	10	10	19	8	5	—
South Dakota	8.9	35	18	—	8	—	—	—	—
Tennessee	5.0	136	64	12	26	16	11	6	—
Texas	5.3	534	207	96	85	67	54	22	—
Utah	5.9	65	29	8	14	6	5	—	—
Vermont	1.9	6	—	—	—	—	—	—	—
Virginia	4.1	147	69	10	31	16	11	9	—
Washington	3.6	102	44	9	18	18	6	7	—
West Virginia	8.2	63	33	—	13	9	—	—	—
Wisconsin	3.9	110	57	8	21	15	5	—	—
Wyoming	15.3	40	22	—	9	—	5	—	—

Source: U.S. Department of Labor, Bureau of Labor Statistics, except rates, which are National Safety Council estimates.
Note: Dashes (—) indicate no data or data that do not meet publication criteria.
[a] Total excludes 2,886 work-related homicide deaths from the terrorist attacks of September 11, 2001.
[b] Includes highway, nonhighway, air, water, and rail fatalities, and fatalities resulting from being struck by a vehicle or mobile equipment.
[c] Includes violence by persons, self-inflicted injury, and attacks by animals.

NONFATAL OCCUPATIONAL INCIDENCE RATES BY STATE

NONFATAL OCCUPATIONAL INJURY AND ILLNESS INCIDENCE RATES[a] BY STATE, PRIVATE INDUSTRY, 2001

State	Total Cases	Lost Workday Cases		Cases Without Lost Workdays
		Total[b]	With Days away from Work[c]	
Private Industry[d]	**5.7**	**2.8**	**1.7**	**2.9**
Alabama	5.9	2.7	1.4	3.2
Alaska	8.5	4.1	3.5	4.4
Arizona	5.8	2.7	1.6	3.0
Arkansas	5.8	2.8	1.5	3.0
California	5.4	3.1	1.8	2.4
Colorado	—	—		
Connecticut	6.3	3.2	2.0	3.1
Delaware	4.8	2.4	1.6	2.5
Dist. of Columbia	—	—	—	—
Florida	5.7	2.7	1.5	3.0
Georgia	4.8	2.1	1.2	2.7
Hawaii	5.7	3.3	2.9	2.4
Idaho	—	—	—	—
Illinois	5.3	2.6	1.6	2.6
Indiana	7.6	3.5	1.6	4.1
Iowa	8.1	3.8	1.8	4.3
Kansas	7.3	3.2	1.6	4.0
Kentucky	7.4	3.8	2.1	3.6
Louisiana	4.6	1.9	1.3	2.7
Maine	8.7	5.0	2.2	3.7
Maryland	4.3	2.2	1.6	2.2
Massachusetts	5.1	2.5	1.9	2.6
Michigan	7.3	3.7	1.6	3.6
Minnesota	6.3	3.1	1.7	3.2
Mississippi	—	—		—
Missouri	6.1	2.8	1.4	3.3
Montana	8.3	3.1	2.4	5.1
Nebraska	7.4	3.2	1.8	4.2
Nevada	6.6	3.1	1.6	3.5
New Hampshire	—	—		—
New Jersey	4.8	2.3	1.6	2.4
New Mexico	4.8	2.5	1.8	2.3
New York	3.6	1.9	1.7	1.8
North Carolina	4.8	2.2	1.2	2.5
North Dakota	—	—	—	—
Ohio	—	—	—	—
Oklahoma	6.5	3.3	1.8	3.1
Oregon	6.2	3.2	1.9	3.0
Pennsylvania	—	—	—	—
Rhode Island	6.8	3.6	2.7	3.1
South Carolina	4.5	2.1	1.2	2.4
South Dakota	—	—	—	—
Tennessee	6.1	2.9	1.6	3.1
Texas	4.9	2.5	1.5	2.4
Utah	6.6	2.7	1.5	3.9
Vermont	7.0	3.2	1.9	3.8
Virginia	4.6	2.3	1.5	2.4
Washington	7.8	3.4	2.5	4.3
West Virginia	7.2	3.9	3.4	3.3
Wisconsin	7.8	3.9	2.3	3.9
Wyoming	—	—	—	—

Source: Bureau of Labor Statistics, U.S. Department of Labor.
Note: Because of rounding, components may not add to totals. Dashes (—) indicate data not available.
[a]Incidence rates represent the number of injuries and illnesses per 100 full-time workers using 200,000 hours as the equivalent.
[b]Total lost workday cases involve days away from work, days of restricted work activity, or both.
[c]Days-away-from-work cases include those that result in days away from work with or without restricted work activity.
[d]Data cover all 50 states.

NONFATAL OCCUPATIONAL AND ILLNESS INCIDENCE RATES BY STATE, PRIVATE INDUSTRY, 2001

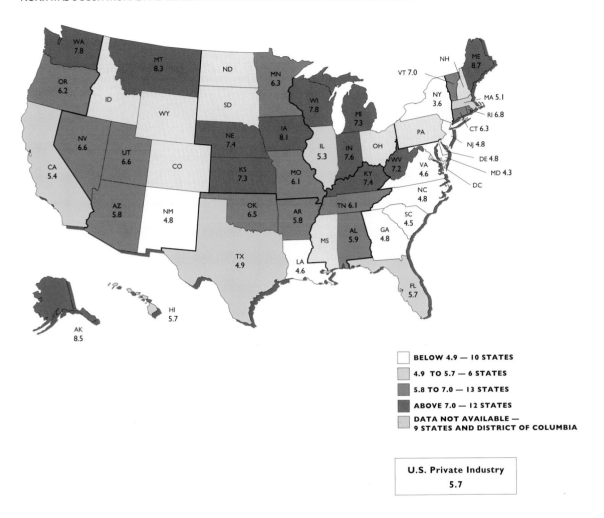

BELOW 4.9 — 10 STATES

4.9 TO 5.7 — 6 STATES

5.8 TO 7.0 — 13 STATES

ABOVE 7.0 — 12 STATES

DATA NOT AVAILABLE —
9 STATES AND DISTRICT OF COLUMBIA

U.S. Private Industry
5.7

MOTOR-VEHICLE DEATHS BY STATE

MOTOR-VEHICLE DEATHS BY STATE, UNITED STATES, 1999–2002

State	Motor-Vehicle Traffic Deaths (Place of Accident)				Total Motor-Vehicle Deaths[a] (Place of Residence)			
	Number		Mileage Rate[b]		Number		Population Rate[b]	
	2002	2001	2002	2001	2000[c]	1999	2000	1999
Total U.S.[a]	44,000	43,700	1.6	1.6	43,354	42,401	15.7	15.5
Alabama	1,004	997	1.7	1.7	1,064	1,162	23.8	26.6
Alaska	85	85	1.8	1.8	132	87	20.2	14.0
Arizona	1,104	1,047	2.1	2.1	999	945	20.8	19.8
Arkansas	641	611	2.1	2.1	680	649	25.8	25.4
California	4,104	3,926	1.3	1.3	3,743	3,641	11.5	11.0
Colorado	732	736	1.7	1.7	751	620	18.0	15.3
Connecticut	325	317	1.0	1.0	340	308	10.3	9.4
Delaware	126	136	1.4	1.6	126	98	16.4	13.0
Dist. of Columbia	50	72	1.3	2.0	56	36	10.7	6.9
Florida	3,137	3,013	2.0	2.0	3,057	2,872	20.0	19.0
Georgia	1,522	1,506	1.4	1.4	1,536	1,521	19.5	19.5
Hawaii	115	141	1.3	1.6	129	90	10.2	7.6
Idaho	265	259	1.9	1.9	271	278	20.1	22.2
Illinois	1,411	1,414	1.3	1.4	1,568	1,537	13.0	12.7
Indiana	792	909	1.1	1.3	918	988	15.1	16.6
Iowa	409	447	1.3	1.5	474	529	16.3	18.4
Kansas	510	494	1.8	1.7	495	570	18.5	21.5
Kentucky	917	850	1.9	1.8	832	814	20.8	20.6
Louisiana	865	957	2.1	2.3	1,014	976	22.9	22.3
Maine	191	191	1.3	1.3	175	199	13.9	15.9
Maryland	650	662	1.2	1.3	612	609	11.6	11.8
Massachusetts	459	477	0.9	0.9	493	441	7.9	7.1
Michigan	1,279	1,328	1.3	1.3	1,507	1,411	15.5	14.3
Minnesota	653	568	1.2	1.1	689	646	14.2	13.5
Mississippi	885	784	2.4	2.2	935	956	33.1	34.5
Missouri	1,203	1,098	1.7	1.6	1,097	1,061	19.8	19.4
Montana	268	230	2.6	2.3	234	210	24.6	23.8
Nebraska	307	246	1.7	1.3	285	295	16.7	17.7
Nevada	380	311	2.0	1.7	303	333	16.2	18.4
New Hampshire	127	142	1.0	1.2	134	129	10.9	10.7
New Jersey	786	745	1.1	1.1	772	727	9.4	8.9
New Mexico	458	464	1.9	2.0	418	415	22.4	23.9
New York	1,523	1,490	1.1	1.1	1,541	1,759	8.5	9.7
North Carolina	1,564	1,523	1.7	1.7	1,693	1,597	21.7	20.9
North Dakota	97	105	1.3	1.4	105	134	15.8	21.1
Ohio	1,301	1,379	1.2	1.3	1,456	1,427	12.8	12.7
Oklahoma	725	670	1.6	1.5	679	686	20.1	20.4
Oregon	436	487	1.2	1.4	478	433	14.0	13.1
Pennsylvania	1,618	—	1.5	—	1,522	1,580	12.4	13.2
Rhode Island	84	81	1.0	1.0	81	89	8.1	9.0
South Carolina	1,053	1,061	2.2	2.3	1,025	996	26.5	25.6
South Dakota	175	171	2.0	2.0	178	174	22.9	23.7
Tennessee	1,159	1,188	1.7	1.8	1,395	1,322	24.6	24.1
Texas	3,722	3,727	1.7	1.7	3,824	3,669	19.0	18.3
Utah	330	291	1.4	1.3	364	364	16.5	17.1
Vermont	78	—	0.8	—	76	83	12.3	14.0
Virginia	913	935	1.2	1.2	981	897	14.0	13.1
Washington	660	649	1.2	1.2	711	732	12.1	12.7
West Virginia	437	376	2.2	1.9	394	387	21.3	21.4
Wisconsin	805	764	1.4	1.3	890	775	16.7	14.8
Wyoming	176	186	2.0	2.3	122	144	23.2	30.0

Source: Motor-Vehicle Traffic Deaths are provisional counts from state traffic authorities; Total Motor-Vehicle Deaths are from the National Center for Health Statistics (see also page 156).
Note: Dashes (—) indicate data not reported.
[a] *Includes both traffic and nontraffic motor-vehicle deaths. See definitions of motor-vehicle traffic and nontraffic accidents on page 175.*
[b] *The mileage death rate is deaths per 100,000,000 vehicle miles; the population death rate is deaths per 100,000 population. Death rates are National Safety Council estimates.*
[c] *Latest year available. See Technical Appendix for comparability.*

MILEAGE DEATH RATES, 2002
MOTOR-VEHICLE TRAFFIC DEATHS PER 100,000,000 VEHICLE MILES

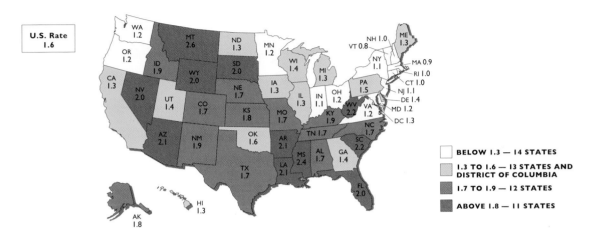

U.S. Rate
1.6

BELOW 1.3 — 14 STATES

1.3 TO 1.6 — 13 STATES AND DISTRICT OF COLUMBIA

1.7 TO 1.9 — 12 STATES

ABOVE 1.8 — 11 STATES

REGISTRATION DEATH RATES, 2002
MOTOR-VEHICLE TRAFFIC DEATHS PER 10,000 MOTOR VEHICLES

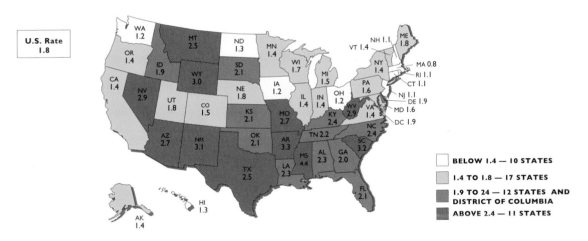

U.S. Rate
1.8

BELOW 1.4 — 10 STATES

1.4 TO 1.8 — 17 STATES

1.9 TO 24 — 12 STATES AND DISTRICT OF COLUMBIA

ABOVE 2.4 — 11 STATES

POPULATION DEATH RATES, 2002
MOTOR-VEHICLE TRAFFIC DEATHS PER 100,000 POPULATION

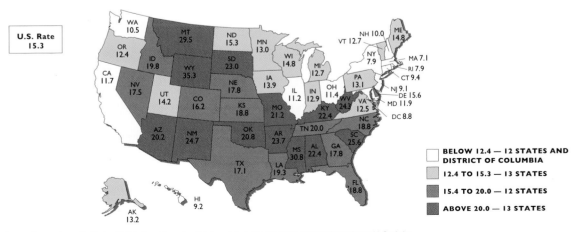

U.S. Rate
15.3

BELOW 12.4 — 12 STATES AND DISTRICT OF COLUMBIA

12.4 TO 15.3 — 13 STATES

15.4 TO 20.0 — 12 STATES

ABOVE 20.0 — 13 STATES

Source: Rates estimated by National Safety Council based on data from state traffic authorities, National Center for Health Statistics, Federal Highway Administration, and the U.S. Census Bureau.

INJURY FACTS®

NATIONAL SAFETY COUNCIL

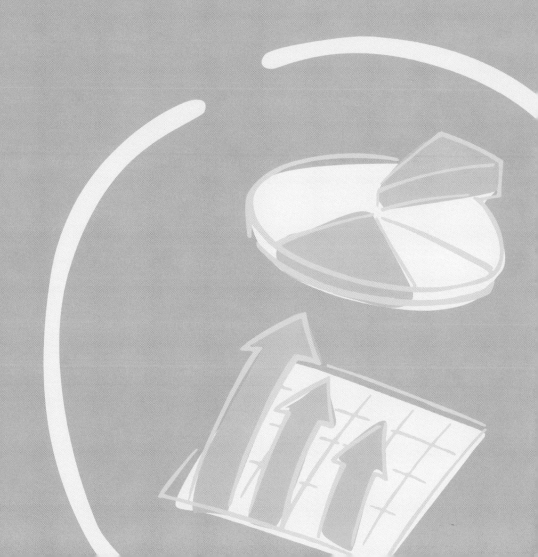

This appendix gives a brief explanation of some of the sources and methods used by the National Safety Council (NSC) Statistics Department in preparing the estimates of deaths, injuries, and costs presented in this book. Because many of the estimates depend on death certificate data provided by the states or the National Center for Health Statistics (NCHS), it begins with a brief introduction to the certification and classification of deaths.

Certification and classification. The medical certification of death involves entering information on the death certificate about the disease or condition directly leading to death, antecedent causes, and other significant conditions. The death certificate is then registered with the appropriate authority and a code is assigned for the underlying cause of death. The underlying cause is defined as "(a) the disease or injury which initiated the train of morbid events leading directly to death, or (b) the circumstances of the accident or violence which produced the fatal injury" (World Health Organization [WHO], 1992). Deaths are classified and coded on the basis of a WHO standard, the *International Statistical Classification of Diseases and Related Health Problems,* commonly known as the International Classification of Diseases or ICD (WHO, 1992). For deaths due to injury and poisoning, the ICD provides a system of "external cause" codes to which the underlying cause of death is assigned. (See pages 18–19 of *Injury Facts*® for a condensed list of external cause codes.)

Comparability across ICD revisions. The ICD is revised periodically and these revisions can affect comparability from year to year. The sixth revision (1948) substantially expanded the list of external causes and provided for classifying the place of occurrence. Changes in the classification procedures for the sixth revision as well as the seventh (1958) and eighth (1968) revisions classified as diseases some deaths previously classified as injuries. The eighth revision also expanded and reorganized some external cause sections. The ninth revision (1979) provided more detail on the agency involved, the victim's activity, and the place of occurrence. The tenth revision, which was adopted in the United States effective with 1999 data, completely revised the transportation-related categories. Specific external cause categories affected by the revisions are noted in the historical tables.

The table at the end of this appendix (page 171) shows the ICD-9 codes, the ICD-10 codes, and a comparability ratio for each of the principal causes of unintentional-injury death. The comparability ratio represents the net effect of the new revision on statistics for the cause of death. The comparability ratio was obtained by classifying a sample of death certificates under both ICD-9 and ICD-10 and then dividing the number of deaths for a selected cause classified under ICD-10 by the number classified to the most nearly comparable ICD-9 cause. A comparability ratio of 1.00 indicates no net change due to the new classification scheme. A ratio less than 1.00 indicates fewer deaths assigned to a cause under ICD-10 than under ICD-9. A ratio greater than 1.00 indicates an increase in assignment of deaths to a cause under ICD-10 compared to ICD-9.

The broad category of "accidents" or "unintentional injuries" under ICD-9 included complications and misadventures of surgical and medical care (E870–E879) and adverse effects of drugs in therapeutic use (E930–E949). These categories are not included in "accidents" or "unintentional injuries" under ICD-10. In 1998, deaths in these two categories numbered 3,228 and 276, respectively.

Under ICD-9, the code range for falls (E880–E888) included a code for "fracture, cause unspecified" (E887). A similar code does not appear in ICD-10 (W00–W19, which probably accounts for the low comparability ratio (0.8409). In 1998, deaths in code E887 numbered 3,679.

Beginning with 1970 data, tabulations published by NCHS no longer include deaths of nonresident aliens. In 2000, there were 868 such deaths, of which 356 were motor-vehicle related.

Fatality estimates. The Council uses four classes to categorize unintentional injuries: Motor Vehicle, Work, Home, and Public. Each class represents an environment and an intervention route for injury prevention through a responsible authority such as a police department, an employer, a home owner, or public health department.

Motor vehicle. The Motor-Vehicle class can be identified by the underlying cause of death (see the table on page 171).

Work. The National Safety Council adopted the Bureau of Labor Statistics' Census of Fatal Occupational Injuries (CFOI) figure, beginning with the 1992 data year, as the authoritative count of unintentional work-related deaths. The CFOI system is described in detail in Toscano and Windau (1994).

The 2-Way Split. After subtracting the Motor-Vehicle and Work figures from the unintentional-injury total (ICD-10 codes V01–X59, Y85–Y86), the remainder belong to the Home and Public classes. The Home class can be identified by the "place of occurrence" subclassification (code .0) used with most nontransport deaths; the Public class is the remainder. Missing "place of occurrence" information, however, prevents the direct determination of the Home and Public class totals. Because of this, the Council allocates nonmotor-vehicle, nonwork deaths into the Home and Public classes based on the external cause, age group, and cases with specified "place of occurrence." This procedure, known as the 2-Way Split, uses the most recent death certificate data available from the NCHS and the CFOI data for the same calendar year. For each cause-code group and age group combination, the Motor-Vehicle and Work deaths are subtracted and the remainder, including those with "place of occurrence" unspecified, are allocated to Home and Public in the same proportion as those with "place of occurrence" specified.

The table on page 171 shows the ICD-10 cause-codes and CFOI event codes for the most common causes of unintentional-injury death. The CFOI event codes (BLS, 1992) do not match exactly with ICD cause codes, so there is some error in the allocation of deaths among the classes.

State reporting system. The Council operates a reporting system through which participating states send monthly tabulations of unintentional-injury death data by age group, class, and type of event or industry. This is known as the Injury Mortality Tabulation reporting system. These data are used to make current year estimates based on the most recent 2-Way Split and CFOI data.

Linking up to current year. The benchmark data published by NCHS are usually two years old and the CFOI data are usually one year old. The link-relative technique is used to make current year estimates from these data using the state vital statistics data. This

method assumes that the change in deaths from one year to the next in states reporting for both years reflects the change in deaths for the entire nation. The ratio is calculated and multiplied times the benchmark figure, resulting in an estimate for the next year. It may be necessary to repeat the process, depending on the reference year of the benchmark. For example, the 2000 NCHS and CFOI data were used this year for a 2-Way Split, and state data were used to make estimates for 2001 and 2002 Home and Public classes using the link-relative technique. CFOI data for 2001 were also available, so it was necessary only to make 2002 Work estimates.

Revisions of prior years. When the figures for a given year are published by NCHS, the 2-Way Split based on those figures and the CFOI become the final estimate of unintentional-injury deaths by class, age group, and type of event or industry. Subsequent years are revised by repeating the link-relative process described above. For example, in the 2003 edition of *Injury Facts®*, the 2000 NCHS and CFOI data were used to produce final estimates using the 2-Way Split, the 2001 estimates were revised using more complete state data and 2001 CFOI figures, and the new 2002 estimates were made with the state data available in the spring of 2003.

Nonfatal injury estimates. The Council uses the concept of "disabling injury" to define the kinds of injuries included in its estimates. See page 23 for the definition of disabling injury and the National Health Interview Survey (NHIS) injury definitions.

Injury to death ratios. There is no national injury surveillance system that provides disabling injury estimates on a current basis. The National Health Interview Survey, a household survey conducted by the NCHS (see page 23), produces national estimates using its own definition of injury, but the data are not published until well after the reference year (Adams, Hendershot, & Marano, 1999). For this reason, the Council uses injury-to-death ratios to estimate nonfatal disabling injuries for the current year. Complete documentation of the background and new procedure, effective with the 1993 edition, may be found in Landes, Ginsburg, Hoskin, and Miller (1990).

The ratios, one for each class, are a 3-year moving average of the NHIS injury data and the corresponding Council estimates of deaths. Because the NHIS does not use the Council's definition of disabling injury, the NHIS data are adjusted to approximate the disabling concept. The adjustment involves counting only injuries that result in two or more days of restricted activity. (The NHIS counts only whole days of restricted activity even though the definition is stated in terms of half days. One day counted includes from one-half day up to one and one-half days of actual restriction. Two days counted includes from one and one-half up to two and one-half.)

Comparability over time. Even though the injury to death ratios are updated each time a new NHIS is released, the resulting estimates are not direct measures of nonfatal injuries and should not be compared with prior years.

Population sources. All population figures used in computing rates are taken from various reports published by the Bureau of the Census, U.S. Department of Commerce, on their Internet web site (www.census.gov). *Resident* population is used for computing rates.

Costs (pp. 4–7). The procedures for estimating the economic losses due to fatal and nonfatal unintentional injuries were extensively revised for the 1993 edition of *Accident Facts®*. New components were added, new benchmarks adopted, and a new discount rate assumed. All of these changes resulted in significantly higher cost estimates. For this reason, it must be re-emphasized that the cost estimates should not be compared to those in earlier editions of the book.

The Council's general philosophy underlying its cost estimates is that the figures represent income not received or expenses incurred because of fatal and nonfatal unintentional injuries. Stated this way, the Council's cost estimates are a measure of the economic impact of unintentional injuries and may be compared to other economic measures such as gross domestic product, per capita income, or personal consumption expenditures. (See page 91 and "lost quality of life" [p. 169] for a discussion of injury costs for cost-benefit analysis.)

The general approach followed was to identify a benchmark unit cost for each component, adjust the benchmark to the current year using an appropriate inflator, estimate the number of cases to which the component applied, and compute the product. Where

possible, benchmarks were obtained for each class: Motor Vehicle, Work, Home, and Public.

Wage and productivity losses include the value of wages, fringe benefits, and household production for all classes, and travel delay for the Motor Vehicle class.

For fatalities, the present value of after-tax wages, fringe benefits, and household production was computed using the human capital method. The procedure incorporates data on life expectancy from the NCHS life tables, employment likelihood from the Bureau of Labor Statistics household survey, and mean earnings from the Bureau of the Census money income survey. The discount rate used was 4%, reduced from 6% used in earlier years. The present value obtained is highly sensitive to the discount rate; the lower the rate, the greater the present value.

For permanent partial disabilities, an average of 17% of earning power is lost (Berkowitz & Burton, 1987). The incidence of permanent disabilities, adjusted to remove intentional injuries, was computed from data on hospitalized cases from the National Hospital Discharge Survey (NHDS) and nonhospitalized cases from the National Health Interview Survey and National Council on Compensation Insurance data on probabilities of disability by nature of injury and part of body injured.

For temporary disabilities, an average daily wage, fringe benefit, and household production loss was calculated, and this was multiplied by the number of days of restricted activity from the NHIS.

Travel delay costs were obtained from the Council's estimates of the number of fatal, injury, and property damage crashes and an average delay cost per crash from Miller et al. (1991).

Medical expenses, including ambulance and helicopter transport costs, were estimated for fatalities, hospitalized cases, and nonhospitalized cases in each class.

The incidence of hospitalized cases was derived from the NHDS data adjusted to eliminate intentional injuries. Average length of stay was benchmarked from Miller, Pindus, Douglass, and Rossman (1993b) and adjusted to estimate lifetime length of stay. The cost per hospital day was benchmarked to the National Medical Expenditure Survey (NMES).

Nonhospitalized cases were estimated by taking the difference between total NHIS injuries and hospitalized cases. Average cost per case was based on NMES data adjusted for inflation and lifetime costs.

Medical cost of fatalities was benchmarked to data from the National Council on Compensation Insurance (1989) to which was added the cost of a premature funeral and coroner costs (Miller et al., 1991).

Cost per ambulance transport was benchmarked to NMES data and cost per helicopter transport was benchmarked to data in Miller et al. (1993a). The number of cases transported was based on data from Rice and MacKenzie (1989) and the National Electronic Injury Surveillance System.

Administrative expenses include the administrative cost of private and public insurance, which represents the cost of having insurance, and police and legal costs.

The administrative cost of motor-vehicle insurance was the difference between premiums earned (adjusted to remove fire, theft, and casualty premiums) and pure losses incurred, based on data from A. M. Best. Workers' compensation insurance administration was based on A. M. Best data for private carriers and regression estimates using Social Security Administration data for state funds and the self-insured. Administrative costs of public insurance (mainly Medicaid and Medicare) amount to about 4% of the medical expenses paid by public insurance, which were determined from Rice and MacKenzie (1989) and Hensler et al. (1991).

Average police costs for motor-vehicle crashes were taken from Miller et al. (1991) and multiplied by the Council's estimates of the number of fatal, injury and property damage crashes.

Legal expenses include court costs, and plaintiff's and defendant's time and expenses. Hensler et al. (1991) provided data on the proportion of injured persons who hire a lawyer, file a claim, and get compensation. Kakalik and Pace (1986) provided data on costs per case.

Fire losses were based on data published by the National Fire Protection Association in the *NFPA Journal*. The allocation into the classes was based on the property use for structure fires and other NFPA data for nonstructure fires.

Motor-vehicle damage costs were benchmarked to Blincoe and Faigin (1992) and multiplied by the Council's estimates of crash incidence.

Employer costs for work injuries is an estimate of the productivity costs incurred by employers. It assumes each fatality or permanent injury resulted in 4 person-months of disruption, serious injuries 1 person-month, and minor to moderate injuries 2 person-days. All injuries to nonworkers were assumed to involve 2 days of worker productivity loss. Average hourly earnings for supervisors and nonsupervisory workers were computed and then multiplied by the incidence and hours lost per case. Property damage and production delays (except motor-vehicle related) are not included in the estimates but can be substantial.

Lost quality of life is the difference between the value of a statistical fatality or statistical injury and the value of after-tax wages, fringe benefits, and household production. Because this does not represent real income not received or expenses incurred, it is not included in the total economic cost figure. If included, the resulting *comprehensive costs* can be used in cost-benefit analysis because the total costs then represent the maximum amount society should spend to prevent a statistical death or injury.

Work deaths and injuries (p. 48). The method for estimating total work-related deaths and injuries is discussed above. The breakdown of deaths by industry division for the current year is obtained from the CFOI and state Injury Mortality Tabulation figures using the link-relative technique (also discussed above).

The estimate of nonfatal disabling injuries by industry division is made by multiplying the estimate of employment for each industry division by the BLS estimate of the incidence rate of cases involving days away from work for each division (e.g., BLS, 2002) and then adjusting the results so that they add to the work-injury total previously established. The "private sector" average incidence rate is used for the government division, which is not covered in the BLS survey.

Employment. The employment estimates for 1992 to the present were changed for the 1998 edition. Estimates for these years in prior editions are not comparable. The total employment figure used by the Council represents the number of persons in the civilian labor force, aged

16 and older, who were wage or salary workers, self-employed, or unpaid family workers, plus active duty military personnel resident in the U.S. The total employment estimate is a combination of three figures — total civilian employment from the Current Population Survey (CPS) as published in *Employment and Earnings,* plus the difference between total resident population and total civilian population, which represents active duty military personnel.

Employment by industry division is obtained from an unpublished Bureau of Labor Statistics table titled "Employed and experienced unemployed persons by detailed industry and class of worker, Annual Average [year] (based on CPS)."

Time lost (p. 51) is the product of the number of cases and the average time lost per case. Deaths average 150 workdays lost in the current year and 5,850 in future years; permanent disabilities involve 75 and 565 days lost in current and future years, respectively; temporary disabilities involve 17 days lost in the current year only. Off-the-job injuries to workers are assumed to result in similar lost time.

Off-the-job (p. 52) deaths and injuries are estimated by assuming that employed persons incur injuries at the same rate as the entire population.

Motor-Vehicle section (pp. 86–117). Estimates of miles traveled, registered vehicles and licensed drivers are published by the Federal Highway Administration in *Highway Statistics* and *Traffic Volume Trends.*

In addition to the death certificate data from NCHS and state registrars, the Council receives annual summary reports of traffic crash characteristics from about 15 states. Most national estimates are made using various ratios and percent distributions from the state crash data.

Beginning with the 1998 edition of *Accident Facts®,* national estimates of crashes by manner of collision (p. 90) and motor-vehicles involved in crashes by type of vehicle (p. 100) are made using the percent changes from the previous year to the current year as reported by the states. This percent change is then applied to benchmark figures obtained from the National Highway Traffic Safety Administration (NHTSA), Fatality Analysis Reporting System (FARS), and General Estimates System (GES) data for the previous year, which yields the current year estimates. These current year estimates are then adjusted to add to the Council's overall number of deaths, injuries, and fatal, injury, and property damage-only crashes that are listed on page 86. Because of these changes, comparisons to previous years should not be made.

Adams, P. F., Hendershot, G. E., & Marano, M. A. (1999). Current estimates from the National Health Interview Survey, 1996. *Vital and Health Statistics* 10(200). Hyattsville, MD: National Center for Health Statistics.

Berkowitz, M., & Burton, J. F., Jr. (1987). *Permanent Disability Benefits in Workers' Compensation.* Kalamazoo, MI: W. E. Upjohn Institute for Employment Research.

Blincoe, L. J., & Faigin, B. M. (1992). *Economic Cost of Motor Vehicle Crashes, 1990.* Springfield, VA: National Technical Information Service.

Bureau of Labor Statistics [BLS]. (1992). *Occupational Injury & Illness Classification Manual.* Itasca, IL: National Safety Council.

Bureau of Labor Statistics [BLS]. (2002, December 19). *Workplace Injuries and Illnesses in 2001.* Press release USDL-02-687.

Hensler, D. R., Marquis, M. S., Abrahamse, A. F., Berry, S. H., Ebener, P. A., Lewis, E. D., Lind, E. A., MacCoun, R. J., Manning, W. G., Rogowski, J. A., & Vaiana, M. E. (1991). *Compensation for Accidental Injuries in the United States.* Santa Monica, CA: The RAND Corporation.

Hoyert, D. L., Arias, E., Smith, B. L., Murphy, S. L., & Kochanek, K. D. (2001). Deaths: final data for 1999. *National Vital Statistics Reports, 49*(8).

Kakalik, J. S., & Pace, N. (1986). *Costs and Compensation Paid in Tort Litigation.* R-3391-ICJ. Santa Monica, CA: The RAND Corporation.

Landes, S. R., Ginsburg, K. M., Hoskin, A. F., & Miller, T. A. (1990). *Estimating Nonfatal Injuries.* Itasca, IL: Statistics Department, National Safety Council.

Miller, T., Viner, J., Rossman, S., Pindus, N., Gellert, W., Douglass, J., Dillingham, A., & Blomquist, G. (1991). *The Costs of Highway Crashes.* Springfield, VA: National Technical Information Service.

Miller, T. R., Brigham, P. A., Cohen, M. A., Douglass, J. B., Galbraith, M. S., Lestina, D. C., Nelkin, V. S., Pindus, N. M., & Smith-Regojo, P. (1993a). Estimating the costs to society of cigarette fire injuries. *Report to Congress in Response to the Fire Safe Cigarette Act of 1990.* Washington, DC: U.S. Consumer Product Safety Commission.

Miller, T. R., Pindus, N. M., Douglass, J. B., & Rossman, S. B. (1993b). *Nonfatal Injury Incidence, Costs, and Consequences: A Data Book.* Washington, DC: The Urban Institute Press.

Rice, D. P., & MacKenzie, E. J. (1989). *Cost of Injury in the United States: A Report to Congress.* Atlanta, GA: Centers for Disease Control and Prevention.

Toscano, G., & Windau, J. (1994). The changing character of fatal work injuries. *Monthly Labor Review, 117*(10), 17–28.

World Health Organization. (1977). *Manual of the International Statistical Classification of Diseases, Injuries, and Causes of Death.* Geneva, Switzerland: Author.

World Health Organization. (1992). *International Statistical Classification of Diseases and Related Health Problems — Tenth Revision.* Geneva, Switzerland: Author.

Manner of Injury	ICD-9 Codes[a]	ICD-10 Codes[b]	Comparability Ratio[c]	OI & ICM[d] Event Codes
Unintentional Injuries	E800–E869, E880–E929[e]	V01–X59, Y85–Y86	1.0305 (1.0278–1.0333)[f]	00–60, 63–9999
Railway accident	E800–E807	V05, V15, V80.6, V81(.2–.9)	n/a	44
Motor-vehicle accident	E810–E825	V02–V04, V09.0, V09.2, V12–V14, V19.0–V19.2, V19.4–V19.6, V20–V79, V80.3–V80.5, V81.0–V81.1, V82.0–V82.1, V83–V86, V87.0–V87.8, V88.0–V88.8, V89.0, V89.2	0.9754 (0.9742–0.9766)	41, 42, 43
Water transport accident	E830–E838	V90–V94	n/a	45
Air transport accident	E840–E845	V95–V97	n/a	46
Poisoning by solids & liquids	E850–58, E860–66	X40–X49	n/a	344
Poisoning by gases and vapors	E867–E869			341
Falls	E880–E888	W00–W19	0.8409 (0.8313–0.8505)	1
Fires and burns	E890–E899	X00–X09	0.9743 (0.9568–0.9918)	51
Drowning	E910	W65–W74	0.9965 (0.9716–1.0213)	381
Suffocation by ingestion or inhalation	E911–E912	W78–W80	n/a	382
Mechanical suffocation	E913	W75–W77, W81–W84	n/a	383, 384, 389
Firearms	E922	W32–W34	1.0579 (1.0331–1.0828)	0220, 0222, 0229 with source = 911[g]

Source: National Safety Council.
Note: n/a means comparability ratio not calculated or does not meet standards of reliability or precision.
[a]*WHO (1977).*
[b]*WHO (1992).*
[c]*Hoyert, Arias, Smith, et al. (2001). Table III.*
[d]*BLS (1992).*
[e]*The National Safety Council has used E800–E949 for unintentional injuries. The code group in the table omits complications and misadventures of surgical and medical care (E870–E879) and adverse effects of drugs in therapeutic use (E930–E949).*
[f]*Figures in parentheses are the 95% confidence interval for the comparability ratio.*
[g]*Struck by flying object where the source of injury was a bullet.*

The following organizations may be useful for obtaining more current data or more detailed information on various subjects in *Injury Facts®*.

American Association of Poison Control Centers
3201 New Mexico Avenue, Suite 310
Washington, DC 20016
(202) 362-7217
www.aapcc.org
aapcc@poison.org

Bureau of Labor Statistics
U.S. Department of Labor
2 Massachusetts Avenue, NE
Washington, DC 20212
(202) 691-7828
www.bls.gov
blsdata_staff@bls.gov

Bureau of the Census
U.S. Department of Commerce
Public Information Office
Washington, DC 20233-8200
(301) 457-2794
www.census.gov

Bureau of Justice Statistics
810 7th Street, NW
Washington, DC 20531
(202) 307-5933
www.ojp.usdoj.gov

Bureau of Transportation Statistics
U.S. Department of Transportation
400 7th Street, SW, Room 3103
Washington, DC 20590
(800) 853-1352
www.bts.gov
answers@bts.gov

Centers for Disease Control and Prevention
1600 Clifton Road
Atlanta, GA 30333
(404) 639-3534 or (800) 311-3435
www.cdc.gov

Chemical Safety Board
2175 K Street, NW, Suite 400
Washington, DC 20037
(202) 261-7600
www.chemsafety.gov
info@csb.gov

Eno Transportation Foundation
1634 I Street, NW, Suite 500
Washington, DC 20006
(202) 879-4700
www.enotrans.com

Environmental Protection Agency, U.S.
1200 Pennsylvania Avenue, NW
Washington, DC 20460
(202) 260-2090
www.epa.gov
public-access@epa.gov

European Agency for Safety and Health at Work
Gran Via, 33
E-48009 Bilbao, Spain
Phone: +34 944-794-360
Fax: +34 944-794-383
http://europe.osha.eu.int
information@osha.eu.int

Federal Aviation Administration
U.S. Department of Transportation
National Aviation Safety Data Analysis Center
800 Independence Avenue, SW
Washington, DC 20591
(202) 366-4000
www.faa.gov

Federal Bureau of Investigation
935 Pennsylvania Avenue, NW
Washington, DC 20535-0001
(202) 324-3000
www.fbi.gov

Federal Highway Administration
U.S. Department of Transportation
400 7th Street, SW
Washington, DC 20590
(202) 366-0660
www.fhwa.dot.gov
execsecretariat.fhwa@fhwa.dot.gov

Federal Motor Carrier Safety Administration
U.S. Department of Transportation
400 7th Street, SW
Washington, DC 20590
(800) 832-5660
www.fmcsa.dot.gov

Federal Railroad Administration
U.S. Department of Transportation
1120 Vermont Avenue, NW
Washington, DC 20590
(202) 366-2760
www.fra.dot.gov

Federal Transit Administration
400 7th Street, SW
Washington, DC 20590
www.fta.dot.gov

FedStats
Gateway to official statistical information available to the public from more than 100 federal agencies.
www.fedstats.gov

FirstGov
Gateway to federal, state, local, tribal, and international government web sites.
www.firstgov.gov

Insurance Information Institute
110 William Street
New York, NY 10038
(212) 346-5500
www.iii.org

Insurance Institute for Highway Safety
1005 N. Glebe Road, Suite 800
Arlington, VA 22201
(703) 247-1500
www.highwaysafety.org

International Hunter Education Association
P.O. Box 490
Wellington, CO 80549-0490
(970) 568-7954
www.ihea.com
ihea@frii.com

International Labour Office
4, rue des Morillons
CH-1211 Geneva 22
Switzerland
Phone: +41-22-799-6111
Fax: +41-22-798-8685
www.ilo.org
ilo@ilo.org

Mine Safety and Health Administration
1100 Wilson Boulevard, 21st Floor
Arlington, VA 22209-3939
(202) 693-9400
www.msha.gov

Motorcycle Safety Foundation
2 Jenner Street, Suite 150
Irvine, CA 92718-3812
(714) 727-3227
www.msf-usa.org

National Academy of Social Insurance
1776 Massachusetts Avenue, NW, Suite 615
Washington, DC 20036-1904
(202) 452-8097
www.nasi.org
nasi@nasi.org

National Center for Education Statistics
U.S. Department of Education
1990 K Street, NW
Washington, DC 20006
(202) 502-7300
http://nces.ed.gov

National Center for Health Statistics
3311 Toledo Road, Room 2217
Hyattsville, MD 20782
(301) 458-4636
www.cdc.gov/nchs

National Center for Injury Prevention and Control
Office Of Communication Resources, Mail Stop K65
4770 Buford Highway, NE
Atlanta, GA 30341-3724
(770) 488-1506
www.cdc.gov/ncipc
ohcinfo@cdc.gov

National Clearinghouse for Alcohol and Drug Information
P.O. Box 2345
Rockville, MD 20847-2345
(301) 468-2600 or (800) 729-6686
www.health.org

National Climatic Data Center
151 Patton Avenue
Asheville, NC 28801-5001
(828) 271-4800
http://lwf.ncdc.noaa.gov/oa/ncdc.html
ncdc.info@noaa.gov

National Collegiate Athletic Association
700 W. Washington Street
P.O. Box 6222
Indianapolis, IN 46206-6222
(317) 917-6222
www.ncaa.org

National Council on Compensation Insurance
901 Peninsula Corporate Circle
Boca Raton, FL 33487
(800) NCCI-123 (800-622-4123)
www.ncci.com

National Fire Protection Association
P.O. Box 9101
Batterymarch Park
Quincy, MA 02269-0910
(617) 770-3000 or (800) 344-3555
www.nfpa.org
osds@nfpa.org

National Highway Traffic Safety Administration
U.S. Department of Transportation
400 7th Street, SW
Washington, DC 20590
(202) 366-0123 or (800) 424-9393
www.nhtsa.dot.gov
    National Center for Statistics and Analysis (NRD-30)
    (202) 366-4198 or (800) 934-8517
    NCSAweb@nhtsa.dot.gov

National Institute for Occupational Safety and Health
Clearinghouse for Occupational Safety and Health
    Information
4676 Columbia Parkway
Cincinnati, OH 45226
(800) 356-4674
www.cdc.gov/niosh
eidtechinfo@cdc.gov

National Spinal Cord Injury Association
6701 Democracy Boulevard, Suite 300-9
Bethesda, MD 20817
(301) 588-6959
www.spinalcord.org
nscia2@aol.com

National Sporting Goods Association
1601 Feehanville Drive, Suite 300
Mt. Prospect, IL 60056
(847) 296-6742
www.nsga.org
info@nsga.org

National Transportation Safety Board
490 L'Enfant Plaza East, SW
Washington, DC 20594
(202) 314-6000
www.ntsb.gov

Occupational Safety and Health Administration
U.S. Department of Labor
Office of Statistics
200 Constitution Avenue, NW
Washington, DC 20210
(800) 321-OSHA (6742)
www.osha.gov

Prevent Blindness America
500 E. Remington Road
Schaumburg, IL 60173
(800) 331-2020
www.preventblindness.org
info@preventblindness.org

Transportation Research Board
500 5th Street, NW
Washington, DC 20001
(202) 334-2934
www.nas.edu/trb

U.S. Coast Guard
2100 2nd Street, SW
Washington, DC 20593-0001
(800) 368-5647
www.uscgboating.org
uscginfoline@gcrm.com

U.S. Consumer Product Safety Commission
National Injury Information Clearinghouse
Washington, DC 20207-0001
(301) 504-0424
www.cpsc.gov
clearinghouse@cpsc.gov

World Health Organization
20, avenue Appia
CH-1211 Geneva 27
Switzerland
Phone: +41-22-791-2111
Fax: +41-22-791-0746
www.who.int
info@who.int

Accident is that occurrence in a sequence of events that produces unintended injury, death, or property damage. *Accident* refers to the event, not the result of the event (see *unintentional injury*).

Cases without lost workdays are cases that do not involve lost workdays but result in medical treatment other than first aid, restriction of work or motion, loss of consciousness, transfer to another job, or diagnosis of occupational illness.

Death from accident is a death that occurs within one year of the accident.

Disabling injury is an injury causing death, permanent disability, or any degree of temporary total disability beyond the day of the injury.

Fatal accident is an accident that results in one or more deaths within one year.

Home is a dwelling and its premises within the property lines including single-family dwellings and apartment houses, duplex dwellings, boarding and rooming houses, and seasonal cottages. Excluded from *home* are barracks, dormitories, and resident institutions.

Incidence rate, as defined by OSHA, is the number of occupational injuries and/or illnesses or lost workdays per 100 full-time employees (see formula on page 61).

Injury is physical harm or damage to the body resulting from an exchange, usually acute, of mechanical, chemical, thermal, or other environmental energy that exceeds the body's tolerance.

Lost workdays are those days on which, because of occupational injury or illness, the employee was away from work or limited to restricted work activity. *Days away from work* are those days on which the employee would have worked but could not. *Days of restricted work* activity are those days on which the employee was assigned to a temporary job, worked at a permanent job less than full time, or worked at a permanent job but could not perform all duties normally connected with it. The number of lost workdays (consecutive or not) does not include the day of injury or onset of illness or any days on which the employee would not have worked even though able to work.

Lost workday cases are cases that involve days away from work, days of restricted work activity, or both.

Motor vehicle is any mechanically or electrically powered device not operated on rails, upon which or by which any person or property may be transported upon a land highway. The load on a motor vehicle or trailer attached to it is considered part of the vehicle. Tractors and motorized machinery are included while self-propelled in transit or used for transportation. *Nonmotor vehicle* is any road vehicle other than a motor vehicle, such as a bicycle or animal-drawn vehicle, **except** a coaster wagon, child's sled, child's tricycle, child's carriage, and similar means of transportation; persons using these latter means of transportation are considered pedestrians.

Motor-vehicle accident is an unstabilized situation that includes at least one harmful event (injury or property damage) involving a motor vehicle in transport (in motion, in readiness for motion, or on a roadway but not parked in a designated parking area) that does not result from discharge of a firearm or explosive device and does not directly result from a cataclysm. [See Committee on Motor Vehicle Traffic Accident Classification (1997), *Manual on Classification of Motor Vehicle Traffic Accidents*, ANSI D16.1-1996, Itasca, IL: National Safety Council.]

Motor-vehicle traffic accident is a motor-vehicle accident that occurs on a trafficway — a way or place, any part of which is open to the use of the public for the purposes of vehicular traffic. *Motor-vehicle nontraffic accident* is any motor-vehicle accident that occurs entirely in any place other than a trafficway.

Nonfatal injury accident is an accident in which at least one person is injured and no injury results in death.

Occupational illness is any abnormal condition or disorder other than one resulting from an occupational injury caused by exposure to environmental factors associated with employment. It includes acute and chronic illnesses or diseases that may be caused by inhalation, absorption, ingestion, or direct contact (see also page 61).

Occupational injury is any injury such as a cut, fracture, sprain, amputation, etc., which results from a work accident or from a single instantaneous exposure in the work environment (see also page 61).

Pedalcycle is a vehicle propelled by human power and operated solely by pedals; excludes mopeds.

Pedestrian is any person involved in a motor-vehicle accident who is not in or upon a motor vehicle or nonmotor vehicle. Includes persons injured while using a coaster wagon, child's tricycle, roller skates, etc. Excludes persons boarding, alighting, jumping, or falling from a motor vehicle in transport who are considered occupants of the vehicle.

Permanent disability (or permanent impairment) includes any degree of permanent nonfatal injury. It includes any injury that results in the loss or complete loss of use of any part of the body or in any permanent impairment of functions of the body or a part thereof.

Property damage accident is an accident that results in property damage but in which no person is injured.

Public accident is any accident other than motor-vehicle that occurs in the public use of any premises. Includes deaths in recreation (swimming, hunting, etc.), in transportation except motor-vehicle, public buildings, etc., and from widespread natural disasters even though some may have happened on home premises. Excludes accidents to persons in the course of gainful employment.

Source of injury is the principal object such as tool, machine, or equipment involved in the accident and is usually the object inflicting injury or property damage. Also called *agency* or *agent*.

Temporary total disability is an injury that does not result in death or permanent disability but that renders the injured person unable to perform regular duties or activities on one or more full calendar days after the day of the injury.

Total cases include all work-related deaths and illnesses and those work-related injuries that result in loss of consciousness, restriction of work or motion, or transfer to another job, or require medical treatment other than first aid.

Unintentional injury is the preferred term for accidental injury in the public health community. It refers to the *result* of an accident.

Work hours are the total number of hours worked by all employees. They are usually compiled for various levels, such as an establishment, a company, or an industry. A work hour is the equivalent of one employee working one hour.

Work injuries (including occupational illnesses) are those that arise out of and in the course of gainful employment regardless of where the accident or exposure occurs. Excluded are work injuries to private household workers and injuries occurring in connection with farm chores that are classified as home injuries.

Workers are all persons gainfully employed, including owners, managers, other paid employees, the self-employed, and unpaid family workers but excluding private household workers.

Work/Motor-vehicle duplication includes *work injuries* that occur in *motor-vehicle accidents* (see definitions for work injuries and motor-vehicle accident on this page).

INDEX